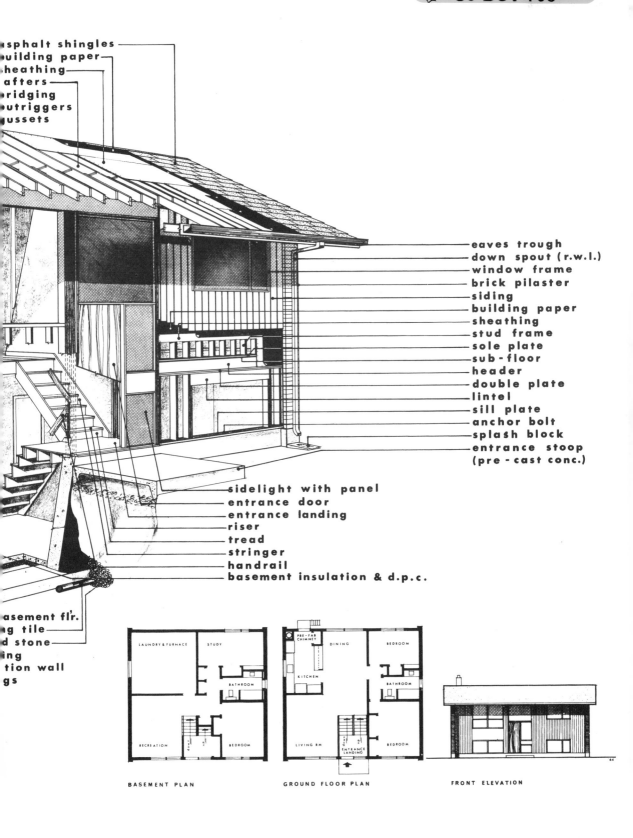

asphalt shingles
building paper
sheathing
rafters
bridging
outriggers
gussets

eaves trough
down spout (r.w.l.)
window frame
brick pilaster
siding
building paper
sheathing
stud frame
sole plate
sub-floor
header
double plate
lintel
sill plate
anchor bolt
splash block
entrance stoop
(pre-cast conc.)

sidelight with panel
entrance door
entrance landing
riser
tread
stringer
handrail
basement insulation & d.p.c.

basement flr.
g tile
d stone
ing
tion wall
gs

LAUNDRY & FURNACE   STUDY

BATHROOM

RECREATION   BEDROOM

BASEMENT PLAN

PRE-FAB CHIMNEY   DINING   BEDROOM

KITCHEN

BATHROOM

LIVING RM   ENTRANCE LANDING   BEDROOM

GROUND FLOOR PLAN

FRONT ELEVATION

BUILDING CONSTRUCTION
materials and methods

BUILDING CONSTRUCTION
materials and methods

H. G. MILLER
Technical Director
General Brock High School
Burlington, Ontario

Illustrated by Tony Langdon and Bernard Loates

Macmillan of Canada   Toronto

ISBN 0-7705-0595-3

Cover design based on a drawing from National Forest Products Association.

Printed in Canada by the Bryant Press Limited

CONTENTS

PREFACE

This text is written with the sincere hope that it will stimulate the clear, constructive thinking that will enable students to solve problems and that it will provide information that will assist in the development of the skills required in the building industry. It is also hoped that it will foster an appreciation of the economic and social importance that good home building plays in the life of a community.

An attempt has been made to encourage students to take an active interest in building construction by pointing out the many vocational opportunities at present available to them in the various branches of the industry. The need to obtain the basic knowledge and skills that will make it possible for students to adapt themselves to changing employment requirements that will offer opportunities in construction fields not yet known or developed is stressed.

The material covered in this text follows the Ontario Department of Education Building Construction Course of Study Outline for grade 10 of the four- and five-year Science, Technology and Trades Branch. We have, however, expanded on the topics listed and have also added others in an effort to make this text of value beyond the grade 10 level, especially to those students studying building construction as a related subject. It is hoped that this book will be of value to all those interested in the basic principles of home construction, whether they are students, apprentices, tradesmen, or home owners.

Because of its importance, one section of the book has been devoted to construction safety. It has been placed at the back of the text immediately following the chapters on building construction as a ready reference. Questions that refer directly to this safety information have been included in many of the chapter assignments.

In so far as was practicable, the material in this text has been arranged in a logical sequence of operations in the order in which they would generally be performed in the actual building of the main structural portion of a house. Sections of residential construction such as foundations, interior trim, and interior wall coverings, as well as some other important aspects of building construction, are not included in this text, as it would not be feasible to incorporate all phases of building construction in an adequate manner in a single textbook. It was, therefore, considered advisable to restrict this book to describing in some detail the basic framing materials and operations involved in construction. Some of the other aspects of building are sufficiently important and involved to warrant a textbook dealing exclusively with them. These texts should be made available to all students continuing in the study of building construction.

An individual author's knowledge and experience is limited; only by reading the words and sharing the experiences of many authors can one hope to obtain a comprehensive understanding of any subject.

It is hoped, therefore, that all shop libraries will contain an adequate number of good reference books dealing directly or indirectly with building construction that can be used in conjunction with this text. To keep abreast of the latest developments in the building industry, the most recent building periodicals and trade catalogues should be available.

Students should be encouraged to observe new buildings being erected in the community, and to familiarize themselves with new building materials and construction techniques. The best way to learn a trade is to actually work at it; the second-best method is through first-hand observation. Students studying building construction have ample opportunity for this observation because of the vast amount of residential, commercial, and industrial building taking place in almost all parts of our country.

If this book serves the purpose for which it was intended — that of providing building construction information in an efficient and interesting manner — it will, in no small measure, be due to the valuable assistance I have received from government agencies, private associations, and individuals who provided me with authentic information and who made objective criticisms of draft copies of the manuscript.

I owe thanks to the Industrial Training Branch of the Ontario Department of Labour, to Mr. G. R. Henderson of the Construction Safety Associations of Ontario, and to the Canadian Wood Council, all of whom supplied valuable material and spared no effort giving me advice and encouragement in this project.

To all the manufacturers of building materials who so willingly supplied illustrative material I am indebted. Their names appear below the illustrations of their products.

To the members of my family, special thanks: their forbearance during the last two years made this work much easier.

If in some small measure this text assists in the promotion of technical education and better Canadian housing, I shall have been amply rewarded for my efforts.

H. G. M.

BUILDING CONSTRUCTION
materials and methods

Chapter 1

INTRODUCTION

It would be difficult to imagine our present way of life without the results of *builders*. Our spacious houses, compact but comfortable apartments, attractive public buildings, and large, efficient industrial plants all represent the progress and prosperity we enjoy, and should be constant reminders of the important role the construction industry plays in our daily lives.

During the past generation, home building has developed from an individual craft into one of North America's largest industries. The result of this continuing expansion will be improved construction methods. With this progress will also come new and different materials, ideas, and designs for making our homes more comfortable and convenient.

The contribution made by the upsurge in building construction has played a large part in the economic growth and social progress of our nation. The continued expansion of the building industry will require an ever increasing number of well-trained, highly skilled men to design, plan, erect, and service these buildings.

The building industry is composed of a great number of occupations all dealing with different materials and skills. Some of these tradesmen and professional people directly connected with building construction are architects, engineers, draftsmen, bricklayers, operators of heavy earth-moving equipment, plasterers, plumbers, electricians, tile setters, floorlayers, roofers, steam fitters, painters, sheet metal workers, cabinet-makers, lathers, glaziers, landscape gardeners, interior decorators, cement masons, steel erectors, refrigeration and air conditioning installers, and millworkers. These and many others all play their part in the building industry. In residential construction the carpenter, as well as being responsible for all the woodwork, often has the added responsibility of co-ordinating the work of all other tradesmen. He is generally the first worker on the site and remains there until the home has been completed. In commercial and industrial construction a graduate engineer is generally in charge of co-ordination and over-all supervision of the tradesmen. Often the foreman or building superintendent is an experienced carpenter. The carpentry work and some of the other major trades are generally handled directly by the builder or contractor, while the work done by some of the other tradesmen such as the plasterers and painters is referred to as a "sub-trade". This work is supervised by the builder or the architect, but may be done by other companies that have contracted to complete certain portions of the building.

Whether your interest lies in working with wood, metal, brick, plastics, electrical equipment, plumbing supplies, or any other building materials, there is an excellent opportunity for you in the building industry. Those of you who will be employed in occupations or trades not directly connected with the building industry should still find this study of interest and value, since housing and home ownership will be of vital concern to you for a large part of your lifetime. You will find the carpentry information in your course of valuable assistance in building, repairing, and maintaining your own home.

How does one get started in any one of the building trades? Enrolling in a technical course is the first step toward making some form of technical endeavour one's life's work. The immediate goal of all students should be to complete their secondary school education in the course of their choice. Without this groundwork of academic and technical knowledge, one will find that opportunities for employment in any line of work are limited and chances of advancement in such work as is available are few. Although grade 10 is the minimum entrance requirement for most trades, grade 12 is preferred.

The best method of entering any of the building trades is through *apprenticeship training.* This is a practical on-the-job plan that enables you to learn by doing. The education you receive from a technical course is an excellent preparation for apprenticeship; you can start making plans and preparing yourself for any one of the numerous building trades. Apprenticeship is a well-organized, long-term program of on-the-job and in-the-classroom training.

To be an *apprentice* a person must be over sixteen years of age, and have completed grade 10. It is, however, strongly recommended that prospective apprentices complete grade 12. Apart from the many other advantages of a secondary school diploma, recognition may be given by granting credit hours off the apprenticeship training period.

The apprentice enters into a three-way agreement between himself, his employer, and the Industrial Training Branch of the Department of Labour, the sponsoring body for this training plan. Terms of the contract state the length of the training plan, working conditions, and wages to be paid. Apprenticeship is the period during which the apprentice is fulfilling the terms of his agreement to work and to learn as much about the trade as possible. The length of the training time varies with the trade and is listed in units of hours. A carpentry apprentice, for instance, must serve four units of 1,800 hours, or the equivalent of three to four years depending on the number of hours worked per week. As has been stated previously, the time is generally reduced for grade 12 technical graduates.

During his apprenticeship, the apprentice must attend trade school for what normally consists of two ten-week day courses. The first course is basic and is taken during the first or second work period of the contract, and the second, or advanced, course is taken near the end of the contract.

The technical school graduate usually does not attend the basic course as the information would be a repetition of work he has already covered. The courses consist of specific technical and academic information relating to the trade being studied. The tuition cost of these courses, as well as a subsistence allowance to cover the cost of room and board while attending, is paid by the Department of Labour.

The wages paid during the apprenticeship period differ with the various trades, but all are based on a percentage of the average rate of pay of a *journeyman* (an experienced, qualified tradesman who has served his apprenticeship). This percentage gradually increases, from 40 per cent for the first period of hours to 80 per cent for the last period.

The Industrial Training Branch of the Department of Labour and the school often assist the qualified student in locating an employer who requires an apprentice in his business and who is willing to undertake this training.

The Department of Labour sponsors apprenticeship programs for the following building trades: bricklaying, carpentry, masonry, painting and decorating, plastering, electrical, plumbing, sheet metal working, steamfitting, refrigeration and air conditioning, lathing, and structural steel erection. Others, no doubt, will be added.

The contract simply ensures that the apprentice will be taught a trade by the employer and at the trade school, provided he has the desire to learn and will perform his assigned duties conscientiously and to the best of his ability. When the apprenticeship training has been successfully completed, the apprentice is issued a *certificate of apprenticeship* in all provinces except Quebec, stating that the holder is qualified to practise the trade. In some trades after the apprentice has passed a written examination, the certificate is stamped with an interprovincial "red seal", which means the certificate is recognized in all provinces.

Some of the advantages in taking apprenticeship training are that it (a) provides further education (with concurrent pay); (b) provides a sound trade training that will serve as a foundation for the future; (c) increases earning power and provides a good chance of future economic security.

Apprenticeship can be considered the road to a skilled job along which one earns as he learns.

While the rating of "journeyman tradesman" in one of the building trades is a worth-while goal and while it provides a measure of economic security and community standing, it need be only a stepping-stone to success for an ambitious and competent tradesman. There is a great need for well-trained building construction tradesmen and technicians to act in supervisory capacities as estimators, layoutmen, foremen, and construction superintendents for large building construction companies. There is a greater shortage of this type of personnel than for the hourly-rated journeyman tradesmen. As various aspects of building construction become more complex, better-trained men are required to supervise the work involved.

These are men who have studied mathematics, science, drafting, and English at the secondary school level and who have also acquired a sound basic trade knowledge through taking a technical course. This demand for better-educated and more highly skilled men brings greater opportunities for advancement than were available a few years ago. Preparing yourself now for a better than average position in the building industry will pay big dividends in the future.

Another opportunity open to grade 12 graduates interested in entering the industry is enrolment in one of the special two-year building construction technicians' courses offered at the vocational centres or junior colleges. In the post-high-school training centres operated by the Ontario Department of Education, students study more advanced aspects of all phases of building construction than are covered in either technical or apprenticeship trade schools. The special technicians' course covers in depth such building topics as planning, surveying, estimating, and studying strength of materials, as well as architectural drafting and mathematics. A somewhat similar post-high-school course is sponsored by the Mechanical Contractors Association. This course deals mainly with the mechanical aspects of building, such as plumbing, steamfitting, and refrigeration and air conditioning, rather than the structural aspects of building. Graduates from such courses as these help to fill the need for trained mechanical building technicians who install and maintain the vast amount of complex mechanical equipment that is required in commercial and industrial building. These courses are designed to graduate men at the *technicians' level* who will eventually fill many of the top planning and supervisory positions connected with building construction.

After gaining technical knowledge and skill as well as business ability while working for others, many building tradesmen decide to go into the building business for themselves. There are several ways of doing this. Some builders specialize in building new homes on a speculative basis to sell to prospective home owners; others operate as general contractors who contract to erect homes or other buildings to the specifications of their customers; still others specialize in repairs and alterations. Many builders will, of course, be involved in all three of these building operations.

Additional employment opportunities directly or indirectly connected with building construction are found in the non-designated trades or in such areas as lumber wholesale or retail outlets. Other areas include the manufacture and sale of special building materials, land and subdivision development, town or municipal planning (as architects' and surveyors' assistants), the servicing and operating of mechanical building equipment, and many other related occupations that all require a background of basic building construction knowledge or training. No other industry encompasses such a wide variety of occupations or uses so many different materials.

There is a wonderful opportunity for a rich and rewarding future for any young man willing to work and prepare himself for employment in any one of the branches of the building industry.

4

In the chapters that follow you will be introduced to some of the basic building materials and operations required in residential construction. The assignment questions included in each chapter should make the study of the topic more effective. As safety is an important aspect of all phases of building, questions on this topic have been included in many of the chapters. These refer to a special section on construction safety at the back of the book, where the subject is covered in some detail.

It is hoped, however, that you will carry the study of building construction far beyond the limits of the information presented in this book.

ASSIGNMENT

1. List six trades that are directly involved in building construction.
2. What are five employment possibilities for people who are not trades-men but who have a basic knowledge of building construction?
3. What should be the immediate goal of all secondary school students?
4. (a) What is meant by apprenticeship training?
   (b) What are the advantages of apprenticeship training?
   (c) List the building trades for which the Department of Labour sponsors apprenticeship training plans.
5. What future opportunities are there for a person engaged in one of the building trades after he has served his apprenticeship and worked for some time as a journeyman tradesman?
6. State any specific interest that you have in any branch of the building industry.

Chapter 2

BLUEPRINT READING

To be successful in any branch of the building industry it is essential that you acquire the ability to read *blueprints.* Your advancement in any of the building trades may well depend upon your ability to interpret quickly and accurately all of the information shown on the blueprints. It may mean the difference between being a junior tradesman and being a foreman or building superintendent. Opportunity and responsibility come only to those who prepare themselves. There is no better preparation than the study of architectural working drawings.

As the written word is the only means of communication between author and reader, so the architectural drawing is the means of communication between the engineer or architect and the tradesman. If you are unable to read or interpret this language of lines and symbols shown on working drawings, your value and your rewards as a tradesman will be very limited indeed. If, on the other hand, you become proficient in reading these drawings, your value will soon be recognized.

It is not our intention here to attempt to offer any instruction in drafting. No doubt you have been studying this subject and realize the very important part it plays in our industrial economy. It is hoped some of you may choose to specialize in this branch of technical education.

Since many more building construction personnel are required to read architectural drawings than to be involved in making them, we are including blueprint reading in this textbook. We cannot, however, hope to cover the complete field of architectural blueprint reading but can only introduce the topic and point out some of the basic principles of these drawings as well as some of the terms and symbols used.

For further study many fine books are available that deal exclusively with this topic. Some of these books are included in the bibliography of this text.

Architectural drawings may be artistic or technical. The artistic or *presentation drawings* will show the customer or prospective home owner what the house will look like when completed, but will give few details. This type of drawing is used extensively in advertising brochures and magazines and may include such effects as landscaping and shading to give a general impression of the over-all finished appearance of the house. These drawings are sometimes referred to as renderings. The technical or *working drawings* will be used by the builder and all the tradesmen working on the house. These drawings consist of *elevations, plan views, detail views,* and *sectional views.* They include all the dimensions, construction details, and other information necessary to build the structure exactly as the architect or the draftsman intended. No one view will give the complete picture, but by looking at several views you should get a good mental image of the completed house.

TYPES OF VIEWS

Elevation Views

Let us consider first some of the information to be found on the elevation views. Elevations are views of the exterior of a building in the vertical plane. The front elevation includes all exterior building lines and features that one would see when standing directly in front of the building. The other elevations are referred to as rear, right, or left elevations according to their position relative to the front of the building. See Figure 2:1.

The three elevations in Figure 2:1 show the exterior of the house as viewed from the front and the two ends. You will notice that certain lines representing definite corners of the building are shown on two elevations. Lines A and B on the front elevation represent the same corners of the house as lines A and B on the left elevation. Likewise, lines D and E on the front elevation represent the same corners of the building as lines D and E on the right elevation. Lines F and G will also appear on the rear elevation. Certain features of the house will appear on all three elevations, such as the front offset and the chimney, with the width shown on the front elevation and the thickness or depth shown on the right and left elevations. The dormer is shown on the right and left elevations and would also appear on the rear elevation. Features such as windows and doors that appear only in one plane will be shown in only one elevation because each face of the building will be shown on only one elevation.

LEFT ELEVATION   FRONT ELEVATION   RIGHT ELEVATION

Fig. 2:1   Elevation Views

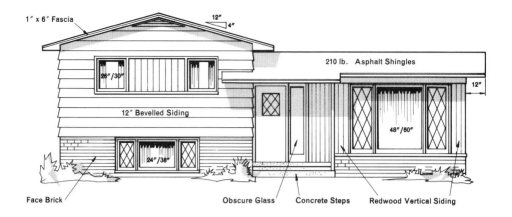

Fig. 2:2   Some information to be found on elevations.

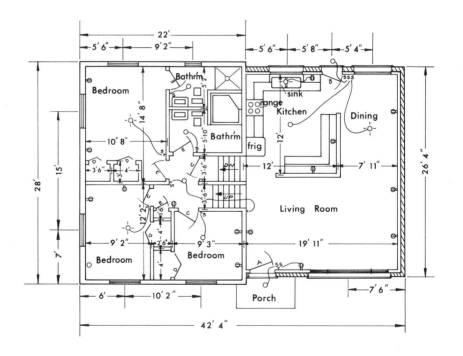

Fig. 2:3   First floor plan of a split-level house.

Some of the information to be found on the elevations include exterior wall covering, roof covering and pitch, window sizes (the glass size is generally given), porches, steps, planters, dormers, and bay windows. Figure 2:2, a front elevation, shows some of these.

Plan Views

Elevations are vertical views of the exterior of a house; plan views are horizontal views of the interior of a house that show the following features:

(a) the arrangement of the rooms, their shape and size;

(b) location of all doors and windows;

(c) wall and partition thicknesses;

(d) the location of all items such as closets, chimneys, fireplaces, cupboards, stairways, and other structural parts of the building as they would be seen when viewed from above if the building were cut through horizontally at window level.

Plan views are referred to as floor plans. At least one view will be required of each floor of the house, including the basement. Figure 2:3 shows a typical floor plan.

Where there is a great deal of information required regarding electrical or mechanical installations, more than one view of a floor plan may be drawn, with one floor plan dealing almost entirely with the electrical layout.

Sectional Views

Often there are structural details that cannot be clearly shown on either an elevation or a plan view. The architect will then provide a sectional view: generally of a wall section that shows the thickness of the wall and the materials used. See Figure 2:4 and 2:5 on page 10.

Detail Views

For further clarification and ease of dimensioning, many detail views are shown. They are drawn to a larger scale than the elevation and plan views, as otherwise the details shown on them could not be easily seen. Some of the items shown in detail views are windows, stairs, fireplaces, and cupboards.

DEVICES USED BY ARCHITECTS

Symbols

Because of the vast amount of information necessary to designate different building materials used and to indicate the type and location of plumbing, heating, ventilating, and electrical installation and equipment, a system of architectural symbols has been devised that is more or less standard on all architectural drawings. The symbols are, in fact, a form of architectural shorthand: they save space and add to the clarity of the working drawings. Some of the symbols commonly used are shown in Figure 2:6. There is no short cut to familiarity with these symbols. The only sure way is to memorize them so that at a glance you understand what the architect wants.

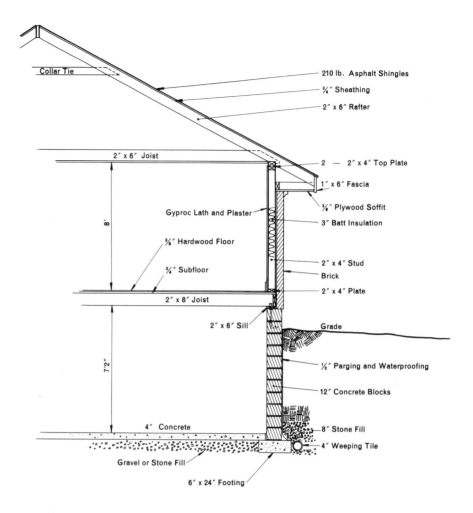

Collar Tie

210 lb. Asphalt Shingles

¾″ Sheathing

2″ x 6″ Rafter

2″ x 6″ Joist

2 — 2″ x 4″ Top Plate

1″ x 6″ Fascia

⅜″ Plywood Soffit

Gyproc Lath and Plaster

3″ Batt Insulation

8′

⅜″ Hardwood Floor

2″ x 4″ Stud

Brick

¾″ Subfloor

2″ x 8″ Joist

2″ x 4″ Plate

2″ x 6″ Sill

Grade

7′2″

½″ Parging and Waterproofing

12″ Concrete Blocks

4″ Concrete

8″ Stone Fill

4″ Weeping Tile

Gravel or Stone Fill

6″ x 24″ Footing

Fig. 2:4   Sectional view of a brick veneer wall.

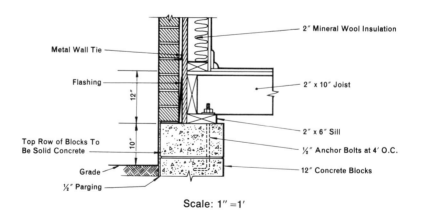

2″ Mineral Wool Insulation

Metal Wall Tie

Flashing

2″ x 10″ Joist

12″

10″

2″ x 6″ Sill

Top Row of Blocks To
Be Solid Concrete

½″ Anchor Bolts at 4′ O.C.

Grade

12″ Concrete Blocks

½″ Parging

Scale: 1″ = 1′

Fig. 2:5   Section Detail

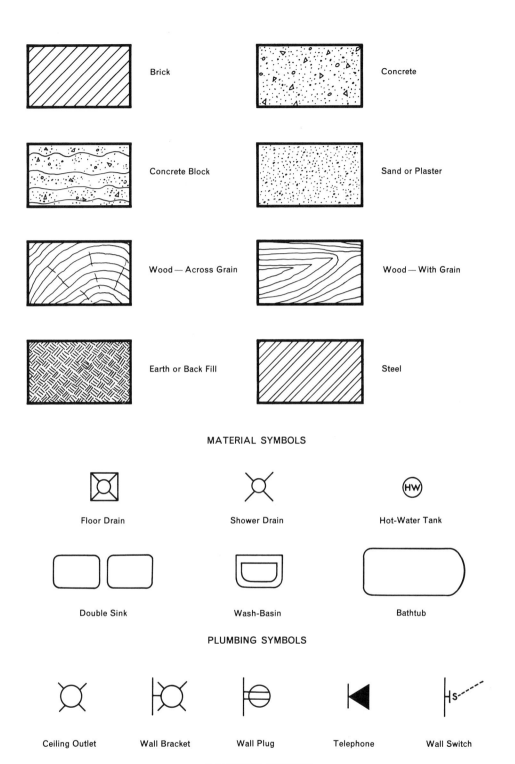

Brick

Concrete

Concrete Block

Sand or Plaster

Wood — Across Grain

Wood — With Grain

Earth or Back Fill

Steel

MATERIAL SYMBOLS

Floor Drain

Shower Drain

Hot-Water Tank

Double Sink

Wash-Basin

Bathtub

PLUMBING SYMBOLS

Ceiling Outlet

Wall Bracket

Wall Plug

Telephone

Wall Switch

ELECTRICAL SYMBOLS

Fig. 2:6   Architectural Symbols

Conventions

Conventions are the standard methods of showing structural parts of a house on the working drawings. They have been standardized and accepted as the method by which the architect shows on the drawings the facts he wants the builder to know. A basement window, for instance, will be shown in the same manner on all architectural drawings.

Exterior dimensions of frame and brick-veneer houses are taken from the outside face of the wall studs. For solid masonry or concrete the dimensions are taken from the exterior face of the building. The dimensions of doors and windows are to their centres. Room dimensions are given to the centre of the partitions.

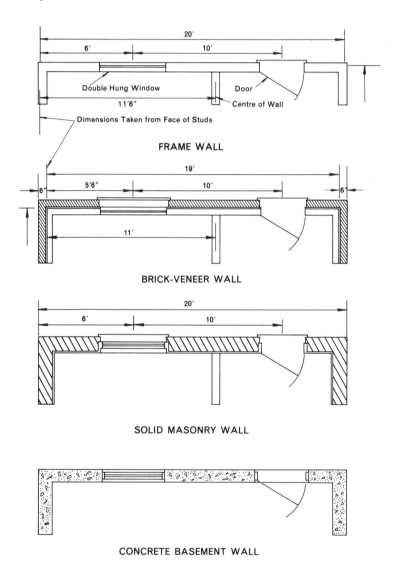

Fig. 2:7 Conventions used on the plan views of working drawings.

Schedules

A schedule is another device used by architects as a convenient and efficient way of listing information on working drawings. Schedules may be used to specify the types, sizes, style, and location of doors, windows, and room interior materials and finishes. All that need appear on the drawing is a circled number beside the part. By referring to the schedule, one can easily see all the particulars concerning a certain window or door.

ROOM SCHEDULE				
ROOM	WALLS	CEILING	FLOORS	TRIM
Living-Rm.	Plaster	Plaster	Oak	Oak
Dining-Rm.	Mah. Plywood	Tile	Maple	Mahogany
Kitchen	Plaster	Tile	Vinyl Tile	Pine-Painted
Bathroom	"	Tile	Vinyl Tile	Pine-Painted
Entry	"	Plaster	Flagstone	Oak
Hall	"	"	Oak	Oak
Bedroom 1	"	"	Maple	Mahogany
Bedroom 2	"	"	Maple	Mahogany

DOOR SCHEDULE				
NO.	QUAN.	TYPE	SIZE	REMARKS
A	1	Exterior	3' x 7' x 1¾"	3 — Light Birch
B	2	Exterior	2'10" x 6'10" x 1¾"	½ Light Fir
C	6	Interior	2'6" x 6'6" x 1⅜"	Mahogany Slab
D	4	Closet	2' x 6'6" x 1⅜"	Mahogany Louver
E	2	Closet	1'6" x 6'6" x 1⅜"	Mahogany Slab

Fig. 2:8   Schedules

Specifications

Specifications are written instructions that are not part of the drawings but they give detailed information concerning the construction of the building. Specifications are generally drawn up in point form, listing sizes, types, and grades of materials to be used as well as special equipment and other features that are to be incorporated into the building by the contractor. Some of this information may also be found on the drawings, but much of it is of such a nature that it is best to list it on a separate document. Generally the working drawings are readily available to all tradesmen on the job, while copies of the specifications are held only by the owner, the contractor, and the architect. Specifications are very important in that they protect both the home owner and the contractor. They stipulate exactly what the owner is to receive for his money and what the builder must supply. They are, in effect, the terms of the contract that both have signed. Any changes in the specifications while the house is under construction must be agreed to in writing.

Scales

An important aspect of architectural drawings is that all drawings are made to scale: that is, the size of the drawing has a definite relationship to the actual size of the building. The scale to which the drawing is made is stated on each view. Detail views are generally drawn to a larger scale.than floor plans or elevations. A scale of ¼″ = 1′ is most often used for elevations and plan views. Even though the draftsman has carefully drawn the plans to a stated scale, never attempt to determine a dimension by measuring the drawing, or scaling the drawing, as it is commonly called. The architect or draftsman will have stated the correct dimensions on one of the views. You will be able to locate the dimensions easily once you are accustomed to reading blueprints.

One of the reasons why you should learn as much as possible about reading architectural drawings is that this skill enables you to visualize the house as it is to be built, and to know how and where to locate the information required to build it.

ASSIGNMENT

1. Why is it important that anyone connected with the building industry be able to read and understand architectural drawings?
2. Briefly describe the two basic types of architectural drawings.
3. List three pieces of information to be found on:
   (a) elevation views; (b) plan views; (c) sectional views.
4. When is it necessary for the architect to include a detailed view of a certain section of a house?
5. (a) Draw the symbols that indicate these structural materials:
      concrete; steel; wood (cross-grain).
   (b) Draw the symbols that indicate these plumbing fixtures:
      floor drain; wash basin; double kitchen sink.
   (c) Draw the symbols that indicate these electrical outlets:
      wall switch; ceiling outlet; telephone.
6. On the first floor plan show how a double window would be indicated on:
   (a) a solid brick house; (b) a brick-veneer house; (c) a frame house.
7. From what points are the exterior dimensions taken on:
   (a) a brick-veneer wall; (b) a solid masonry wall; (c) a frame wall?
8. List the information generally found on a room schedule.
9. From the isometric drawing of the house shown in Figure 2:9, make drawings of the front and left elevation views.
10. List the following information about the floor plan shown in Figure 2:9:

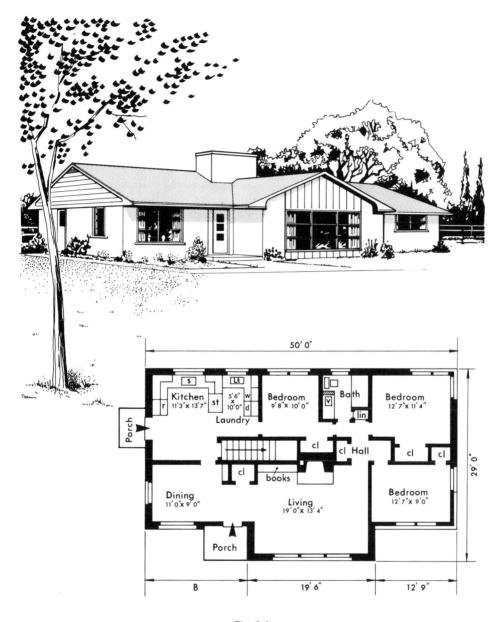

Fig. 2:9

(a) What is dimension "B"?
(b) How many windows would be shown on the rear elevation?
(c) How many closets are shown?
(d) From which room do the stairs descend to the basement?

Construction Safety (see pages 399 to 417)
11. (a) State the two major causes of accidents in the construction industry.
    (b) How could many of these accidents be prevented?

15

Chapter 3

BUILDING STANDARDS AND BUILDING TRADES

Building in Canada would soon be in hopeless confusion without regulations and standards. Imagine what would happen if people could erect any type of building wherever they could locate a piece of land big enough to put it on. This is why new homes being built in most parts of Canada are subject to many regulations and restrictions. It is also necessary to assure the public that new houses will be built with good materials, that a high standard of workmanship will be maintained, and that proper precautions will be taken for fire and public health protection. Building standards and regulations provide such assurance. It is in the best interest of everyone in the community that houses be built that are permanent, attractive, and a credit to their owner and the community. It is important that a high level of building standards be rigidly maintained for good city and town planning. We have all seen the results of insufficient planning and the lack of adequate building standards in the costly redevelopment projects that have been necessitated in some areas of our large cities.

For all these reasons government authorities have established building codes, restrictions, and regulations, governing not only the size of the dwelling and the type of the material to be used in it, but also the lot size and the placement of the house on the property. To some these regulations might seem restrictive, but when we consider that there is nothing more important to our social and economic growth than attractive, well-built homes, we realize that these regulations must be enforced.

The highest authority on building standards in Canada is to be found in the *National Building Code of Canada.* This fairly large volume, published by the Queen's Printer in Ottawa, was compiled by the Housing Standards Division of Building Research of the National Research Council in Ottawa. This council spends a great deal of time and money carrying out extensive research into such matters as the strength of materials, the effects of climate on materials and types of construction, the insulation, fire resistance, and acoustic qualities of materials, as well as other phases of building construction.

A supplement to the National Building Code that stipulates the minimum requirements for planning, construction, and materials for houses built under the National Housing Act is *Residential Standards.* This publication is revised each year by a committee of the National Research Council.

The *Central Mortgage and Housing Corporation* is the government agency that administers the National Housing Act for homes built with mortgage money supplied either directly from the government or from financial companies where the mortgage repayment is guaranteed by the government. This agency is responsible for the actual inspection and enforcement of the regulations as set out in the book *Residential Standards* for all homes built under the Act.

There are, of course, many houses built that are financed privately or from funds supplied by insurance companies or other firms that supply mortgage money for home building. The Central Mortgage and Housing Corporation has no direct control over these houses, but they must be constructed according to local building codes and by-laws. In nearly all areas the local building codes very closely parallel that which is outlined in *Residential Standards,* and in fact most of them are taken from this book. Where municipal by-laws or provincial regulations require higher standards than those stated in the *Residential Standards* as issued by Central Mortgage and Housing, the higher standards prevail.

Other building regulations and codes that govern certain phases of residential house construction can be found in *The Canadian Electric Code Part 1, The Residential Electric Heating Standards,* and other publications of the Canadian Standards Association; *The National Plumbing Code,* and *The Code of National Warm Air Heating and Air Conditioning Association of Canada.*

In addition to the regulations laid down in the codes, the subdivider or the owner of the housing development may place some stipulations on the type and size of the houses to be built on the lots that are sold. In this way he has some control over the finished subdivision. It also assures anyone who purchases a lot in the subdivision that the value of his property will not be adversely affected by someone building an inferior house next to his.

The minimum regulations listed in *Residential Standards* cover most phases of home construction. Starting with planning, requirements are stated governing the minimum size and number of rooms, ceiling heights, sizes and placement of windows and exterior doors, location and design of stairs, and many other planning details. Regulations governing the actual construction cover such items as foundation walls, thickness and width of footings, and type and spacing of framing members such as girders, supporting columns, studding, and rafters. Tables are included listing the required size and spacing of framing members to be used for a given span and supporting a specified load. Many regulations are listed concerning solid masonry walls, as well as veneer walls of brick, stone, or stucco. The mechanical services such as electrical, plumbing, heating, and air conditioning are dealt with in a general manner in *Residential Standards* but are covered more specifically in some of the other regulations mentioned above. They are enforced by inspectors who deal specifically with this phase of home construction. A copy of *Residential Standards* should be available for your further study.

The building regulations mentioned state only the minimum requirements that must be met in the public interest. Designers, architects, and builders may, and generally do, go beyond these requirements. Building regulations are not intended to restrict the development of better designs and improved methods of construction.

However, all the general building regulations in the world would be to no avail if the individual pieces of material and equipment were not inspected, tested, and proved to be of acceptable quality before they are used in home construction. There are two organizations mainly responsible for the quality of building materials: (1) The *Canadian Lumbermen's Association*, and (2) The *Canadian Standards Association.*

The Canadian Lumbermen's Association and its associate companies are authorized to grade and stamp lumber before it is sold to builders and home owners. Most building regulations state definitely which grade of lumber is to be used for specific parts of the building. The approved grading stamp must appear on the material used. For example, the Canadian Lumbermen's Association grade mark shown here will be stamped near the end of most 2″ construction spruce used for framing members in N.H.A. homes.

Fig. 3:1   Labels of the Canadian Lumbermen's Association and the Canadian Standards Association

The Canadian Standards Association is an independent organization authorized by the government to operate laboratories for the testing and inspection of such building materials as electrical appliances, fuel-burning equipment, plumbing fixtures and fittings, safety equipment, plastic products, and various other items. The CSA stamp of approval is assurance that samples of the product have been thoroughly inspected for uniformity and safety and tested to ensure an acceptable level of performance under normal use.

Good houses do not "just grow" like Topsy, although some houses may appear to have done so. Before starting the actual construction of a good house, a great deal of thought and planning must be done by the new home owner, the architect, or the builder — and often by all three. The home owner must decide on the type and size of house he would like. He must also carefully analyse his needs or requirements and assess his financial ability to pay for them. Often, painful compromises must be made before the plans are finalized.

The selection of the neighbourhood and the particular building lot is the responsibility of the home owner. He should begin by choosing an area that is within a convenient distance from his employment, or at least, within easy commuting distance. It should have the normal community services: good schools, a shopping centre, churches, parks, playground, and a community centre. If the lot is situated in a suburban area it should be provided with local services such as storm and sanitary sewers, water, gas, and electricity. It should also have good connecting roads and a dependable public transportation service. A large proportion of the homes should be well-built, attractive, single-family dwellings that are owner-occupied. The immediate area should be predominantly residential, preferably in a young, growing community where real estate values are rising. There should be adequate local building restrictions and/or local zoning by-laws that dictate the type and size of the dwelling, thus protecting the home owner's investment. On the other hand, the restriction should not be so severe as to make the building of a new home too expensive.

It has often been debated which should be selected first: the house plans or the lot. It is generally considered better to select a building lot and then choose a house design to fit the size, shape, and topography of the lot and to blend in with surrounding buildings and landscape.

Many prospective home owners simply purchase, from a builder or a subdivider, a new house already erected in a new housing development. This is a convenient method of acquiring a home, since all the planning, building, and financing arrangements have already been completed. The prospective owner need only choose an area, pick out a house that he likes and can afford, make the down payment, move in — and, of course, keep up the payments.

The people most directly responsible for planning new homes are the architects who draw the plans, either for the prospective home owners or for the Central Mortgage and Housing Corporation. C.M.H.C. in turn sells them for a small fee to the contractors and builders who build homes under the National Housing Act. House plans are available from many sources, but most of them are produced by architects, whose years of training and experience enable them to incorporate the many good features that make our modern homes both attractive and functional. Some builders either draw the plans for the houses they build or modify the plans originally drawn by architects. Years of practical building experience and technical know-how are necessary before a builder can thus place himself in the role of designer and architect.

The major responsibility for the completion of the new house rests with the builder or general contractor. He is responsible for all work done on the house from the layout of the building on the lot to the final interior trim and paint. He must supervise and co-ordinate the work of all the tradesmen involved in completing the house. This means that he may have to schedule the work of as many as twenty different types of tradesmen who may be employed by twenty different firms. These firms or individuals are generally under contract to the builder to complete one phase of the work. They are referred to as *subcontractors* while the builder is referred to as the *general contractor.*

It is no mean feat to see that each of these groups of tradesmen arrive on the building site at the proper time and complete their allotted tasks so that subsequent groups may complete their work. Several groups of tradesmen, of course, may be at work on the house at the same time. Throughout the whole operation the builder must display considerable organizing ability in dovetailing all operations together, in seeing that all the material used is as specified, and also in making sure it arrives on the site when it is needed. This task becomes more difficult when the builder has several homes under construction at the same time. He must contend with labour problems, shortages of building materials, adverse weather conditions which greatly affect some phases of construction, and many other problems. In spite of these difficulties good builders find the home construction industry a challenging and rewarding business to be in.

Generally, even though the builder is technically in charge of all the labour and material required to complete the home, the subcontracting firms that have contracted to complete certain parts of the house such as the bricklaying, electrical installation, and plumbing must share the responsibility with the builder. The terms of their contract with the builder, or directly with the owner, stipulate the extent and quality of the work to be done. Not only are they responsible to the builder, but the work they have completed is subject to inspection by municipal and/or National Housing building inspectors.

All the tradesmen involved in building a house must work as a team, with the builder acting as captain, if a good home is to be built.

ASSIGNMENT

1. Why is it necessary to have building regulations and restrictions on new home building?

2. (a) What is the most complete authority governing building standards in Canada?

    (b) What government agency is responsible for writing these building standards?

    (c) What type of research does this agency carry out in establishing these standards?

3. Name the government agency responsible for administering the National Housing Act.

4. What regulations govern the building of homes not built under the National Housing Act?

5. What building regulations govern:
   (a) the electrical work;
   (b) the plumbing;
   (c) the furnace work?

6. List some of the points covered in *Residential Standards* concerning minimum requirements for these phases of house building:
   (a) planning;
   (b) the frame construction.

7. In the selection of a building lot, what factors should the prospective home owner consider?

8. What restrictions do local zoning by-laws place on new homes?

9. Which should be selected first, the building lot or the house plans? Give reasons for your answer.

10. Explain the duties and responsibilities of the builder in the construction of a new house.

11. List some of the problems a builder may encounter in the construction of a new home.

12. (a) What is meant by a subcontractor?
    (b) What are the responsibilities of a subcontractor in the construction of a new house.

Construction Safety (see pages 399 to 417)

13. What are the responsibilities of the construction company in preventing accidents?

14. List three legislative acts passed by the Ontario government aimed at the prevention of accidents in the construction industry.

Chapter 4

TYPES OF CONSTRUCTION AND BUILDING MATERIALS

Before going into the details of home-building, let us first consider some of the various types of home construction and some of the materials that are used.

TYPES OF HOME CONSTRUCTION

The type of home construction chosen will depend on such factors as the preference of the owner, local building restrictions, cost, and geographic location. For instance, homes built in a warm climate will differ structurally from those built in a colder climate.

Frame Construction

Houses built with a wood frame are used extensively in all areas, and in many places they far exceed any other type of construction. Some cities, however, in the interest of fire prevention, have local building by-laws that restrict frame construction to larger lots where there is a greater distance between houses. The popularity of frame houses is due to their low cost and their ease of erection. They can be built more quickly by fewer tradesmen than most other types of construction, yet still provide attractive, durable homes.

The term "frame construction" originated with the older frame houses. The main structural members consisted of large, square timbers for corner posts, plates and sills making up the frame in the same manner as for frame barns. Timbers are no longer used for frame houses. The structural members are made from 2″ x 4″ uprights with 2″ x 8″s or 2″ x 10″s for floor joists and 2″ x 4″s or 2″ x 6″s for ceiling joists and rafters. The exterior is covered with wood or fibreboard sheathing over which is placed some type of wood or other siding. Much of this book will deal with this type of construction.

Platform Frame Construction. Figure 4:1 shows some of the structural details of platform frame construction. This type of construction is in general use in most parts of Canada, especially for one-storey houses. It consists of building the floor unit on the foundation and using the subfloor as a platform or base on which to erect the exterior walls and partitions. It is a fast and economical form of construction but has the disadvantage of con-considerable shrinkage because of the large number of horizontal bearing

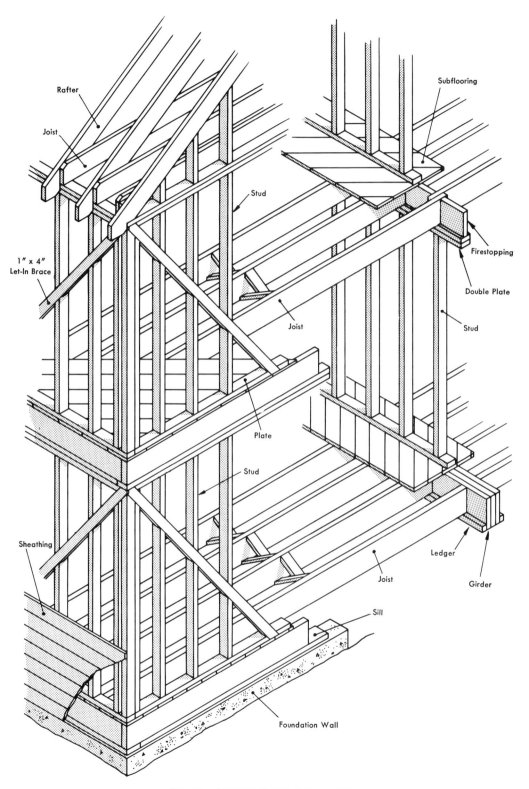

Rafter

Joist

Stud

1″ x 4″
Let-In Brace

Joist

Plate

Stud

Sheathing

Subflooring

Firestopping

Double Plate

Stud

Ledger

Girder

Joist

Sill

Foundation Wall

Fig. 4:1 Platform Frame Construction

23

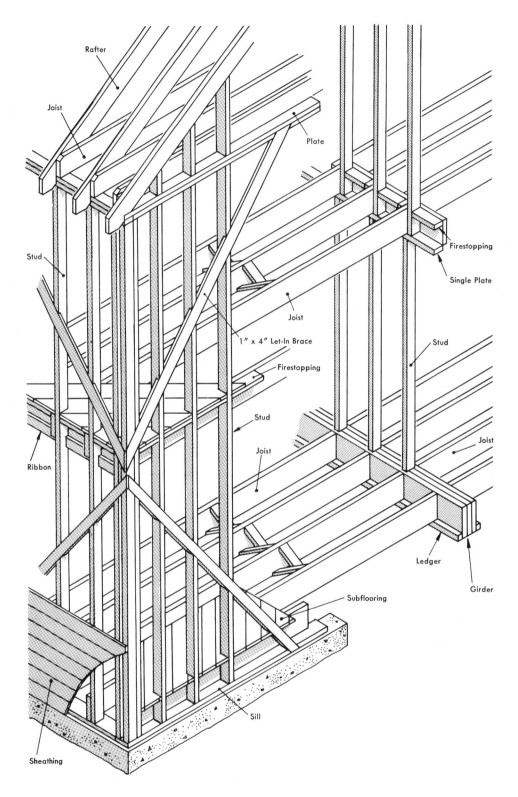

Fig. 4:2   Balloon Frame Construction

24

members. Platform frame construction lends itself well to the erection of prefabricated homes because the floors and walls can be built as units and erected one on another like blocks.

Balloon Frame Construction. Figure 4:2 illustrates the structural details of balloon frame construction. It can be noted here that the 2″ x 4″ exterior wall studding runs continuously from the sill on the foundation to the plate under the rafters. The advantage of this arrangement is that it minimizes the wall shrinkage; lumber shrinks very little in length but considerably in width and thickness. Since most of the bearing members in balloon construction are vertical, it is a preferred type of construction, especially for two-storey houses, even though it requires more labour. The second-floor joists are supported by a 1″ x 6″ board that is notched into the inside edge of the studding at the correct height.

Post and Beam Construction. This type of frame construction is now extensively used for modern homes as a method of framing walls and ceilings. In some ways it resembles the timber framing that was used in many older homes. However, many new features in design and materials have been added to make it a desired type of construction.

The conventional platform and balloon framing consist of upright studding and other framing members spaced at 16″ intervals. The post and beam method of construction requires larger but fewer members spaced farther apart. The subfloor and roof sheathing are usually made of 2″ material. They are supported by solid or laminated transverse or longitudinal beams spaced at intervals of not more than 8′. The beams, in turn, are supported by posts at the outside walls. The spaces between the main bearing posts consist of

Fig. 4:3 Post and Beam Construction

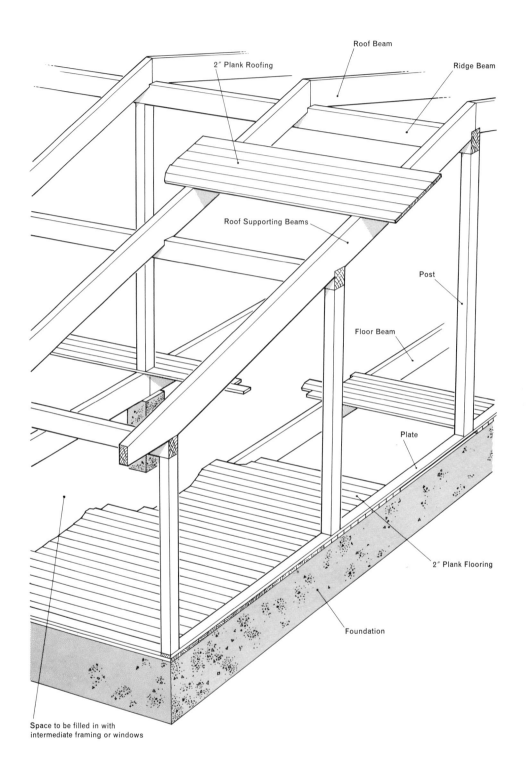

Roof Beam

Ridge Beam

2″ Plank Roofing

Roof Supporting Beams

Post

Floor Beam

Plate

2″ Plank Flooring

Foundation

Space to be filled in with
intermediate framing or windows

Fig. 4:4   Post and Beam Construction for a One-Storey House

26

window and door openings or supplementary framing members to which the interior and exterior finishing materials are applied. This section of the walls between the posts does not support the roof load but serves only to enclose the house and provide lateral bracing for the walls.

There are several advantages to post and beam construction, such as the rustic architectural effect presented by the exposed beams and plank ceilings. The planks used as roof sheathing may also serve as the interior finish, thus saving the time and material required to build a ceiling. This adds height to the living area and provides for a greater circulation of air.

Post and beam construction allows for a greater flexibility of window arrangement. Windows can be extended into the gables, permitting more light to enter and adding variety to the interior and exterior architectural design of the house. Figure 4:4 illustrates some of the structural details of the post and beam construction.

Plank Wall Framing. This is a type of frame wall construction that has been described as truly Canadian. Although little known in many areas, it is ex-

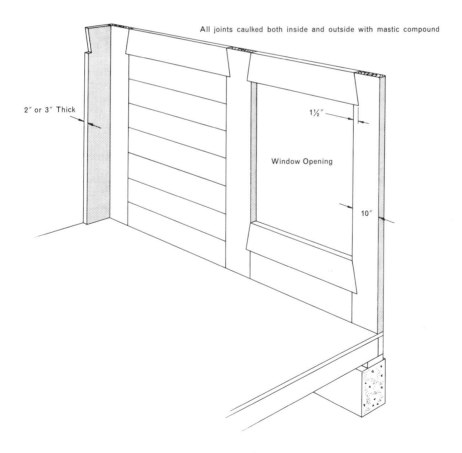

All joints caulked both inside and outside with mastic compound

2″ or 3″ Thick

1½″

Window Opening

10″

Fig. 4:5   Plank Wall Construction

tensively used in the province of Quebec and is recognized as an acceptable form of frame construction in many municipalities in and around Montreal. It is acknowledged by the National Building Code and by the *Residential Standards* as being acceptable for National Housing loans.

Plank wall construction consists of planks 2″ or 3″ thick and 10″ wide placed vertically at intervals of not more than 8′ to support the roof or the floor above them. Other planks are placed on edge horizontally between the uprights, many of them above or below the windows. If 2″ planks are used, 1″ vertical sheathing must be used on the outside of the wall. If 3″ planks are used, the wall is strapped on the outside and any type of exterior wall covering may be used. The inside of the wall is covered with a vapour-barrier material, 1″ x 2″ furring strips, and lath and plaster.

No upright 2″ x 4″ studding is used; the vertical and horizontal planks provide a strong rigid wall with good insulating and sound-deadening qualities, at a reasonable cost. Figure 4:5 shows some of the details of plank wall construction.

All of the types of construction described above may be built on a conventional masonry foundation wall with a full basement, or they may be built on a specially prepared concrete slab that has been poured directly on the ground. *Slab Floor Construction* has become quite common in most parts of our country. It provides a home all on one floor – considered an advantage in modern living. This type of construction lends itself well to the prevailing architectural styling of low houses that spread over a fairly large area.

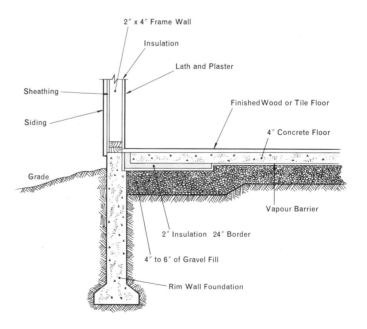

Fig. 4:6 Slab Floor Construction with Rim Wall Foundation.

The area on which the house is to rest must be prepared to provide drainage. Insulating materials must be used below the concrete in most climates. Figure 4:6 shows one type of slab floor construction.

Although frame construction is one of the oldest methods of building homes in this country, changes continue to take place in this type of construction, due to the development of new materials and to improvements in home design.

Masonry Construction

Brick Veneer Construction. This is a combination of masonry and wood frame construction. It is widely used because it incorporates the better features of both frame and masonry construction.

A wood frame with sheathing is erected on the foundation and one thickness of brick is applied. The wood framing members must be kept to the inner edge of the foundation wall as the brick must have a full bearing on it. An air space of 1″ is left between the brick and the sheathing, which must be provided with vents at sill level to allow passage of air, thus preventing condensation within the wall. Metal ties nailed to the sheathing and the

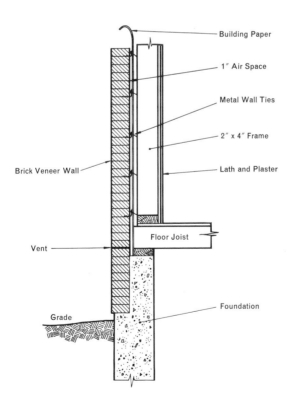

Fig. 4:7 Brick Veneer Construction

Fig. 4:8   Brick Veneer Construction

frame, and set in the cement mortar, act as a bond between the brick and the frame. A brick veneer wall is shown in Figures 4:7 and 4:8. A *stone veneer wall* can be built in the same manner, using natural or manufactured cut stone.

Brick-and-Block Construction. This is another type of brick veneer. A brick face is built on hollow concrete blocks. The backup blocks may be 4″, 6″, or 8″ in thickness depending on the thickness of the wall desired or the

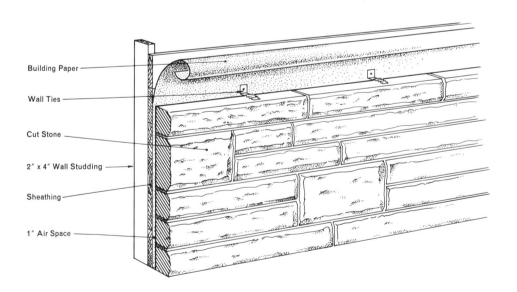

Building Paper

Wall Ties

Cut Stone

2″ x 4″ Wall Studding

Sheathing

1″ Air Space

Fig. 4:9   Stone Veneer Wall

30

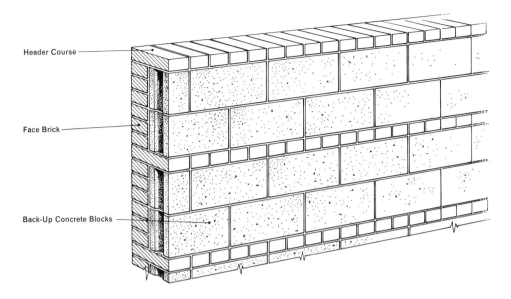

Header Course

Face Brick

Back-Up Concrete Blocks

Fig. 4:10   Brick and Block Wall

load to be carried. No air space is left between the block and brick; they are built as a solid wall. The hollow space in the block provides the necessary air space. Generally, every seventh course of brick is laid with the end of the brick facing out, allowing the bricks to extend over the block to form a bond which ties the wall together. These are called header courses.

Manufactured or natural cut stone may be used instead of brick on the face of this type of wall.

The inside of the wall should be parged (plastered) with cement mortar before the wall is insulated, and strapped with 1″ x 2″ furring pieces. The furring pieces provide the nailing base for gyproc or other plaster base. Figure 4:10 illustrates such a wall.

Solid Brick Construction.   Walls may be made by laying two or three thicknesses of brick, as illustrated in Figure 4:11, to make a wall 8″ or 12″ thick. This type of construction is gradually being replaced by brick-and-block construction. There is a considerable saving both in the cost of the material and in the labour when back-up blocks are used. The interior of the wall is strapped, insulated, lathed, and plastered.

Concrete Block Construction.   Many houses have exterior walls built almost entirely of concrete blocks 8″ or 10″ thick. The exterior face of the block can be plastered with a cement, lime, and sand mortar, and spray-painted. A fairly presentable appearance can also be obtained by applying a special masonry paint directly on the face of the blocks. If this method is used, care must be taken when laying the blocks to see that all mortar joints are neatly trowelled and flush with the face of the block, or the joints

Every seventh course
is a header course.

Fig. 4:11   Solid Brick Wall, Two Bricks Thick

may be recessed or V'd for effect. The interior of the wall is given the same treatment as the brick-and-block wall.

Stucco. In some localities many stucco houses are built. These houses are a combination of frame and masonry construction. The wood frame is made of 2″ x 4″ material with a wood or fibreboard sheathing over which is placed a heavy building paper covered with a metal lath. Smooth or stone-covered stucco is then applied. Better results are obtained when 1″ x 2″ strapping is nailed to the sheathing at 16″ intervals and the wire lath nailed to it. The stucco will come through the wire and form a better key.

If properly applied so that no moisture is allowed to get behind it, stucco affords a durable, attractive, fire-resistant exterior finish that will last for many years.

Poured Concrete. Houses are built by erecting forms for the walls and filling them with concrete in the same way that concrete basement walls are built. It is more economical if several houses of the same design are to be constructed so that the same forms can be used several times. The exterior is finished by plastering it with cement mortar or by painting it. On the inside the wall should be strapped, insulated, and plastered. The concrete should be reinforced with horizontal and vertical steel rods. See Figure 4:14.

Pre-cast Concrete. Several types of *pre-cast concrete wall sections* are made for industrial, commercial, and residential construction. The concrete is poured in sections, or panels, at a factory; the sections are then transported to the building site where they are assembled to make a complete building. One type of pre-cast concrete wall section is shown in Figure 4:15; other types are described later in this chapter.

32

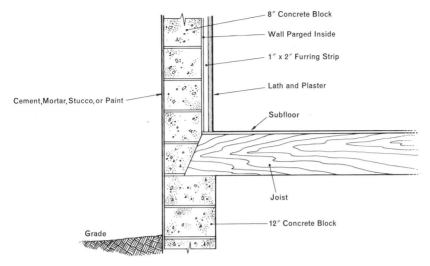

8″ Concrete Block

Wall Parged Inside

1″ x 2″ Furring Strip

Lath and Plaster

Cement, Mortar, Stucco, or Paint

Subfloor

Joist

12″ Concrete Block

Grade

Fig. 4:12   Concrete Block Wall

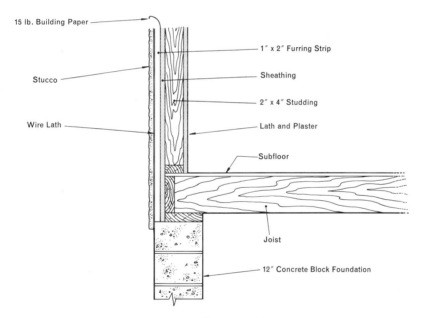

15 lb. Building Paper

1″ x 2″ Furring Strip

Stucco

Sheathing

2″ x 4″ Studding

Wire Lath

Lath and Plaster

Subfloor

Joist

12″ Concrete Block Foundation

Fig. 4:13   Stucco Wall

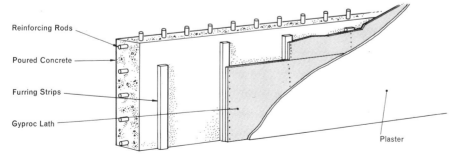

Reinforcing Rods

Poured Concrete

Furring Strips

Gyproc Lath

Plaster

Fig. 4:14   Section of a Poured Concrete Wall

33

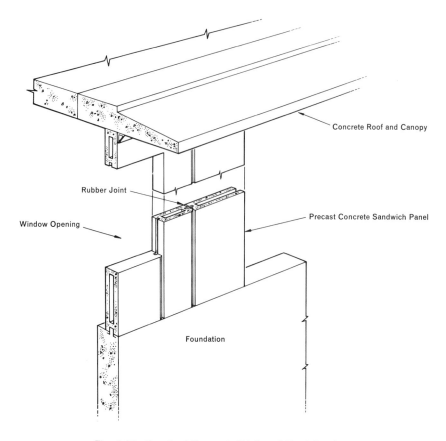

Fig. 4:15 Pre-Cast Concrete Wall and Roof Sections

There are other types and combinations of types of construction than those described here, but these are some of the more commonly used ones with which you should be familiar.

Prefabricated Construction

Like nearly every other industrial field, the building industry is becoming automated. This is coming about through factory-built homes and the use of the most modern engineered production methods and labour-saving devices. Such time-saving devices as automatic nailing and stapling machines are used to assemble wall sections and other component house parts in or on precision frames or jigs. These *prefabricated sections,* completely fitted with all doors and windows, are transported to the building site where the house can be quickly assembled on the prepared foundation. The floor, wall, and roof sections can be assembled and the house completely enclosed and under lock and key in less than two days.

Formerly, *prefabricated homes* were restricted to the smaller, one-storey frame houses with some type of wood siding. Factory-built homes are no longer limited to this type of dwelling but can be built in such styles as ranch-type bungalows, split-level homes, two-storey homes, or almost any

34

other style or size of house that can be built by the conventional on-the-site method. The wall sections generally consist of frames made with 2" x 4" members covered with fibreboard sheathing. They may be covered with wood siding, but more often a brick or stone face is applied at the site in the same fashion as for conventionally built houses. Some manufactured-home builders are completing the interior of the walls by laminating plywood sheets to the studs. This is done by placing the panel sections in a press and applying heat and pressure. They achieve what is termed a *stressed-skin* wall section, which is extremely strong and cannot be duplicated in houses that are built on the site. These manufacturers also install the insulation, electrical wiring, and plumbing services that are required in the wall sections, as well as the electrical heating units.

Some of the advantages of *factory-built homes* are the speed with which the building can be erected and closed in from the weather, and the high degree of precision arrived at by the use of assembly jigs and machine cutting, which is difficult to achieve when all the pieces are individually cut, fitted, and assembled on the site. Home construction need not be curtailed to certain areas during certain seasons when skilled tradesmen are not available. To enable builders to control the cost of building units more closely, prefabricated houses, complete with the frame, trim, doors, windows, and finishing materials, are delivered as a package unit at a stated price.

This type of home construction is gradually changing the role played by skilled and semi-skilled carpenters or woodworkers. Many people directly engaged in building construction will, in the future, be employed on a full-time basis in an enclosed assembly plant just as machinists or other skilled tradesmen are employed today in the manufacture of automobiles or other factory-built products. This type of building construction requires men with varying degrees of skill, ranging from foremen, lead hands, and layoutmen to the semi-skilled production worker.

It must, of course, be realized that the success of the prefabricated home industry is due largely to the fact that there is a considerable amount of uniformity in the homes that are built. The manufacturer is able to set up efficient production assembly lines for the houses that have been designed and catalogued for sale. Although only certain changes can be made without extra cost, the choice of home offered by home manufacturers is, nevertheless, wide enough to satisfy most home-buyers. It is not expected that prefabricated homes will ever replace on-the-site, custom-built homes, but it is expected that a much larger percentage of Canadian homes will be wholly or partially prefabricated.

It is difficult to classify houses as prefabricated or as built on the site because most builders prefabricate, at least partially, the houses they build. Although the walls may not have been pre-assembled as prefabricated sections, such members and components as roof trusses, window and door frames, cupboard units, stairs, and other parts are made as production units and transported to the site.

A

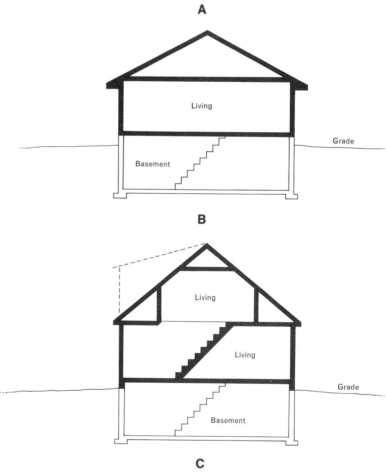

Fig. 4:16 (A) One-Storey Pitched Roof House; (B) Conventional One-Storey House, with Flat Ceiling and Pitched Roof; (C) One-and-a-Half-Storey House, with or without Dormer Windows.

36

A

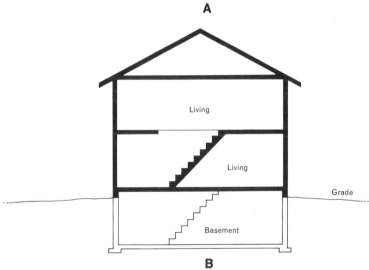

B

Fig. 4:17 (A) Modern Two-Storey House, with Porch and Garage; (B) Conventional Two-Storey House, with Flat Ceilings and Pitched Roof.

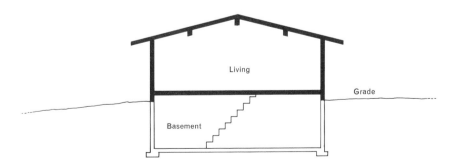

Fig. 4:18 Post and Beam Construction—Pitched Roof, Sloping Ceilings

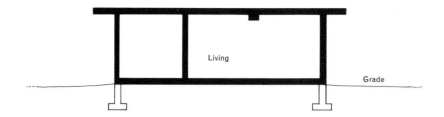

Fig. 4:19 Post and Beam Construction—Flat Roof, Slab Floor

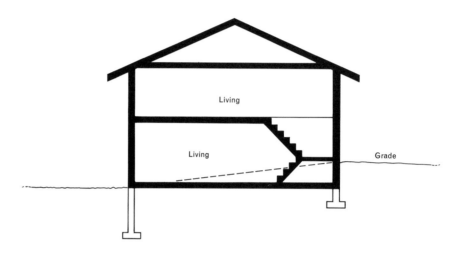

Fig. 4:20 Bi-Level House, with Split-Level Entrance, Two Living Levels, and No Basement

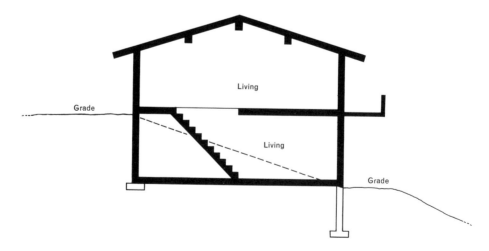

Fig. 4:21 Bi-Level House, Top Level With Open Ceiling, Lower Level With Flat Ceiling. Built on Hillside Lot.

A

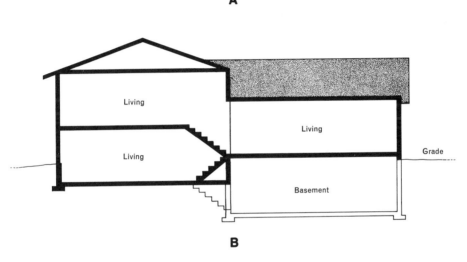

B

Fig. 4:22 (A) Split-Level House; (B) Split-Level House, with Three Living Levels and Flat Ceilings.

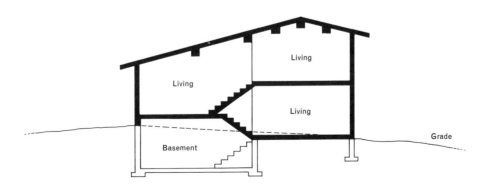

Fig. 4:23 Split-Level House, Post and Beam Construction, with Three Living Levels, Pitched Roof, and Open Ceilings

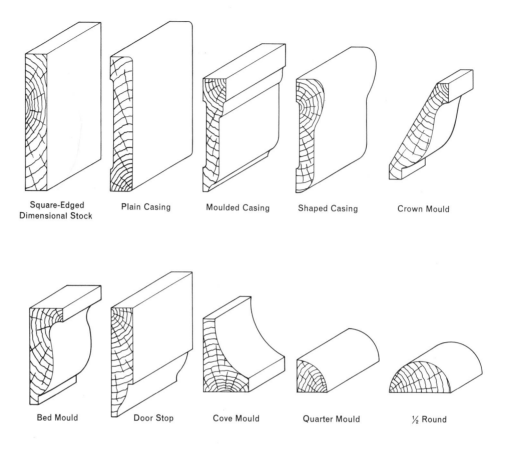

Square-Edged
Dimensional Stock

Plain Casing

Moulded Casing

Shaped Casing

Crown Mould

Bed Mould

Door Stop

Cove Mould

Quarter Mould

½ Round

Fig. 4:24 Trim Stock

Figures 4:16 to 4:23 illustrate some of the basic architectural styles currently being used in home construction, whether the house is to be built on the site or prefabricated in a factory.

BUILDING MATERIALS

A large variety of building materials are in general use in the construction of houses of all types. We cannot hope to consider all of them, but you should be familiar with some of those most frequently used in Canada.

Building materials fall into five categories, according to what they are manufactured from: wood, fibre, plastics, masonry materials, or metal.

Lumber

Let us first consider some of the forms of lumber products. Most lumber is sold as *dimensional stock,* which means that it has been cut and planed to nominal sizes with square edges such as 1″ x 8″, or 2″ x 4″. *(Actual sizes are slightly smaller.)* Lumber is also cut to special sizes and shapes such as *trim*

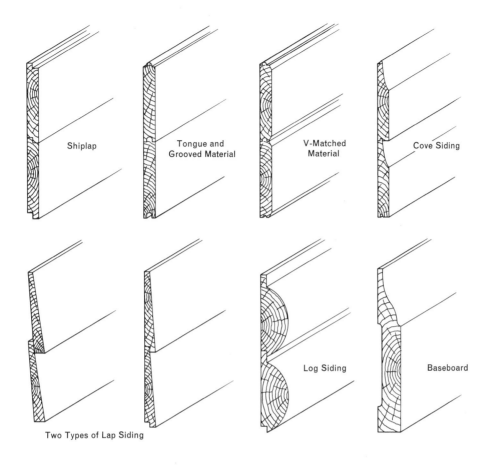

Fig. 4:25 Types of Lumber

stock, which has been milled to a special shape and used for such purposes as door and window trim. Some of these shapes are shown in Figure 4:24.

Mouldings. These are generally milled from smaller stock and sold by the lineal foot. Some of them are also shown in Figure 4:24.

Other lumber building products are siding materials, milled to a variety of shapes and widths; sheathing material such as shiplap, tongue and grooved stock, V-matched material; and many others, some of which are shown in Figure 4:25.

Plywood. This is a manufactured type of wood that has revolutionized the building industry. Carpenters are no longer limited to using wood in board widths. The use of large plywood sheets has made many building operations easier and faster and the finished structure neater and stronger. Plywood is an economical method of utilizing wood for many building materials. In the manufacturing of logs into plywood, there is little waste, and a much *higher strength-weight ratio* is obtained than when lumber is cut into solid, square-edged stock. In fact, plywood is stronger in proportion to its weight than steel. This is because it is made up of layers of veneers, or thin layers of wood, which are laminated (glued) together, with the grain of alternate layers generally at right-angles to each other. The layers are sliced or peeled from the log in thicknesses of 1/20″ or more. These layers are called *plies.* The centre ply is often thicker than this, however, and is referred to as core stock. To achieve a balanced construction and to reduce the tendency to cupping, an odd number of plies, usually three, five, or seven, is used, depending on the thickness of the plywood. The grain of the two outer plies runs lengthwise on the sheet. Standard sheets vary in thickness from 3/16″ to 1″ but are always 4′ wide and 8′ long. Other sizes are made for special applications.

Some plywoods have a solid lumber core up to ¾″ in thickness.

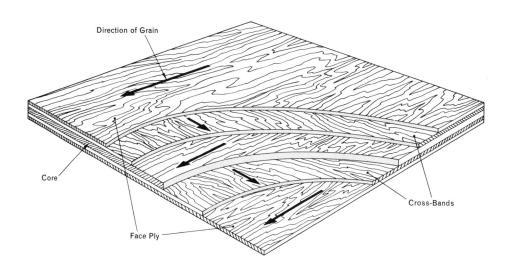

Direction of Grain

Core

Cross-Bands

Face Ply

Fig. 4:26 Five-Ply Plywood with Veneer Core

Plywood is made in many grades to suit the purposes for which it is to be used. Sheathing grade is unsanded and may have defects on both sides; it is used for roof and wall covering under the siding or shingles. Some plywood is listed as *G. 1 S.* (good one side) and has one face that is sanded and has no defects. *G. 2 S.* plywood has two good faces. Other plywood is labelled as *improved back,* indicating that the defects have been cut out and patches of sound wood inserted.

Some plywood is milled with a tongue and groove for use as subflooring.

Plywood is used extensively as a finished interior wall covering, and, for

42

this purpose, it is made in many decorative patterns and finishes, in either plain or plank design. Many have *"pre-finished" surfaces* – that is, a varnish-like finish which is applied to the plywood sheets at the factory. This saves time on the job and provides a uniform finish.

Fibre

Sheets also made from wood but in different forms than plywood are the numerous types of fibreboard building materials. Rather than using solid wood, a better insulating value can be obtained when the wood is first made into pulp and then pressed into sheets. This value arises because the *fibreboard* is porous, having millions of air spaces between the fibres. Because of its insulating qualities, this rather loosely compressed type of fibreboard makes excellent wall sheathing under siding or brick, or for plaster base on interior walls or ceilings.

Hardboards. These more tightly compressed fibreboards, sometimes referred to as *hardboards*, have little insulation value but have a hard finish. Although these sheets will bend, they are tough and resistant to knocks and other abuses. This durability makes them excellent for recreation room wall coverings and for other uses. They are made plain or pre-finished in colours or wood-grained patterns for interior wall coverings.

Particle Boards. These are made from tightly compressed wood particles or wood fibres. They may have a veneer of hardwood on each side.

There are many other building products made partially or wholly from wood fibres, such as batt insulation and acoustic tile.

Plastics

Plastics are playing an ever-increasing role in the manufacture of building materials. Sometimes they are used in conjunction with fibreboards that have a plastic surface, such as the arborite-type counter-top materials. They are also used in conjunction with asbestos and other materials in the manufacture of floor tiles. Other building products made entirely of plastic are floor coverings and coloured corrugated sheets used over sundecks and patios. Many plumbing, electrical, and hardware components are also made of solid plastic.

Masonry Products

There have been important technological developments in the manufacture and utilization of masonry products, especially concrete, which has become increasingly important as a construction material. One of the building products made from concrete is the *concrete block.*

Concrete Blocks. The foundations and basements of a large percentage of Canadian homes are built of concrete blocks. Their use has proved to be

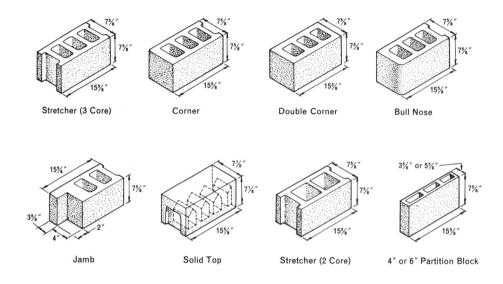

Fig. 4.27   Concrete Blocks

very economical in the construction of basement walls. Concrete blocks are made in shapes and sizes to fit the construction needs. Some of these are shown in Figure 4:27.

Concrete blocks, like planed lumber, are smaller than the nominal sizes. An 8″ x 8″ x 16″ block will actually measure 7⅝″ x 7⅝″ x 15⅝″, but laid up in a wall with ⅜″ mortar joints it will occupy a space that is the full nominal size. Such a block is generally referred to simply as an 8″ block. Concrete blocks used for exterior bearing walls are made from sand, fine gravel, and cement. Back-up blocks and blocks used for partitions are often made from cinders, expanded shale or slag, and cement, which makes them lighter and gives them a better insulating value than blocks made with sand, fine gravel, and cement. However, they do not have as great a compression strength, so they are not acceptable for bearing walls.

Concrete Bricks.   These are made and used with blocks or they may be utilized where smaller concrete units are required. They may also be used for the exterior face brick of a house. Similar bricks, made from sand, lime, and cement, are coloured and used extensively for the walls of brick houses. Many of them are the same size as the standard clay brick, but others are twice the length and are referred to as roman brick. The same material is used to make artificial coloured stone. The face of the unit bears a rough finish to make the completed wall appear like a cut-stone surface.

Pre-cast Panels.   Concrete is poured into moulds or forms to make solid or hollow panels for walls, floors, and roofs. The panels used for walls

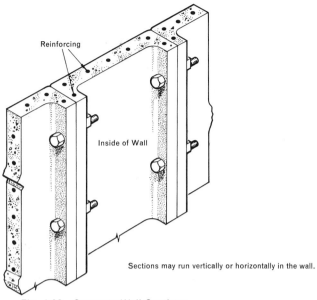

Reinforcing

Inside of Wall

Sections may run vertically or horizontally in the wall.

Fig. 4:28   Concrete Wall Sections

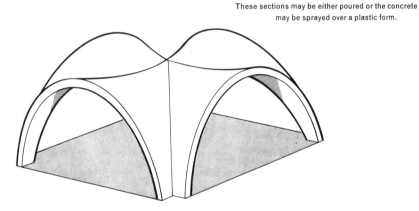

These sections may be either poured or the concrete may be sprayed over a plastic form.

Fig. 4:29   Concrete Roof Made from Shell Sections

(often called curtain walls) are made in many shapes and sizes and are used extensively in apartment and commercial buildings. Some pre-cast panels are shown in Figures 4:15, 4:28, and 4:30.

Pre-cast Units. These are concrete parts of a building that can be made separately, transported to the site, and set in place as the building is being erected. They include such units as concrete steps, sidewalk blocks, and concrete floor joists.

For industrial and commercial building, *pre-stressed* concrete shapes are made for bridge beams, trusses, and the shell roof sections for domed

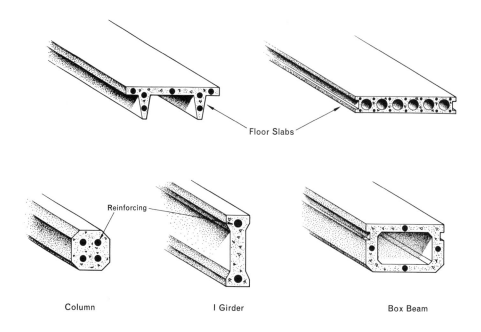

Floor Slabs

Reinforcing

Column

I Girder

Box Beam

Fig. 4:30   Pre-Cast Concrete Building Units

and curved roofs used in modern architecture. See the roof shape illustrated in Figure 4:29. There are two types of pre-stressed concrete: pre-tensioned and post-tensioned.

Pre-tensioned Concrete. Units of pre-tensioned concrete are made at a factory under carefully controlled conditions. A ridged form is made for the required concrete shape. High-tensile steel cables are laid in the form and stretched taut by hydraulic jacks or other mechanical means. Concrete is then poured around the cables. When the concrete has set to its full strength the cables are released. This puts the concrete under compression, greatly increasing its strength and its load-bearing capacity.

Post-tensioned. Units of post-tensioned concrete can be made at the building site. The form is made but the cables are encased in a tubing to prevent them from bonding to the cement. After the concrete has fully hardened, the cables are pulled taut by jacks and anchored to the ends of the concrete unit to compress it. Some of the pre-stressed units in common use are shown in Figure 4:30.

Screen Wall Blocks. Ornamental concrete blocks are made in a wide variety of designs for garden and patio screens and fences. They may be set up dry or with cement mortar. They may be 4", 6", or 8" thick, with a square or rectangular face. Figure 4:31 illustrates some of the designs used for this type of masonry wall.

46

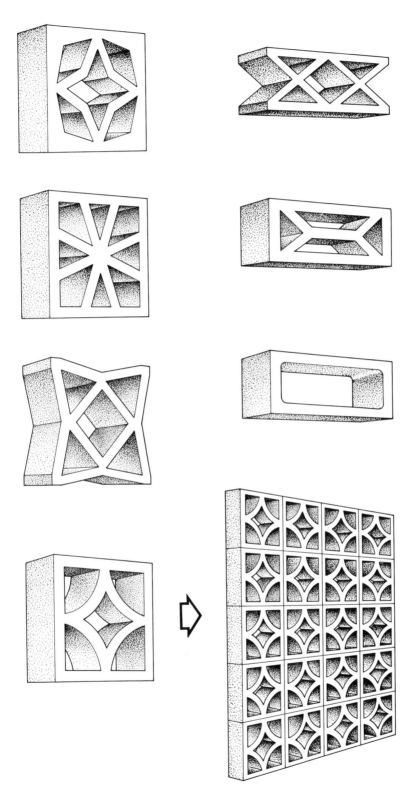

Fig. 4:31   Artistically designed concrete blocks used for screen walls.

Clay Brick.   The most popular masonry exterior finish is clay brick. It is fortunate that most parts of Canada have suitable clay deposits for the manufacture of good brick. The clay is taken from the ground in its natural state, baked in a kiln, and then allowed to cure. Most bricks are made in the standard 2″ x 4″ x 8″ dimensions, but other sizes are sometimes used. They are made in a wide range of colours and with variously textured finishes. Building tiles are also made from clay, and may be used as back-up material behind the brick for a solid masonry wall, or they may be used by themselves, as a complete wall for barns, warehouses, or other large buildings.

We have not touched on paints or other finishing materials or on products made from such materials as asbestos, rock wool, steel, aluminum, brass, glazed tile, asphalt, glass, and ceramics. These and many other materials are important in building construction. You should try to keep abreast of the most recent developments by taking advantage of advertising literature and of the many trade magazines that provide detailed illustrations and descriptions of new building products.

ASSIGNMENT
Types of Construction
1. List four factors that will determine the type of construction chosen by a builder or prospective home owner.
2. What factors contribute to the popularity of frame homes in most parts of Canada?
3. Draw a sectional view of the exterior wall of a frame house, and label six frame members.
4. (a) How does platform frame construction differ from balloon frame construction?
   (b) Which type is considered to be superior? Why?
   (c) Which is the most commonly used type of construction in Canada?
5. (a) What is meant by post-and-beam construction?
   (b) List two advantages of post-and-beam construction.
6. Describe plank-wall construction.
7. Make a sectional drawing of the foundation and floor for a house with a slab floor. Label the materials used.
8. Briefly describe brick veneer construction.
9. How are the face bricks banded to the back-up blocks on a brick-and-block wall?
10. Why is solid brick construction being replaced by brick-and-block masonry walls?
11. How is the outside of concrete blocks treated on a concrete block house?

12. How is stucco attached to a frame wall?

13. What is the limiting factor in the construction of houses with solid concrete walls?

14. What is meant by a prefabricated house?

15. List three advantages of prefabricated housing units.

16. Define the term "stressed-skin" as it refers to wall sections.

17. How is the role of the skilled or semi-skilled carpenter likely to be affected by the increased popularity of the factory-manufactured homes?

Building Materials

18. From what four basic raw materials are building products made?

19. Make a sectional drawing of:
    (a) four types of trim stock;   (b) four types of mouldings.

20. Why is plywood made with an odd number of plies?

21. Why is plywood stronger than a piece of solid wood of comparable thickness?

22. In reference to plywood what is the meaning of:
    (a) G. 1 S.? (b) G. 2 S.? (c) Improved back? (d) Pre-finished?

23. Why has fibreboard more insulating value than solid wood?

24. What is the difference between insulating fibreboard and hardboards?

25. On a drawing of a piece of five-ply plywood, name the veneers used in the plywood.

26. Make a sketch of three types of concrete blocks and show their dimensions.

27. Explain the terms "pre-cast concrete" and "pre-stressed concrete".

28. List three components used in house construction that are often pre-cast.

29. Where are ornamental concrete screen wall blocks used?

30. How are clay bricks made?

31. Name two building products you have seen in your home or in other buildings that are not described in this chapter.

Construction Safety (see pages 399-417)

32. What is the Workmen's Compensation Board and what is its function?

33. Why has it been difficult to control the accident rate in the residential construction field?

34. Why was the Construction Safety Act amended in 1964?

Chapter 5

HAND TOOLS OF THE TRADE

The quality of the work performed by a craftsman in any of the building trades depends not only on his knowledge and skill, but also on the tools he uses. The carpenter probably uses a greater number of tools than any other trades-man. A thorough knowledge of these tools is of the utmost importance to him.

HAND TOOLS

The hand tools used in building construction have greatly improved in recent years. Many of them have been redesigned to make them lighter, stronger, and easier to handle. One of the greatest improvements has been the de-velopment of electric hand tools. These are equipped with a variety of at-tachments that enable the craftsman to perform, with one tool, operations that would formerly have required the use of several tools.

Hand tools may be grouped under the following broad classifications, according to the operations for which they are to be used: measuring, layout, testing, cutting, smoothing, boring, assembling, and dismantling. Many tools, however, fall into several of these groups.

We will deal here with only those tools that are extensively used in building construction, omitting those that are used more specifically in cabinet-making and general woodworking, although many tools are basic to all branches of the woodworking industry.

Measuring Tools
Pull-out Steel Tapes. These tapes have, to a large extent, replaced wooden folding rules, over which they have several advantages: they are longer, easier to carry and use, and are also more versatile as they can be hooked over the end of work for outside measurements or used for inside measure-ments by adding two inches to the measurement shown to allow for the width of the case. They are commonly made in 6', 8', 10', and 12' lengths.

For measuring longer distances, there are steel tapes made in 25', 50', 75', and 100' lengths with steel or plastic cases. These tapes have a convenient loop and barbed hook on the end as shown in Figure 5:2. This arrangement makes it easy to attach the tape onto the end of a piece of stock, or the loop can be set over a nail driven into the centre of a layout stake.

Wooden Rules. A standard type of wooden rule that can be folded into a compact size and has clearly marked graduations is shown in Figure 5:3.

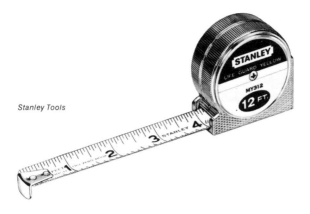

Fig. 5:1   12′ Steel Pull-out Tape

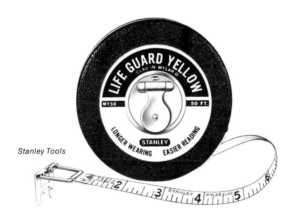

Fig. 5:2   50′ Steel Tape

Fig. 5:3   Zigzag Folding Wooden Rule

This type of rule is generally made in six-foot lengths and manufactured from boxwood or some other species of good soft wood. It can be used for inside measuring but not as conveniently as the more flexible steel rule.

Layout Tools

The Adjustable Square. This is a versatile tool that can be used for laying out lines at right angles to an edge, at a 45° angle to an edge, or parallel to an edge. The blade is adjustable and the head is equipped with a spirit level.

Fig. 5:4   Adjustable Square

Fig. 5:5   Sliding T Bevel

The Sliding T Bevel. This is not a square but is used to lay out lines at any desired angle. The blade is completely adjustable.

The Framing Square. Because of its importance as the major layout tool used by the builder, the framing square will be described in greater detail than the other building tools. The information inscribed on it, when intelligently used, is of such value that a good framing square can be termed the carpenter's handbook. There are many makes of framing squares. They are sold in a wide price range depending on the number of tables and other information stamped on them, and also on the finish of the tool, which may be blued, coppered, or nickel-plated. They may be made from stainless steel. The type of square described here is one that is commonly used in this country.

The framing square consists of two parts: the body, which is 2″ wide and 24″ long, and the tongue, which is 1½″ wide and 16″ long. The face of the square is the side that has the maker's name stamped on it. The outer edge, where the tongue and the body meet, is called the heel. There are eight gra-

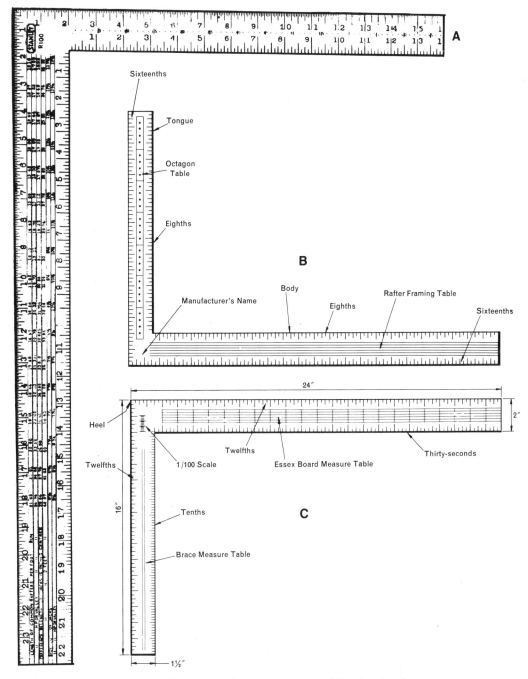

Fig. 5:6 (A) Framing Square; (B) Tables on the Face of the Framing Square; (C) Tables on the Back of the Framing Square.

duated scales on a framing square, which divide the inch into the following fractions: 1/2, 1/4, 1/8, 1/10, 1/12, 1/16, 1/32, and 1/100. The 1/100 scale is on the tongue near the heel. The location of these scales is indicated in Figure 5:6.

In addition to these scales, most framing squares have four tables stamped on them: the Essex Board Measure Table, the Octagon Table, the Brace Measure Table, and the Rafter Framing Table. The Rafter Framing Table is described in some detail in Chapter 17.

Essex Board Measure Table. This table, found on the back of the body of the framing square, consists of a series of numbers and lines that are designed to tell you, at a glance, the number of board feet in a piece of material of any given size. This table is based on lumber 1″ thick; other lumber thicknesses must be calculated accordingly. The key to this board measure table is the inch graduation figures on the outer edge of the body of the square. These figures represent the width of the material. The length of the material is found in the small figures under the 12″ mark on the outer scale. The number of board feet is found under the figure representing the width and on the line representing the length. The amount is given in feet and twelfths of feet. The figure to the left of the long line indicates the feet and the figure to the right indicates the twelfths. Study Figure 5:7.

EXAMPLE: Find the number of board feet in a piece of stock 1″ thick, 9″ wide, and 8′ long.

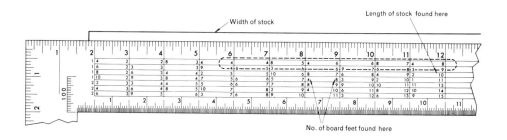

Fig. 5:7   Essex Board Measure

Begin by looking under the 12″ graduation on the scale on the outer edge directly above the table. On the first line below it will be found the figure 8, representing the length in this example. Follow this line to the left until you reach the column of figures under the 9″ mark. The figure 6 appears on the top line. Thus, there are six board feet in this piece of material.

If the stock were 1″ thick, 9″ wide, and 9′ long, you would look on the line below and find the answer to be 6 9/12 board feet. If the stock were 2″ thick, the figure stated in the table would be doubled.

Although there are only seven lines in the table representing seven lengths of stock, any multiple or fraction of any of these seven lengths can be used.

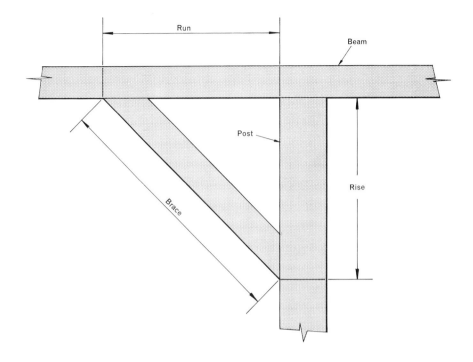

Fig. 5:8 Brace between post and beam.

For example, if the stock were 18′ long, the number of board feet stated on the rafter table for a piece 9′ long would be doubled, or if the stock were 4′ long, it would contain half the board feet stated for a piece 8′ long. There is no small number 12 to indicate stock 12′ long. This is not necessary as the number of board feet in a piece of stock 12′ long will be equal to its width — that is, a piece 12′ long and 7″ wide would contain 7 board feet. Owing to lack of space, only part of the complete Essex Board Measure Table is stamped on the framing square.

Some calculation is necessary to find the number of board feet in a piece of stock whose width is not an even number of inches. For example: if a piece of stock is 6½″ wide, the number of board feet in a piece of stock 6″ wide is subtracted from the number of board feet in a piece 7″ wide and one-half the result added to the figure found for the 6″ width. A similar procedure is followed for a piece of stock whose length is in a fraction of a foot, such as 14½′ long.

Brace Measure Table. The series of numbers running along the back of the centre section of the tongue is known as the Brace Measure Table. This table will tell us quickly and accurately the length required for a brace between a beam and a post when the run and the rise are known. The run is the distance along the beam, or the horizontal member, and the rise is the distance along the post, or the vertical member. See Figure 5:8.

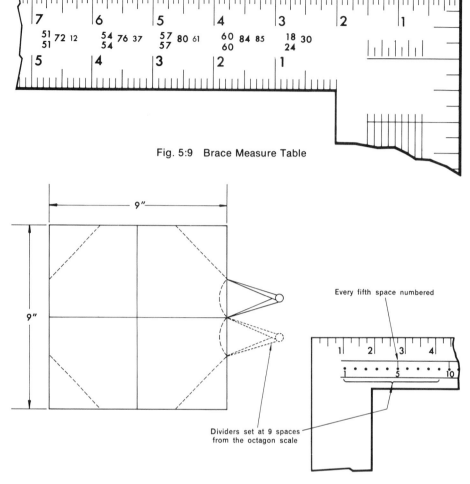

Fig. 5:9   Brace Measure Table

$$\frac{51}{51}\ 72\ _{12}\quad \frac{54}{54}\ 76\ _{37}\quad \frac{57}{57}\ 80\ _{61}\quad \frac{60}{60}\ 84\ _{85}\quad \frac{18}{24}\ _{30}$$

Every fifth space numbered

Dividers set at 9 spaces from the octagon scale

Fig. 5:10   Laying out an octagon.

You will notice in Figure 5:9 that the series of figures on the table read thus:

$$\frac{57}{57}\ 80\ \underline{61}\quad \frac{60}{60}\ 84\ \underline{85}\quad \frac{18}{24}\ 30$$

and so on at 3″ intervals of run and rise distances. The first two figures in each set represent the run and the rise, and the third number, taken to two decimal places, represents the length of the brace at its longest point.

The lengths given on the table for the run and the rise are usually the same. The reason for this is that most braces are placed at a 45° angle, the most efficient angle for a brace. However, the set of figures in the table closest to the heel of the square gives these distances as 18 and 24 and the brace as 30. This is a common brace size. Any multiple of these figures could be used such as 36 and 48, which would require a brace of 60 (twice 30). For a run of 6 and rise of 8 the brace would be 10, that is, ⅓ of 30. Any multiple of any of the other figures can also be used for finding a brace length.

Octagon Table. The Octagon Table, stamped on the face of the tongue, consists of two parallel lines with a series of dots between them. The purpose of this table is to assist you in laying out an octagon (an eight-sided figure). It is an easy table to read and works like this: Suppose you wish to lay out an octagon 9″ across. First draw a 9″ square; then draw lines through the centre dividing it into four equal squares. Now set the points of the dividers from the first to the ninth dot as in Figure 5:10 (one space for each inch in the width of the octagon). Step this distance off from each side of each centre line and join these points to complete the octagon layout. See Figure 5:10.

There are a great many operations, such as the drawing of geometric figures and other layout problems, that can be done with the framing square. Some of these operations are the bisection of angles, the finding of the centre of circles, the laying out of polygons, circles, angles, and ovals, plus the solving of all manner of roof and wall-framing problems. In fact, several books have been written on the use of the framing square; one of these, *Steel Square,* is listed in the bibliography of this book. It would be a good idea to do some reference reading on this subject.

Testing Tools

Spirit Level. To determine if structural members or components are level or plumb, a spirit level is used. This instrument consists of a wood or metal frame with glass tubes, each of which is almost filled with liquid, except for an air bubble that will come to rest between two lines in the centre of the horizontal or vertical tube when the tool is in a true horizontal or vertical position. Spirit levels used on construction range in lengths from 24″ to 72″.

Line Level. Another version of spirit level that is used by builders for arriving at approximate levels and grades is the line level. This instrument is hung on a line. To give an accurate reading the level must be placed near the centre of the line span, and the line must be pulled very taut.

Plumb Bob. A plumb bob is a tool used to establish vertical lines, or to locate a point directly below an already established point, line, or structural member. It consists of a cylindrical metal weight with a point on one end and a line on the other.

Building Line. Building lines in rolls or spools are generally used for laying out building lines or foundations. For laying out straight lines on the subfloor and other places during construction, a self-chalking line and case is used. The case contains powdered chalk that coats the line when it is retracted into the case. The coated line is then drawn out and stretched taut between two points. When the line is raised at mid-point and allowed to snap back on the floor, a straight chalk line is made. This type of line and case can also be used as a plumb bob.

Fig. 5:11   Spirit Level

Fig. 5:12   Line Level

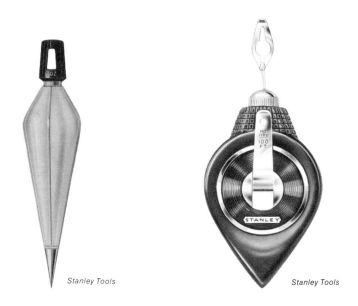

Fig. 5:13   Plumb Bob   Fig. 5:14   Chalk Line and Case

Cutting Tools

Hand Saw. There are many types of hand saws, the two main divisions being the cross-cut and the rip saw. The major difference is in the shape of the teeth, which equip the cross-cut saw to cut at a right angle to the grain and the rip saw to cut parallel with the grain. The saw blades vary in length from 20″ to 26″.

Other saws used in construction are shown in Figures 5:17 and 5:18.

58

Fig. 5:15   Hand Cross-Cut Saw

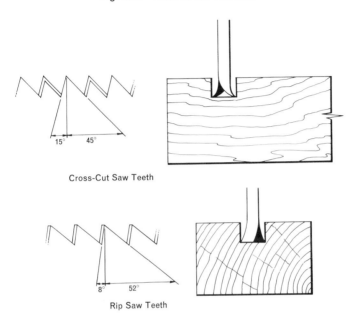

Cross-Cut Saw Teeth

Rip Saw Teeth

Fig. 5:16   Two Types of Saw Teeth

Fig. 5:17   Compass saw with two wood-cutting and one metal-cutting blade.

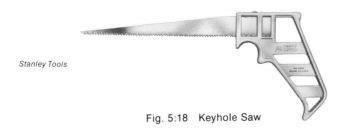

Fig. 5:18   Keyhole Saw

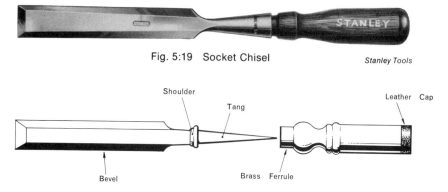

Fig. 5:19   Socket Chisel   *Stanley Tools*

Fig. 5:20   Tang Chisel

Chisels. The socket chisel is the type most often used in construction. However, for finishing work, where the chisel is used only by hand, the tang chisel makes a finer cut. Both chisels are shown above.

Smoothing Tools
Planes. The jack plane is the smoothing tool used for the largest number of planing operations performed by the carpenter. Its medium size makes it large enough for such operations as fitting doors and sashes, and yet light enough to use and carry easily. The jack plane is only one of the family of planes, the members of which vary in size and weight but are similar in design.

The block plane is a special plane designed to be used with one hand. This design makes it useful for cutting end grain when fitting siding or interior trim.

A relatively new tool used for shaping, forming, and smoothing is the surform tool, which has numerous small cutting edges to remove the wood. It is made with flat, round, or curved blades for smoothing different shapes.

Boring Tools
Brace and Bit. Ratchet-type bit braces are made with 8″, 10″, or 12″ sweeps.

The auger bits are the standard bits used with the brace. They come in sizes ranging in sixteenths of an inch, from a No. 4 (¼″) to a No. 16 (1″). For odd-sized or large holes the expansive bit is used.

For drilling pilot or other small holes up to ¼″ for applying hardware, either of the drills shown below can be used.

Assembly Tools
Hammers. The all-steel claw hammer with a neoprene or rubber grip is extensively used for general construction. Its size is determined by the weight of the head which ranges from twelve to twenty ounces. The fact that the head is permanently attached to a strong handle is an advantage in driving and drawing nails, although it does not provide as much spring as the conventional wooden handle.

Stanley Tools

Fig. 5:21   Jack Plane

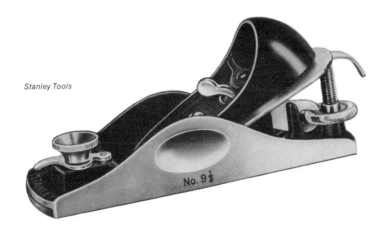

Stanley Tools

Fig. 5:22   Block Plane

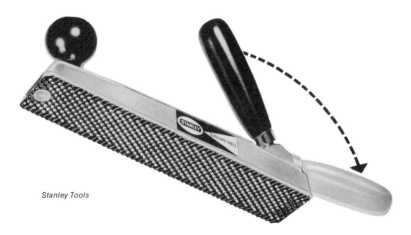

Stanley Tools

Fig. 5:23   Surform Tool

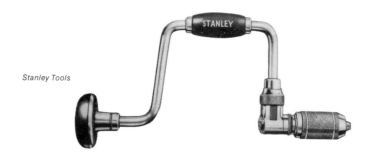

Fig. 5:24   Brace

Fig. 5:25   Auger Bit

Fig. 5:26   Expansive Bit

Fig. 5:27   Hand Drill

Fig. 5:28   Push Drill

Fig. 5:29   All Steel Claw Hammer

Fig. 5:30   Nail Set

Nail Set. For setting finishing nails below the surface, a nail set is used. This tool is made with flat points in sizes from 1/32″ to 1/8″.

Screwdrivers. Also included in assembly tools are the various types and sizes of screwdrivers, which include the socket head, the phillips head (star-shaped), and the conventional straight-slot head.

Dismantling Tools

Ripping Bar and Chisel. The ripping bar, sometimes referred to as a wrecking bar, is a tool designed specifically for dismantling structural members that have been firmly nailed together. It is also used as a lever or a pry to raise or hold members firm while they are being nailed.

Other, smaller tools, used to withdraw nails and dismantle smaller members, include the two ripping chisels such as the ones shown below.

These are only a few of the hand tools required in building construction. They represent some of the most commonly used tools in each of the general classifications. You will become more familiar with these and other carpentry hand tools as you have the occasion to use them.

Stanley Tools

Fig. 5:31   Ripping Bar

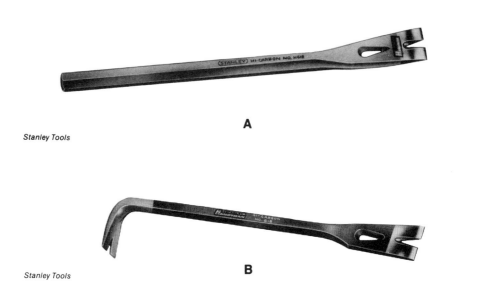

Stanley Tools

A

Stanley Tools   **B**

Fig. 5:32   (A) and (B) Two Ripping Chisels

ASSIGNMENT

1. The quality of the work performed by a craftsman in the building trades depends on several factors. Name them.
2. Building construction hand tools are grouped under certain classifications. List six of these classifications.
3. (a) Name five tools that you consider to be basic to all branches of the woodworking industry.
   (b) Name five tools that would be used more specifically for building construction.
4. List some of the advantages of the pull-out steel tape.
5. List three operations that can be performed with the adjustable square.
6. Why is the framing square referred to as the carpenter's handbook?

7. Make two drawings of the framing square, one showing the face, the other showing the back. On your drawings, indicate the location of six scales and four tables.
8. From the drawing of the section of the Essex Board Measure Table shown below, state how many board feet there are in each of the following:
   (a) 1 piece 1″ x 9″ x 12′
   (b) 4 pieces 2″ x 8″ x 9′
   (c) 6 pieces 1″ x 10″ x 16′
   (d) 3 pieces 1½″ x 13″ x 14′

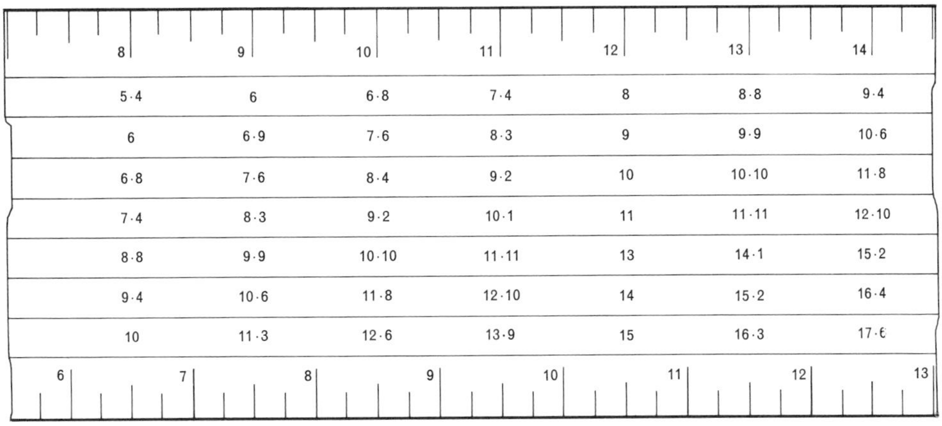

8	9	10	11	12	13	14
5·4	6	6·8	7·4	8	8·8	9·4
6	6·9	7·6	8·3	9	9·9	10·6
6·8	7·6	8·4	9·2	10	10·10	11·8
7·4	8·3	9·2	10·1	11	11·11	12·10
8·8	9·9	10·10	11·11	13	14·1	15·2
9·4	10·6	11·8	12·10	14	15·2	16·4
10	11·3	12·6	13·9	15	16·3	17·6

Fig. 5:33   Part of Essex Board Measure Table

9. Why is the figure 12 omitted in the column of figures representing the length of stock in the Essex Board Measure Table?
10. What is the purpose of the Brace Measure Table on the framing square?
11. Using the partial drawing of the framing square shown here, list the lengths of the braces when:
    (a) the rise is 57 and the run is 57;
    (b) the run is 30 and the rise is 30;
    (c) the run is 36 and the rise is 48.

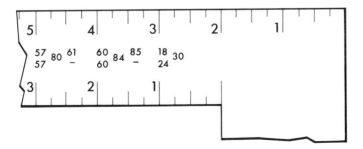

Fig. 5:34   Part of Brace Measure Table

12. List the steps in laying out an octagon, when using the Octagon Table on the framing square.
13. Name some of the geometric figures that can be laid out with the framing square.
14. (a) For what purpose is a spirit level used?
    (b) For what purpose is a line level used?
15. What is the advantage of using a self-chalking line?
16. Make drawings showing the angle of the teeth of a cross-cut saw and a rip saw.
17. Of all the planes used in the woodworking industry, why is the jack plane the one used most extensively by carpenters?
18. List one advantage and one disadvantage of the all-steel claw hammer.

Construction Safety (see pages 399-417)

19. Explain the working principle of explosive actuated tools.
20. List four safety rules that must be observed when using explosive actuated fastening tools.

Chapter 6

GIRDERS AND COLUMNS

After the completion of the foundation, the first operation the carpenter generally performs in erecting the framework is the installation of the main beams or girders and the posts or columns that support them. We will consider each construction operation in the order it would ordinarily be performed by the carpenter or builder. The exact order is not always followed, but the same general sequence of operations is followed in the construction of most homes.

GIRDERS

These are large beams used in house construction to support smaller beams or joists. They generally run the length of the basement to support the inner end of the joist over the long span thus taking the place of a supporting wall. A typical joist and girder arrangement is shown in Figure 6:1. In older homes girders were generally made from solid timbers, but in most modern homes they are of the built-up type — that is, they are made from several pieces of 2″ material bolted or spiked together, or from many

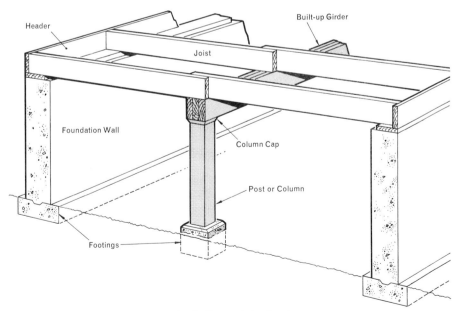

Fig. 6:1   Built-up girder in place.

pieces of 1″ material laminated together. They may also be made of re-inforced concrete, or they may be steel I-beams.

Since girders carry approximately half the floor load and usually part of the ceiling and roof load as well, they must be well designed, rigid, and properly supported on the foundation wall and by the supporting posts or columns. The joist and girder arrangement shown in Figure 6:1, in which the joists rest on top of the girder, is probably the one most used in modern house construction. This arrangement provides a sound construction but has the disadvantage of decreasing the basement headroom. This is a distinct handicap if a finished, level ceiling is desired.

Built-up Girders

A built-up girder generally consists of three or four pieces of 2″ x 8″ or 2″ x 10″ spiked or bolted together. These may be made with a ledger board as shown in Figure 6:2. The ledger board should be a 2″ x 3″ or 2″ x 4″ bolted to the beam. The joists may be notched or they may be set on top of the ledger board allowing a portion of the beam to project below the joist. If this method is used the joist will project above the beam as shown in Figures 6:3A and 6:3B. A method that is more widely accepted with this type of beam is the use of metal joist hangers to support the joists that are butted into the beam. See Figures 6:4A, 6:4B, 6:4C, and 6:4D.

Built-up girders must be securely held together with two rows of 4″ common nails, one row near the top and the other near the bottom, with the nails not more than 18″ apart. Figure 6:5 illustrates the nailing arrangement that should be used. It is preferable to use ½″ or ⅜″ bolts to secure this type of girder. The joints should be situated either over the supporting post, or not more than one-quarter of the distance to the next support. In this way no joints will be in the centre section of the span. See the view of the built-up girder in Figure 6:6.

Steel I-Beams

When steel I-beams are used as girders under the joists, 2″ x 4″s must be bolted to the top to provide a surface to which the joists can be nailed. If the joists are framed into the beam, the 2″ x 4″s should be bolted on top of the lower flange as shown in Figure 6:7B.

A Combination Steel and Wood Beam

This type of beam is sometimes used where a steel plate is bolted on edge between four pieces of 2″ stock, as shown in Figure 6:8.

Hollow Plywood Girders

One type of hollow plywood girder is the plywood box beam. These beams can be made for various building applications: ridge beams, lintels for garages and carports, and floor supports. The depth of the beam, the thickness of the plywood, and the spacing of the stiffeners will depend upon the

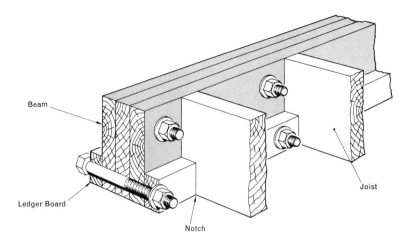

Fig. 6:2   Joist notched to fit over ledger board.

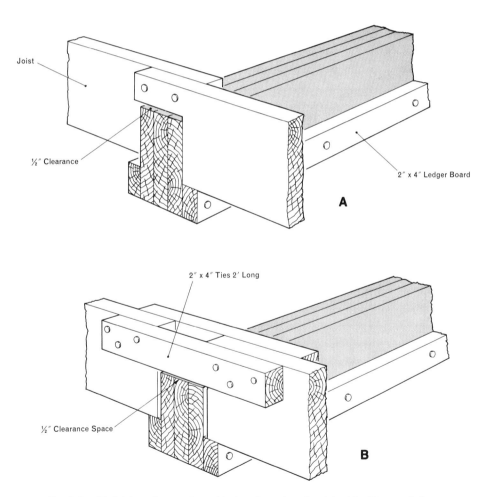

Fig. 6:3   (A) Joist resting on top of ledger board and notched to fit over girder;
(B) Joists resting on top of ledger board and secured by ties.

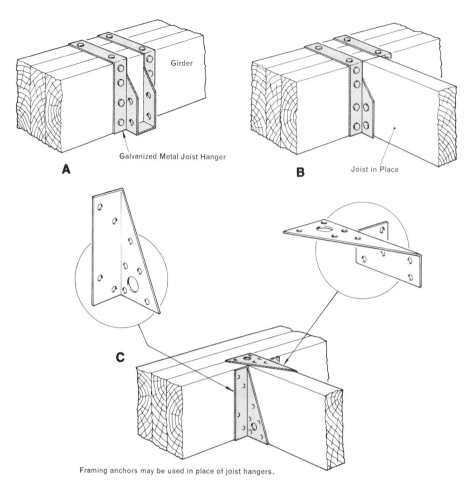

Girder

Galvanized Metal Joist Hanger

A

Joist in Place

B

C

Framing anchors may be used in place of joist hangers.

D

Fig. 6:4 (A), (B), (C), and (D) The use of joist hangers to support joists butted into the beam.

70

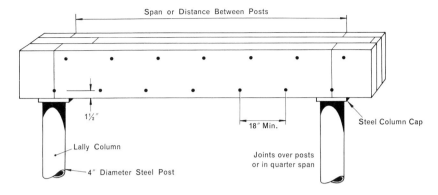

Fig. 6:5   Nailing Arrangement

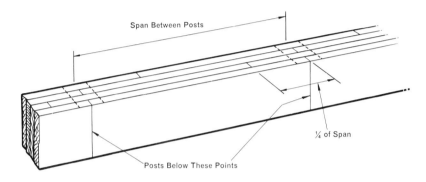

Fig. 6:6   Position of joints of a built-up beam made from four 2″ x 10″ members.

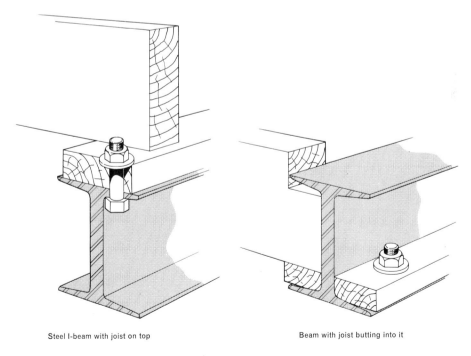

Steel I-beam with joist on top

Beam with joist butting into it

Fig. 6:7   Steel I-beams used as girders.

71

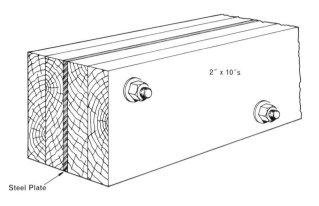

Fig. 6:8   Combination Wood and Steel Beam

span of the beam and upon the load imposed on it. Plywood manufacturers have carried out extensive research on this type of beam and have published their recommended specifications for its construction. These specifications are available and should be closely adhered to. The advantages of plywood beams include their strength and rigidity, the ease with which they can be made, their light weight, and their relative economy. A plywood box beam is shown in Figure 6:9.

Girders may either rest on the sill, which in turn rests on the foundation wall, or they may rest in a pocket in the masonry wall, depending on whether the joists butt against, or rest on, the beam. If the girder is set in the wall as shown in Figure 6:10, a ½″ air space must be left around it for air circulation to prevent rot. It should rest on a metal plate that is larger than the bearing surface of the beam; this will distribute the load over a larger area. All girders must have at least 4″ bearing on the wall. When the girder is recessed in the wall the top must be flush with the top of the sill.

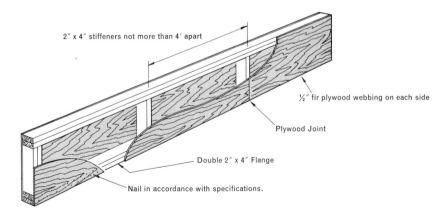

Fig. 6:9   Plywood Box Beam

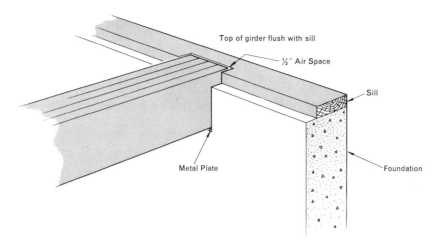

Top of girder flush with sill

½" Air Space

Sill

Metal Plate

Foundation

Fig. 6:10   Girder set in foundation pocket.

The type and size of the girder to be used will depend on these factors:
1. *the span of the girder* (the distance between the supporting posts)
2. *the location of the bearing partition* on the floor above (If the house has a centre bearing partition that carries the ceiling and, in some cases, the second floor, it should be located directly above the girder. If it is a one-storey house with a trussed roof, the weight of one floor only need be considered.)
3. *the load to be imposed on the floor* other than the weight of the building itself
4. *the type of house construction used* (Some houses do not lend themselves to beams that extend below the floor joists. In others it is desirable to have a clear basement with no obstruction from supporting posts or columns, making a large steel beam necessary.)

To increase the strength of a girder it is much more economical to increase the depth rather than the width. To double the width of a girder will double its strength, but to double its depth will increase its carrying capacity four times.

To determine the size of girder required for a given span, consult the table in the *Residential Standards* book. This table lists requirements for houses built under the National Housing Act, and also lists the permissible span for beams used in one- and two-storey dwellings.

COLUMNS

The term *column,* as used in building construction, refers to a vertical member used to support a girder or other main framing member. Columns are generally free-standing and should be in a perfectly vertical position and strong enough to carry the load imposed on them. The material used for columns may be one of the following:
(a) *wood* — either solid timber, laminated material, or a built-up column

73

made from several pieces of 2″ material.

(b) *steel* — a round steel tube 4″ to 6″ in diameter like the one illustrated in Figure 6:5. (These are called "Lally Columns".) Steel I-beams, channel iron or H-beam sections are also used as columns. See Figure 6:11.

(c) *masonry material* — concrete blocks, brick, or poured concrete may be used (concrete block columns are often made from special solid square blocks with the corners rounded, as shown in Figure 6:12).

All columns must have a bearing plate at the top to provide a method of attaching them to the girders and to act as a means of transferring the load from the girder to the column. In the case of wood or masonry columns, the bearing plate may be a short section of 2″ plank, wider and longer than the cross-section of the column. When steel columns are used, a steel plate is welded or bolted to both the top and the bottom.

All columns must rest on a concrete footing that extends from the level of the main wall footings to at least 3″ above the finished concrete floor. The best method is the step-type footing, shown in Figure 6:13. This keeps the bottom of the column dry, preventing rot or rust. When wood columns are used the lower end should be protected with a coat of creosote or other wood preservative.

The columns must be well secured to both the girder and the footings. The top can be spiked or bolted to the girder. The lower end of a wooden column can be secured with a metal rod set into both the column and the footing as shown in Figure 6:13.

The size of the columns will be determined by the load imposed on them and by the span or the distance between them. In residential home construction the distance between columns supporting main girders should not be

H-Column   I-Beam   Channel Iron

Fig. 6:11   Steel shapes used for supporting columns.

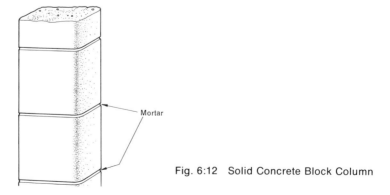

Mortar

Fig. 6:12   Solid Concrete Block Column

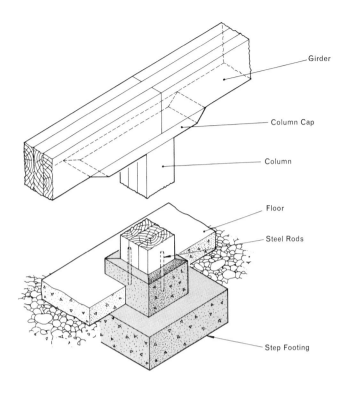

Fig. 6:13   Girder, Column, and Step Footing

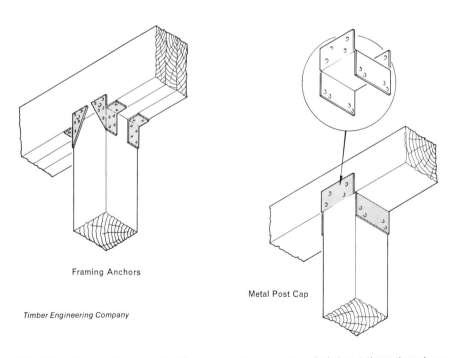

Framing Anchors

Metal Post Cap

Timber Engineering Company

Fig. 6:14   Two methods of attaching wood columns to wood girders (where there is no joint in the girder directly over the column).

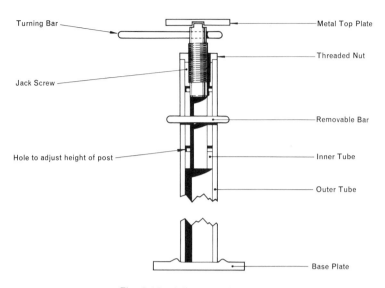

Fig. 6:15 Adjustable Column

more than 10′ if possible. The farther apart the columns, the larger the girder must be.

Where there is a joint in a wooden girder directly over the column, a column cap three times as long as the width of the column should be used. See Figure 6:13.

For repair work and for smaller one-storey houses, an adjustable column consisting of two steel tubes, one sliding inside the other, is used. At the top of the inner tube is attached a jack screw, as shown in Figure 6:15. The height of the girder may be raised or lowered simply by turning the bar in the jack screw. This can be helpful in raising a girder that has sagged or settled in a particular spot.

ASSIGNMENT
Girders
1. What is the function of a girder?
2. How is a built-up girder made?
3. From what materials may girders be made?
4. What proportion of the floor load is supported by the girders?
5. What is the disadvantage of having joists resting on top of the girder?
6. Make a drawing of two methods of attaching joists to wooden girders that are built with a ledger board.
7. What are joist hangers? How are they used?
8. How are wooden joists attached to metal I-beam girders?
9. (a) Why should a ½″ air space be left around the end of a wooden girder that is recessed into a concrete wall?
   (b) Why is a metal plate placed between the girder and the concrete?

10. What is the minimum bearing that a girder must have on the foundation wall?
11. Describe the construction of:
    (a) a combination wood and metal girder;
    (b) a plywood girder.
12. List three factors determining the type and size of girder to be used.
13. If a girder 4″ x 6″ will support 10 tons over a given span
    (a) what weight will a girder 4″ x 12″ support?
    (b) what weight will a girder 8″ x 6″ support?
14. Where can you find information regarding the minimum size of girders that can be used over a given span?

Columns

15. Define the term *column.*
16. From what materials may columns be made?
17. Why should there be a cap or plate between the top of the column and the girder?
18. Make a sketch of the concrete base on which a column should be set.
19. How are columns held in place at the floor level?
20. What is the advantage of the adjustable column used on smaller one-storey homes?

Construction Safety (see pages 399-417)

21. Building construction is not considered a dangerous occupation. Why, then, is the accident rate fairly high?

Chapter 7

SILL FRAMING

The *sill*, sometimes referred to as the "sill plate", is the wood framing member that rests directly on the top of the masonry foundation wall. The two main purposes of the sill are:
(a) to establish a straight, level, solid bearing surface on which the floor joists will rest; and
(b) to provide a member that can be bolted to the foundation, thus tying the wood framework to the masonry wall.

TYPES OF SILLS

Timber Sills

The size and placement of the sill on the foundation wall will depend on the type of house construction used. Older frame houses had timber sills, often referred to as mud sills. They were generally 4" x 6" with half-lap joints made at the corners of the building. Both the studding and the joists rest on this sill. In modern residential construction timber sills are seldom used, because the function of a sill does not warrant a member this thick. This type of sill has the disadvantage of allowing air to circulate between the basement and the space between the wall studs; this causes heating difficulties and creates a fire hazard.

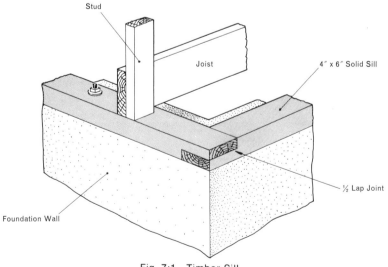

Fig. 7:1   Timber Sill

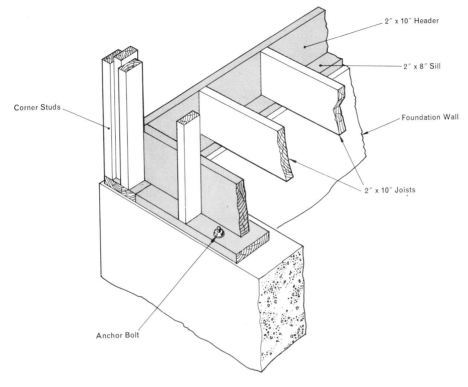

Labels on figure:
2″ x 10″ Header
2″ x 8″ Sill
Foundation Wall
Corner Studs
2″ x 10″ Joists
Anchor Bolt

Fig. 7:2   T-Type Sill

T-type Sill

The *T-type sill* used in balloon frame construction is shown in Figure 7:2. This sill is made of stock-sized material, consisting of a 2″ x 8″ plank laid flat on the top of the foundation. The studs rest on the outer edge with the joists and headers nailed to them. This prevents air circulation between floors and provides sound framing for the support of the joists and subflooring.

Box Sill

The type of sill used most extensively in Canadian homes is the *box sill* shown in Figure 7:3. This sill arrangement is used in platform frame construction; the joists or header rest on the outer edge of the sill with the subfloor and plate in turn nailed to them. This has the advantage of providing a fire stop, as well as forming a firm base on which to erect the wall framing. The greatest advantage of this type of construction, however, is in the saving of time and labour and in the convenience of being able to lay the subfloor before the walls are built. The carpenters are thus able to nail the plates and wall studding together in sections using the subfloor as a platform. One disadvantage, however, is that there are four horizontal members between the foundation and the lower ends of the wall studding. These members may shrink in thickness or width, causing some settlement in the wall.

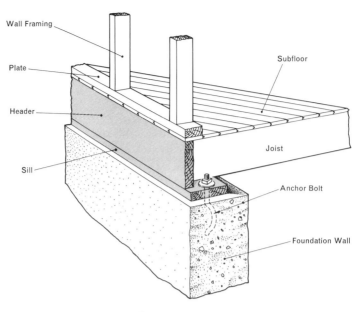

Fig. 7:3 Box Sill

Double Sill

When it is desirable to have the first floor of a house at or near grade level, a *double sill* is sometimes used. A step in the top of the foundation wall is necessary so that the two sills can be set at different levels, as shown in Figure 7:4. Both sills must be secured with anchor bolts into the masonry wall.

Double Box Sill

A type of box sill that affords good nailing between the header and the sill and also provides a 4″ bearing for the ends of the subfloor is shown in Figure 7:5. This sill requires more material and involves more labour than the box sill, as the joists must be notched for both the sill and the plate.

In some cases no flat horizontal sill is used; the joists rest directly on the masonry wall and are back-filled with concrete. The concrete is held in place by the header at the outside of the wall and by short blocks nailed between the joists at the inner edge of the wall, as illustrated in Figure 7:6. This makes for a solid tight joist arrangement. Its disadvantage is that there is too much concrete in direct contact with the joists and header. This prevents ventilation around the ends of the joists and could, in time, cause the wood to decay.

A similar arrangement is used for solid brick construction except that brick rather than concrete is used as back-fill; therefore, no header or blocking is required. In both these types no flat wood sill is needed as the joists rest on top of the concrete wall. This will be covered more fully in a later chapter on joist framing.

Straight stock should be used for sill framing, preferably in long lengths, as the fewer joints there are the straighter the wall sections will be.

In order to fill any gaps that may appear between the top of the foundation

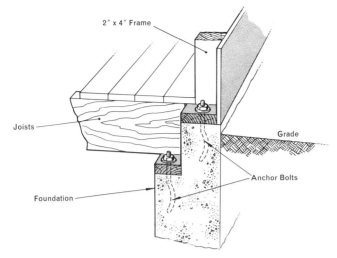

Fig. 7:4 Double Sill

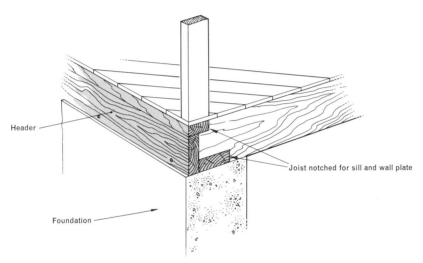

Fig. 7:5 Double Box Sill

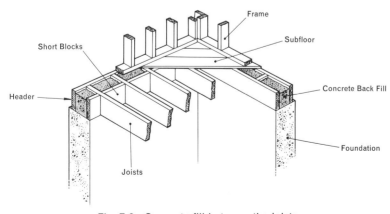

Fig. 7:6 Concrete fill between the joists

81

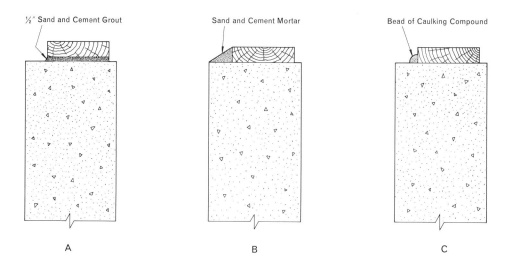

A   B   C

Fig. 7:7   Methods of sealing the joint between the sill and the foundation wall.

and the sill due to the unevenness of the top of the masonry wall, the sills are often "grouted" to the wall. This operation consists of spreading a layer of cement mortar on top of the wall. While the mortar is still wet the sill is set in place and bolted to the wall, as shown in Figure 7:7A. The mortar may be run along the inner edge of the sill in a triangle as shown in Figure 7:7B; or, if the top of the wall is straight and level, a caulking gun may be used to run a bead of caulking compound around the lower edge of the sill where it meets the foundation. See Figure 7:7C.

It is very important that sills be properly installed. The main structural framing members depend on them for an accurately positioned and level base that is well secured to the foundation.

PROCEDURE IN FRAMING SILLS ON THE FOUNDATION WALL

1. Starting from one corner of the building, place the sill members on the top of the walls approximately in their permanent position. Do not allow any joint to occur over basement window or door openings.
2. Cut the ends of the sill pieces square to make well-fitting butt joints. You will find it easier to frame the corners accurately if the sill is allowed to project past the corner until after the holes have been bored for the anchor bolts.
3. Press the sill against the outer edge of the bolts, and with the adjustable square mark a line across the sill opposite the centre of each of the bolts. See Figure 7:8.
4. The location of the bolt holes through the sill will depend on the type of construction of the house. For frame construction, measure over from the outer edge of the sill, a distance equal to the distance from the outer edge of the foundation wall to the centre of the bolt, less ¾″, which is left for the sheathing to rest on the wall. For brick veneer construction,

measure over from the inner edge of the sill, a distance equal to the distance from the inner edge of the wall to the centre of the bolts, as shown in Figure 7:8. Some carpenters, however, prefer to measure back from the inner edge of the brick line plus the 1″ air space to the centre of the bolt. See Figure 7:9.

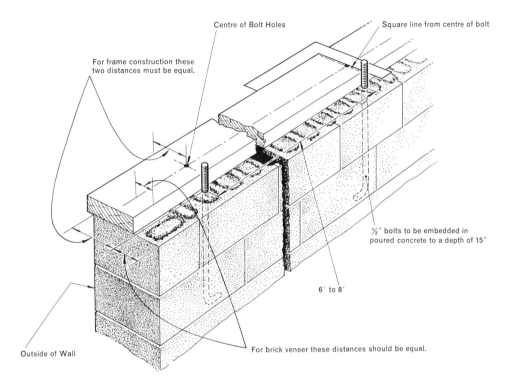

Fig. 7:8   Locating anchor bolt holes for sills.

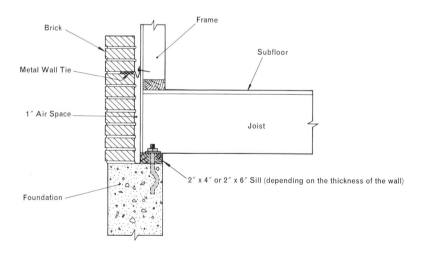

Fig. 7:9   Sill for a brick veneer construction.

Fig. 7:10   2″ x 6″ sill bolted to a 12″ concrete block for a brick veneer wall.

5. After locating the positions for the anchor bolts, bore the holes using an auger bit ¼″ larger than the diameter of the bolts. This clearance will make it easier to keep the sills in a straight line.
6. Place the sills in their correct position over the anchor bolts.
7. At the corners of the building cut the sills where they were allowed to project over.
8. If the method of sealing the joint between the sill and the top of the masonry wall illustrated in Figure 7:7B or 7:7C is to be used, put the washers and nuts on the bolts and tighten to a medium pressure.
9. Using a long straight edge and spirit level, check the sills to see that they are straight and level.
10. Stretch a chalk line along the outer edge of the sill, the full length of each wall in turn. The individual sill members can then be aligned with each other to form a continuous straight line.
11. The nuts can now be tightened firmly.

If the sills are to be grouted to the top of the masonry wall, the sill members must be removed from the wall after step 7 has been completed. The mortar can now be spread over the top of the wall to a thickness of approximately ½″. It may be spread thinner on noticeably high areas and thicker on low areas. Use mortar consisting of three parts sand to one part cement, and enough water to make the mixture pasty but not too thin. Set the sill in place on the soft mortar, level with a straight edge, and tighten the nuts snugly. When all sills have been set in this manner they can be aligned with a chalk line. Tighten the nuts firmly on the anchor bolts when the mortar has hardened.

ASSIGNMENT

1. What are the two main functions of sills?
2. Make a drawing of three types of sills.
3. Which type of sill is most extensively used in modern frame construction? Account for the popularity of this type.
4. Why should there be no joints in the sill over basement window and door openings?
5. What type of sill is used when the first floor is to be at grade level?
6. What is meant by back-filling the joists?
7. List the three methods of sealing the irregular space between the sill and the top of the masonry wall.
8. Explain how the bolt holes are located on the sill.
9. Why is it very important that sills be accurately levelled and positioned?
10. Where on the top of the masonry wall should the sill be placed for:
    (a) frame construction? (b) brick veneer construction?
11. How much larger than the size of the anchor bolts should the holes be bored? Why is this clearance left?
12. What is the final alignment of the sills before the bolts are tightened?
13. What are the ingredients of the mortar that is used between the sill and the top of the wall?
14. What is the disadvantage of the timber sill as it was used in some older homes?

Construction Safety (see pages 399-417)
15. List four safety rules that you consider important and that should be observed in building construction.

Chapter 8

FLOOR JOISTS

One of the main structural members in the framework of a house, and certainly the most important floor-supporting member, is the *floor joist*. The chief functions of floor joists are these:

(a) to support the weight of the floor above them, the weight of the furniture and equipment the floor carries, and also the load of the persons walking on it;

(b) to tie together and stiffen the framework of the building.

In order to carry out these functions, good joist framing must include joists of the correct size to support the weight imposed on them over a given span without deflection or sagging. The joists must be uniformly spaced and have an even level bearing on the plates and girders. They must be all of the same width, to provide a level surface on which to nail the subfloor.

Floor joists that are not the required size or are improperly framed may cause such serious and unsatisfactory results as sagging floors, cracked plaster, and doors that stick or scrub on the floor.

The type, size, and spacing, as well as the material from which joists are made, will depend on the span to be bridged, the load to be carried, and the type of house construction used.

The materials from which floor joists are made are 2″ wood members, steel, or reinforced concrete.

TYPES OF FLOOR JOISTS

Wood Joists

The spacing of wood joists may be 12″, 16″, 20″, or 24″ (from centre to centre) depending on the span and the load. The 16″ spacing is the one most generally accepted for good building practice because it places the joists close enough together that the floor can be supported by standard-sized stock material. The 16″ spacing will also accommodate standard-size plywood or other subfloor materials.

Wood joists may be either butted against the girders or set on top of the girders with the ends lapped as shown in Figure 8:1, in which case the ends should not project more than 1″ over the girders. If the joists project farther, the ends may be forced up due to the weight in the centre of the joist span; this would cause the floor to buckle.

If the ends of the joists are butted on top of the girder, they should be tied together by nailing a cleat against the sides of both joists over the joint.

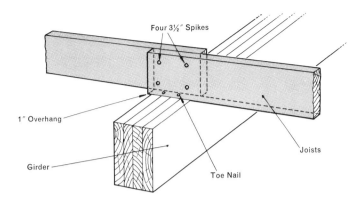

Fig. 8:1   Joist lapped on top of girder.

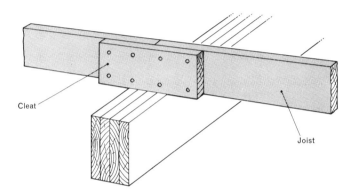

Fig. 8:2   Joist butted on top of girder.

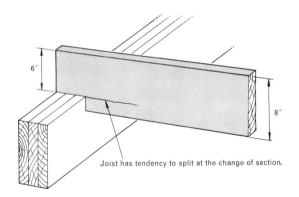

Fig. 8:3   Improper joist framing.

Joists should not be notched to fit over the girder or plate in the manner illustrated in Figure 8:3. Such notching will have a tendency to split the joist at the change of section. The full width of the joist should be supported. To provide for this support a ledger board may be nailed or bolted to the face of the girder. See Figure 8:4. The joist must be notched in such a way as to allow it to extend above and lap over the girder so that it can be spiked to the other joist. A ½″ clearance space must be left between the notched portion of the joist and the top of the girder. All of the joist load is then transferred to the ledger board, which in turn transfers it to the girder.

Where the joists rest on the sill they are held upright by a *header*, a 2″ member of the same width as the joists, which runs at right angles to the joist along the outer edge of the sill. Headers also help to align and space the joists, as well as to provide a means of support for the joists over basement window or door openings. Over large openings the header is doubled to act as a supporting beam. A double header is shown in Figure 8:5B.

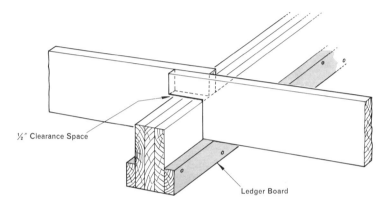

Fig. 8:4   Joist resting on a ledger board.

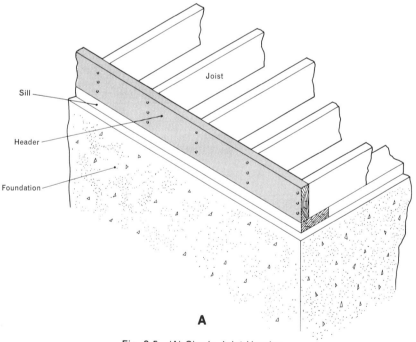

Fig. 8:5   (A) Single Joist Header

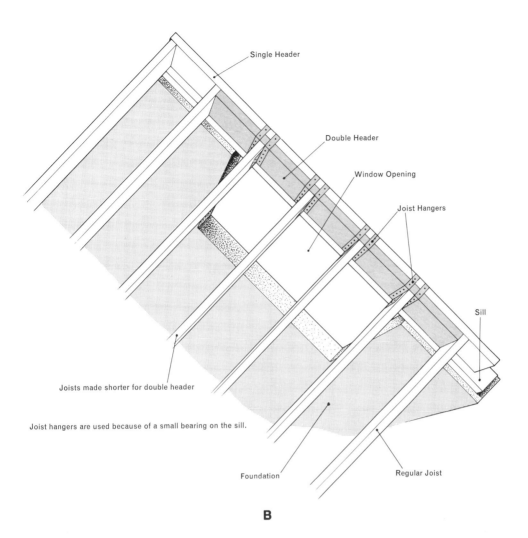

Single Header

Double Header

Window Opening

Joist Hangers

Sill

Joists made shorter for double header

Joist hangers are used because of a small bearing on the sill.

Foundation

Regular Joist

B

C

Fig. 8:5 (B) and (C)
Double Header over
Basement Window

Steel Joists

In industrial and commercial and also in some residential building, *steel joists* are used. These are made from light, fabricated steel rod and angle iron welded together to form a light truss in the manner illustrated in Figures 8:6B and C. A steel joist with one end set into a masonry wall and the other end resting on a steel beam is shown in Figure 8:6A.

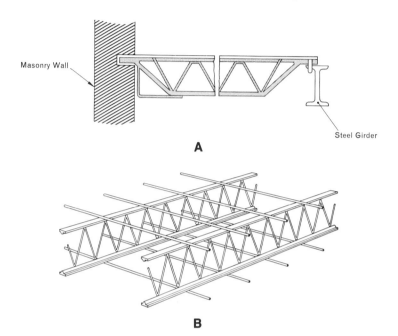

Masonry Wall

Steel Girder

A

B

C

Fig. 8:6 (A) Steel Joists; (B) Steel joists with metal ties; (C) Steel joists supported by a steel I-beam in commercial construction.

90

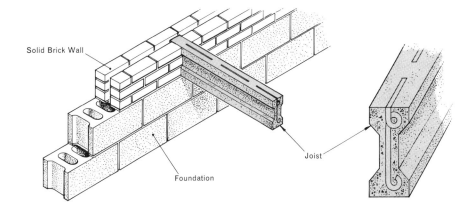

Fig. 8:7 Reinforced pre-cast concrete joist set in place in a solid masonry wall.

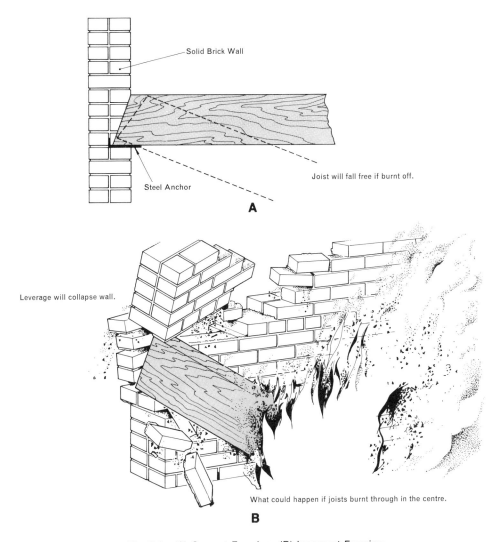

Fig. 8:8 (A) Correct Framing; (B) Incorrect Framing.

91

Reinforced Concrete Joists

This type of joist is often used for heavy construction. Figure 8:7 shows such a joist in place in a masonry wall.

In solid brick construction the ends of the joists rest on the masonry wall rather than on a wood sill at the wall end. The ends of the joists are cut at an angle of approximately 20°, as shown in Figure 8:8A. The reason for this is very important: in the event of a serious fire, should the joists be cut square and should they burn through in the centre, the leverage of the joists and the floor above would cause the walls to topple. When cut at an angle, however, the joists fall free instead of collapsing the wall. For this reason this angle cut is called a fire cut.

TRIMMERS AND HEADERS

When joists are framed around floor openings such as stairwells and chimneys, double headers and trimmers are used. *Headers* are floor framing members of the same material as the joists, and these run at right angles to the joists. *Trimmers* are extra joists that run parallel to the regular joists to support headers, giving added floor strength under partitions. Headers and trimmers are shown in the stairwell framing in Figure 8:9.

Headers used around large floor openings are doubled to support the tail joists framed into them. To carry the added weight of the partitions the joists should be doubled under all partitions that run parallel to the joists. Either the joists and the trimmers may be set tight against each other, or short pieces of 2″ x 4″ may be nailed between the joists and the trimmers as shown in Figure 8:10. This space allows heating, electrical, and water services to be run into the wall above without cutting into the joists.

As an indication of the size of joist that should be used for a given span, part of one of the tables printed in *Residential Standards* is given on page 94.

HOW TO FRAME FLOOR JOISTS

If the floor is to be properly supported, it is just as important to frame the joists properly as it is to use the correct grade and size of material. The joists must be cut to fit, be correctly spaced, be well secured, and have sufficient bearing space on the sills and girders.

An accurate layout of the joist locations on the sills and girders is made with the framing square. The procedure is as follows:
1. Start the layout by measuring 1¾″ over from the end of the sill. The first joist is placed with its outer edge flush with the edge of the sill.
2. Place the end of the tongue (the shorter, 16″ arm) of the framing square even with the end of the sill and draw a line along the outer edge of the body (the larger arm) of the square.
3. Mark an X on the far side of the line. This will be the position of the second joist. The X indicates the side of the line on which the joist will be placed.
4. Move the square along until the end of the tongue is even with the line

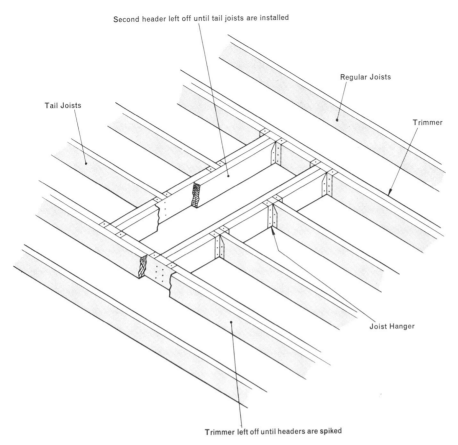

Second header left off until tail joists are installed

Regular Joists

Tail Joists

Trimmer

Joist Hanger

Trimmer left off until headers are spiked

Fig. 8:9   Joist Framing at Stairwell

93

TABLE 2B
FLOOR JOISTS — LIVING QUARTERS

Species	Grade	Nominal Size (1) inches	LIVE LOAD 40 lb. per sq. ft. All ceilings Joist spacing 12 in. ft. in.	16 in. ft. in.	20 in. ft. in.	24 in. ft. in.
Douglas Fir, Western Larch	Construction (dense and non-dense)	2 x 6	11 0	10 0	9 4	8 8
		2 x 8	15 0	13 7	12 8	11 11
		2 x 10	19 0	17 4	16 0	15 1
		2 x 12	23 0	20 11	19 5	18 4
	Standard	2 x 6	11 0	10 0	9 4	8 6
		2 x 8	15 0	13 7	12 8	11 7
		2 x 10	19 0	17 4	16 0	14 8
		2 x 12	23 0	20 11	19 5	17 10
	Utility	2 x 6	—	—	—	—
		2 x 8	12 2	10 6	9 5	8 7
		2 x 10	16 8	14 6	13 0	11 10
		2 x 12	19 8	17 0	15 2	13 11
Pacific Coast Hemlock	Construction	2 x 6	10 10	9 10	9 1	8 7
		2 x 8	14 8	13 4	12 5	11 8
		2 x 10	18 7	16 11	15 8	14 10
		2 x 12	22 6	20 6	19 0	17 11
	Standard	2 x 6	10 10	9 10	9 1	8 6
		2 x 8	14 8	13 4	12 5	11 7
		2 x 10	18 7	16 11	15 8	14 8
		2 x 12	22 6	20 6	19 0	17 10
	Utility	2 x 6	—	—	—	—
		2 x 8	11 2	9 8	8 8	7 11
		2 x 10	15 5	13 5	11 11	10 11
		2 x 12	18 0	15 7	14 0	12 8
Spruce, all western species Lodgepole Pine, Ponderosa Pine	Construction	2 x 6	9 2	8 0	7 1	6 6
		2 x 8	13 4	12 0	11 2	10 4
		2 x 10	16 10	15 2	14 2	13 0
		2 x 12	20 4	18 6	17 1	15 10
	Standard	2 x 6	7 1	6 2	5 6	5 1
		2 x 8	11 5	9 11	8 10	8 1
		2 x 10	15 0	13 0	11 7	10 7
		2 x 12	19 4	16 8	15 0	13 7
	Utility	2 x 6	—	—	—	—
		2 x 8	10 1	8 8	7 10	7 1
		2 x 10	13 6	12 0	10 8	9 6
		2 x 12	16 2	14 0	12 7	11 6
Western Red Cedar Western White Pine (2)	Construction	2 x 6	9 2	8 0	7 2	6 6
		2 x 8	12 10	11 8	10 7	9 8
		2 x 10	16 4	14 10	13 5	12 3
		2 x 12	19 8	17 11	16 2	14 10
	Standard	2 x 6	7 4	6 4	5 8	5 3
		2 x 8	10 10	9 4	8 4	7 7
		2 x 10	14 1	12 2	10 11	10 0
		2 x 12	18 2	15 8	14 1	12 10
	Utility	2 x 6	—	—	—	—
		2 x 8	9 6	8 2	7 4	6 8
		2 x 10	13 0	11 4	10 1	9 3
		2 x 12	15 4	13 2	11 10	10 10

From Residential Standards. Supplement No. 5 to the National Building Code of Canada

Note: Since the strength of various woods differ, all joist tables must specify the species and grade of lumber. Whether the joists are to be used under the main living area, or under the bedroom areas, or whether they are to support rooms with ceilings must also be stated. Most joist tables are based on an average live load of 40 pounds per square foot.

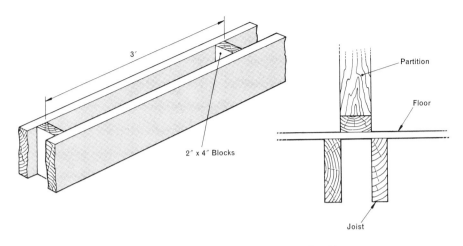

Fig. 8:10   Joist Arrangement under Partition

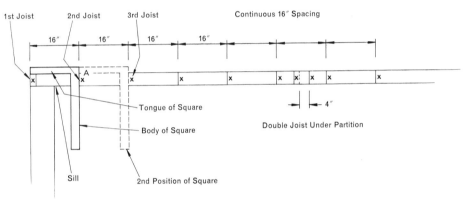

Fig. 8:11   Joist Layout on Sill

representing the edge of the second joist (A on Figure 8:11). Draw a line along the outer edge of the body of the square for the third joist. Mark an X beside the line.

Note: This is a standard layout for framing members that are placed at 16″ spacings. It is used for the location layout of such members as wall studding, ceiling joists, and rafters. You should familiarize yourself with this operation by practising it on a piece of 2″ x 4″, so that you will be able to make this layout accurately and quickly.

5. Continue marking out the joist positions in the same manner as described in Step 4.

6. From the floor plan determine the position of the partitions that run parallel with the joists and locate the centres of these on the sill. Lay out the double joists that are to be placed 3¾″ apart. If there are no plumbing outlets on the wall and electric heat is being used, the joists and trimmer can be placed close together.

7. Determine the location of stairwells so that the double joists can be marked on the sill. The continuous, 16″ spacing must be maintained; this may mean that where a trimmer or a double joist is required under a partition or at a stairwell opening, the spacing may be less than 16″, but it should never be more. If the space is more than 16″, an extra joist must be used.

8. Lay out the joist positions on the girder and the other sill in the same manner. If the joists are to be lapped over the girder the layout on the sill of the opposite wall will need to be started 1¾″ farther away from the corner, or 1¾″ closer.

Layout Rods

A more accurate joist layout can be made by using a *layout rod*: a strip of wood on which the joist layout is marked off. Sometimes two or three strips are nailed end to end to make a continuous strip the same length as the sill on which the joist layout is to be made. The layout rod is then placed on top of one of the sills and the joist locations are transferred to it. The layout is made in a similar manner on the other sill and the girder. The advantage of this method is that the framing-square layout is made only once.

HOW TO CUT THE JOISTS

The procedure in cutting the joists to fit will depend on how they are framed into the girder:

1. If the joists rest on the sill and fit against the header at the wall end and are butted over the girder at the other end, measure with a steel tape the distance between the inner edge of the header and the centre of the girder. If the joists are to be lapped over the girder, measure to the far side of the beam.

2. Square one end of the first joist.

3. From the square end measure the length of the joist.

4. Square and cut the joist to length.

5. Cut the required number of joists using the first one as a pattern.

If notches are required in the end of the joists to fit over the girder, to fit a ledger board, or for a double sill, a pattern should be carefully made and set in place to see that it fits properly before the other joists are cut. Care should be taken before cutting these joists to see that the notches are not on the crowned edge of the stock. The crowned edge is the edge of the stock that is bowed up. See Figure 8:12A. If the crowned edge is placed uppermost, the weight of the floor tends to straighten it out and reduce the crown. Joists that have excessive crown should not be used.

HOW TO INSTALL THE JOISTS

1. The double joists that are placed under the partitions are often nailed together as a unit and set in place before the other joists.

2. Starting from one end, place the joists in their correct location making sure they are on the line and over the X.

3. Check to see that the crowned side is uppermost and nail each joist as it

is set in place, using three 4″ spikes through the header at the wall end and four 2½″ common nails, toe-nailed into the girder.

If the joists are to be butted into a girder or a header around a chimney or stair opening, joist hangers should be set in place on the marks and the joists set into them, as illustrated in Figure 8:13.

In some cases the header at the sill is omitted and a metal joist setter is used to keep the joist upright. See Figure 8:14.

4. Determine the position of the stair or chimney openings from the floor plan. Locate the width of these openings on the sill and/or girder and lay out the position of the trimmers.
5. Nail the inside trimmers in place (A in Figure 8:15).
6. Locate the length of opening and mark on the trimmer. Measure back 1¾″ from this point to locate the outer header. This must be nailed in

Crowned edge placed up

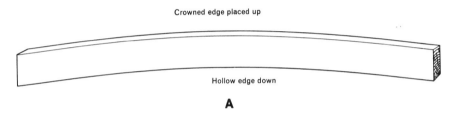

Hollow edge down

A

B   *National Forest Products Association*

Fig. 8:12   (A) Joist with a crown; (B) Installing joists using metal connector plates at the joints.

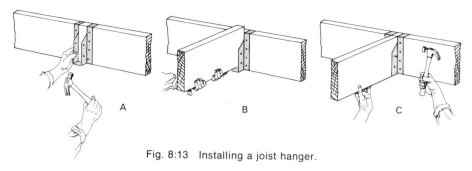

Fig. 8:13   Installing a joist hanger.

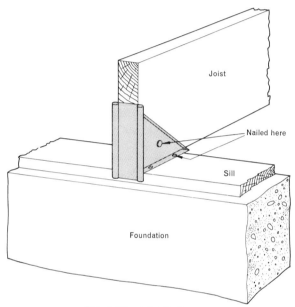

Fig. 8:14   Joist Setter

place first (B in Figure 8:15). Its length can be taken from the layout on the plate or girder.

7. Lay out the position of the tail joist on the header. This layout can be taken from the sill as it should correspond with the original joist layout on the sill for the continuous 16″ spacings.

8. Nail the tail joist in place (C in Figure 8:15). Drive the spikes through the header or use joist hangers.

9. Nail the inside headers with 3½″ spikes through the trimmers, or use joist hangers.

10. Place the outer trimmers in place and spike them to the other trimmers, the header, and the girder.

11. When all joists are in place, check across the top of them with a straight edge. If there are any high points caused by joists with excess crown it may be necessary to replace these joists.

Note: The position of floor openings should be carefully checked for the correct location as they are very difficult to change later.

98

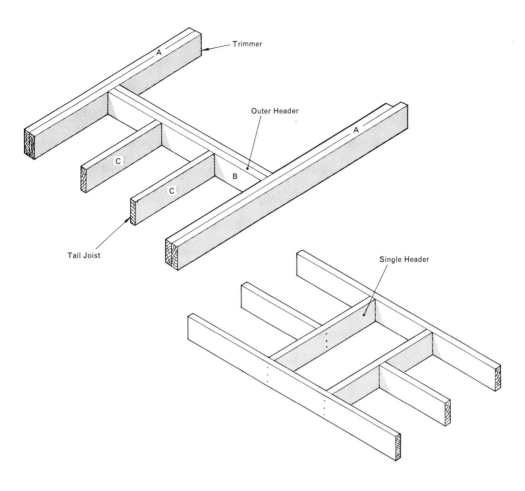

Fig. 8:15   Floor Openings

ASSIGNMENT

1. List the two functions of floor joists.
2. State three features of good joist framing.
3. What building faults often result from improper joist framing?
4. What factors will determine the size and spacing of joists?
5. From what materials are floor joists made?
6. List the spacings at which wood joists are placed.
   Which is the most common spacing?
7. When joists rest on top of the girder, why should the ends not project more than 1"?
8. Why should the full width of the joist be supported on the girder?
9. Make a drawing showing a girder and ledger board with the joist resting on them.
10. What purpose does the header on the sill serve?

11. Why are fire cuts made on the ends of joists that are supported in solid masonry construction?
12. Where are headers and trimmers used?
13. (a) Why are joists doubled under partitions?
    (b) Why are 4″ blocks placed between these doubled joists?
14. What size joist should be used for a span of 14′ if the spacing is 16″ centre to centre? Construction-grade spruce to be used.
15. Explain how the joist locations are laid out on the sill with the framing square.
16. When is the distance between joists less than the regular 16″ spacing?
17. If the joists are lapped over the girder, what allowance will need to be made in the layout?
18. What is the advantage of marking the joist locations by using a layout rod?
19. List the steps required to cut to length a joist that fits against a header on one end and is butted to another joist over a beam at the other end.
20. Why is it necessary to notch certain joists at one or both ends?
21. What is meant by the crowned edge of a joist?
    Why is the crown placed uppermost?
22. What device is used to support a joist that is butted to a girder when no ledger board is used?
23. Describe the steps necessary to lay out and frame a stair opening.
24. Make a sketch of a stairwell showing the trimmers, headers, and tail joists.
25. Why is it very important that floor openings be correctly located?
26. Why is a straight edge placed over the tops of the joists after they have been nailed in place?
27. Why should all the other floor framing members be nailed in place before the headers and trimmers are doubled?

Chapter 9

BRIDGING AND SUBFLOORS

TYPES OF BRIDGING

Wood Diagonal Bridging

To distribute a concentrated load over several floor joists, diagonal bridging is used. Bridging may consist of 2″ x 2″ or 1″ x 3″ stock that runs diagonally from the top of one joist to the bottom of the next, as shown in Figure 9:1. This also helps to space the joists in the centre of the span and prevents them from twisting. The rows of bridging should run continuously the full length of the building except where they are interrupted by chimney or stair openings. The rows should be 7′ or 8′ apart.

Although wood diagonal bridging is the most commonly used method of strengthening and aligning the centre section of joists, there are several other methods.

Metal Strap Bridging

A continuous perforated metal strap ⅛″ x 1″ can be used. Start at the top of the first joist and run the strap under the next joist and so on for the length of the building. The strapping is nailed to each joist. See Figure 9:2.

Solid Bridging

In this method of bridging, pieces of stock the same width and thickness as the joists are cut to a length that enables them to fit snugly between the joists. Solid bridging can be used to advantage when square-edged plywood subfloor is used. The individual pieces of bridging will also serve as battens to

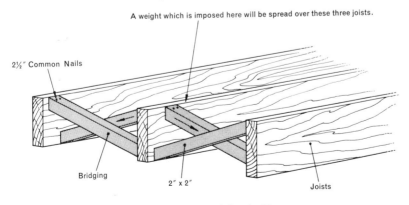

Fig. 9:1   Diagonal Bridging in Place

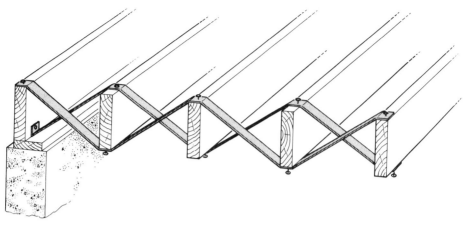

Fig. 9:2 Continuous Metal Strap Bridging

which the edges of the plywood sheets can be nailed. Solid bridging does have the disadvantage, however, of interfering with the installation of electrical and plumbing services. An example of solid bridging is shown in Figure 9:3A.

Pressed Sheet Metal Diagonal Bridging

This type of bridging may be purchased for use with standard-sized joists placed at 16″ centres. It may be nailed to the top and the bottom of the joists rather than to the side. See Figure 9:4A. Another type is made with a pointed end that can be driven into the joists, making nails unnecessary. These bridgings are good only for standard, uniformly spaced joists. See Figure 9:4B.

It is permissible under most building regulations and codes to nail a 1″ x 4″ on the underside of the joist in lieu of bridging provided it is in a continuous strip, fastened with 2¼″ nails to each joist and secured at each end to the header or sill. See Figure 9:5. This will help align and space the joists and prevent their over-all movement. It does little, however, to help distribute a concentrated load over several joists.

HOW TO CUT AND INSTALL DIAGONAL BRIDGING

Since the diagonal wood bridging is the most frequently used joist support, we will list here the steps necessary to cut and fit the pieces. The best method is to lay out and cut one piece to fit and then use that piece as a pattern for the other pieces.

To Cut Bridging

1. Make the two essential measurements: the distance between the joists and the actual width of the joist. For joists that are spaced at 16″ centres the distance between them is generally 14¼″. If 2″ x 10″ joists are used the actual width is 9¾″. These figures would be used on the framing

102

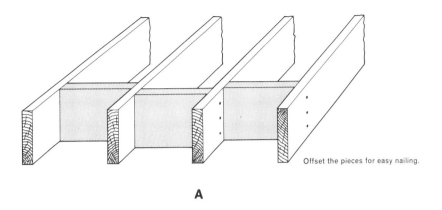

Offset the pieces for easy nailing.

A

B

Fig. 9:3 (A) Solid Bridging; (B) Solid and diagonal bridging used under the same floor.

103

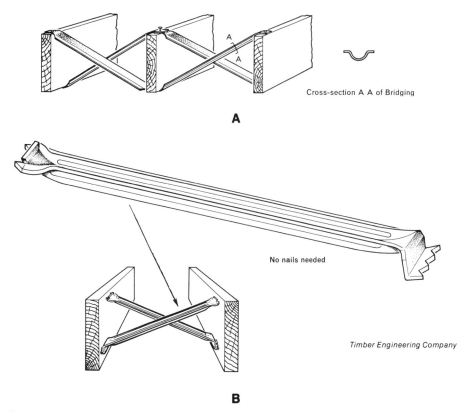

Cross-section A A of Bridging

A

No nails needed

Timber Engineering Company

B

Fig. 9:4 (A) Pressed Sheet Metal Bridging; (B) A type of metal bridging which requires no nails.

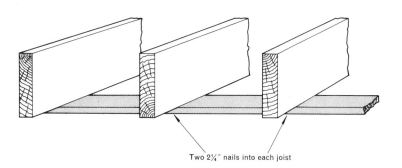

Two 2¼" nails into each joist

Fig. 9:5 Continuous 1" x 4" nailed under the joist in lieu of bridging.

square to lay out the first piece of bridging.

2. Place the framing square on the bridging material as shown in Figure 9:6.

3. Mark across the piece along the tongue of the square at the 9¾" mark. Make another mark on the edge of the stock at the 14¼" mark on the body of the square.

4. Reverse the square, and, using the same figures, mark as shown in Figure 9:7.

104

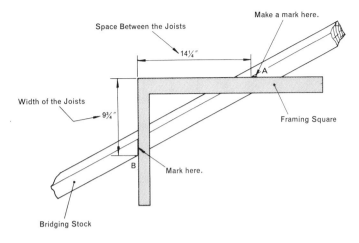

Fig. 9:6   Step 1 in bridging layout.

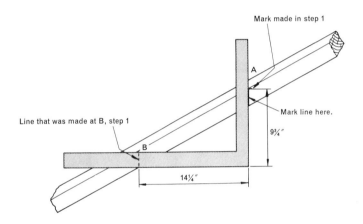

Fig. 9:7   Step 2 in bridging layout.

5. Mark along the tongue of the square at the 9¾″ figure. You should now have two parallel layout lines that represent the length of the bridging.
6. Cut on the layout lines and check the piece for proper fit.
7. Use this piece as a pattern for all the bridging required to fit between joists of the same size and spacing.
8. Bridging of special lengths will be required for the joist and trimmer spacings that, because of partition or floor opening locations, are smaller than the regular spacings. For these odd spacings the bridging is some-times cut to the correct length by placing the cut end of a piece of bridging stock against the face of the joist at the lower edge up a dis-tance equal to the thickness of the bridging. Let the stock rest against the top of the next joist and cut to length using the face of the joist as a guide as illustrated in Figure 9:8.

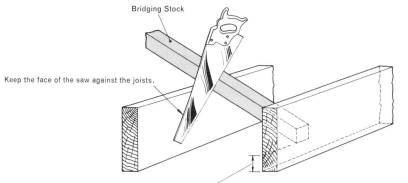

Bridging Stock

Keep the face of the saw against the joists.

Up a distance equal to the thickness of the bridging stock

Fig. 9:8   Cutting bridging for odd-sized joist spaces.

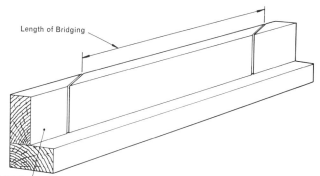

Length of Bridging

Two 2″ x 4″s spiked together

Fig. 9:9   Mitre box for cutting bridging.

Bridging can be cut faster and more accurately if a simple mitre box is made from two 2″ x 4″s like the one shown in Figure 9:9. The pattern that is laid out with the framing square can be used to lay out the correct angles and cuts on the mitre box.

To Install Bridging

1. Determine the location of the rows of bridging, and stretch a chalk line over the tops of the joists at this point.
2. Nail a row of subflooring temporarily to the joists about 6″ away from the bridging location. This will space the joists properly in the centre of the span and will also serve as a platform on which the carpenter can stand while he installs the bridging.
3. Start two 2½″ nails in each end of the individual pieces of bridging.
4. Start from the first joist and nail one end of the bridging to the upper edge of the joists only. *Do not nail the bridging to the lower edge of the joists at this time.* Carry on in this manner across the building. See Figures 9:10A and B.

The lower edge of the bridging should not be nailed until the house is almost completed. This will give the joists, which were placed crown edge

106

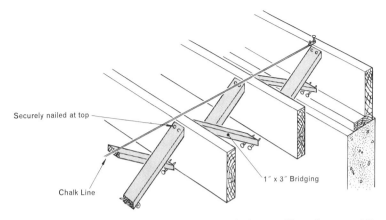

Securely nailed at top

Chalk Line

1″ x 3″ Bridging

Bridging not nailed at bottom until house is near completion

A

B

Fig. 9:10   (A) Nailing bridging in place; (B) 2″ x 2″ bridging in place. Note that the top ends only are nailed.

uppermost, a chance to straighten out due to the weight of the building. Once the bridging is nailed at both ends no further alignment of the top of the joists in the centre of the span can take place.

In estimating the number of lineal feet of bridging material necessary, multiply the number of rows by their length and multiply this again by 3. Example: If a house 40′ long requires 4 rows of bridging, the number of lineal feet required would be 4 x 40 x 3 = 480 lineal feet.

TYPES OF SUBFLOORS

When all the joists and bridging have been set and securely nailed in place, the house is ready for the subfloor. This is the rough floor that is placed directly on the joists. The purpose of the subfloor is:
(a) to provide a solid, level base for the finished floor;
(b) to strengthen the building;
(c) to align the joists and tie them together;
(d) to provide a measure of insulation and a sound-deadening effect.

The materials most often used for subfloors are:
(a) *1″ solid stock* from 4″ to 6″ in width, with square or tongue and grooved edges.
(b) *⅝″ unsanded plywood* which is also made with a square or a tongue and grooved edge. The sheets are generally 4′ x 8′.

Solid Stock Subfloors

Subfloors of solid stock may be laid either at right angles to the joists as shown in Figure 9:11, or diagonally to the joists, as in Figure 9:12.

When the subfloor is laid at right angles to the joists, the lumber need only be cut on one end in order to make the joint come over the joists. Therefore, there is a saving of both labour and material. There is generally very little waste. The disadvantage of this method lies in the fact that while it makes a firm base on which to nail the finished floor it does not brace the building. The direction in which the finished hardwood can be laid is limited as the finished floor must be laid at right angles to the subfloor. If it were laid parallel to the subfloor, it would eventually open up at the joints and buckle due to shrinkage and warpage of the subfloor.

When the subfloor is laid at right angles to the joists, the floor should be started at one side of the building; keep the edge of the first board even with a chalk line or with the edge of the header. The first board should be face-nailed with two 2½″ common nails in each joint. Stagger the joints so that no end joints will occur on adjacent rows on the same joist. See Figures 9:11 and 9:12. If tongue and grooved material is used, drive the nails diagonally through the tongue to draw the boards up tight.

It is preferable to lay solid subfloor diagonally to the joist because of the bracing effect this method provides. Subfloors laid in this way will stiffen the

108

whole building, particularly if it is a two-storey structure and if the two floors are laid at right angles to each other. Another advantage of this type of flooring is that the finished hardwood floor can be laid in either direction as the subfloor will, in any event, be at an angle to it. Any shrinkage or warpage will have little effect on the hardwood floor.

Diagonally laid floors require more labour and material than floors that are laid at right angles to the joists. Each end of the boards must be cut at a 45° angle as the full width of each piece must rest on the joists at the joint.

For the most effective bracing, the subfloor should be at a 45° angle to the joists. The best method of ensuring that this angle is maintained is to measure 8', or any convenient distance, in each direction, along the sill from the corner, that is, along the length and the width of the building, before you start to lay

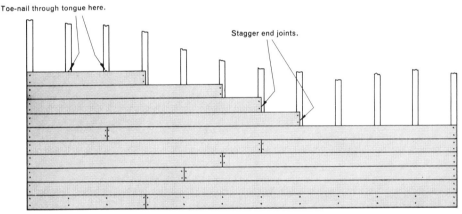

Fig. 9:11 Subfloor laid at right angles to joists.

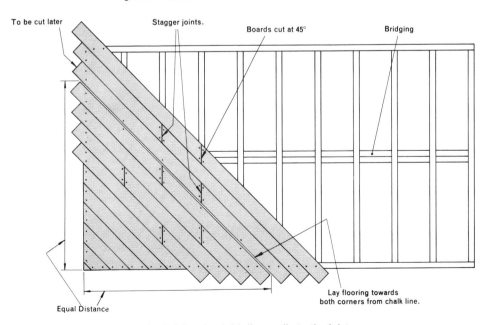

Fig. 9:12 Subflooring laid diagonally to the joists.

the subfloor. *Be sure that the distances in the two directions are equal.* See Figure 9:12. Stretch a chalk line across the joists from these points. Start the flooring from the chalk line. If tongue and grooved material is being used, place the grooved edge of the first board on the line and face-nail the board. Work from here to the opposite corner of the building, nailing diagonally through the tongue into each joist on each piece. Now go back to the first corner and fill it in. Start from the chalk line and work towards the corner. As you did when you started laying the subfloor, place the grooved edge of the first board on the chalk line so that there are two grooved edges together. The two boards at the chalk line are placed with the grooved edges together so that all nails can be driven diagonally through the tongue to draw the board up tight.

The ends of the boards at the edge of the floor may be cut at a 45° angle before each piece is nailed in place, or, more often, they are allowed to project over the edge and are later marked with a straight edge and cut with a hand saw or an electric portable saw.

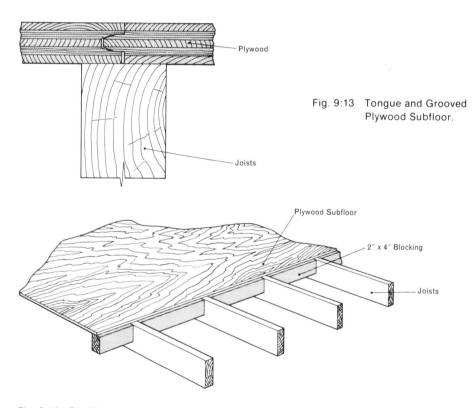

Fig. 9:13   Tongue and Grooved Plywood Subfloor.

Fig. 9:14   Blocking used between joists when square-edged plywood subflooring is used.

Plywood Subfloors

When square-edged plywood subflooring is used for subfloors, 2″ x 4″ blocking must be nailed between the joists and under the joints to support the edges of the sheets. If tongue and grooved plywood sheets are used, no blocking is necessary as the edges of these sheets are self-supporting. Start the sheets at one side of the floor with the square or grooved edge of the sheet flush with the outer edge of the joist header. If the subfloor is being laid with tongue and grooved sheets, the tongue edge should face towards the centre. The ends of the sheets in either type of plywood must rest on the joists.

When spacing the joists, care must be taken to see that they are exactly on the 12″ or 16″ centres. Improperly spaced joists will not accommodate the 8′ sheets and the sheets must then be cut to fit. With properly spaced joists very little cutting is necessary.

The thickness of the plywood used for subfloors will depend on the joist spacing. The most common thickness is ⅝″ for use on joists spaced at 16″. The sheets must be laid with the surface grain of the plywood at right angles to the joists. They should be fastened down with 2″ common nails at 6″ intervals along the edges of the sheet, and at 12″ intervals along intermediate supports. The end joints of the sheets should be staggered so that no two joints are adjacent on the same joist.

ASSIGNMENT
Bridging
1. Why is bridging used in floor framing?
2. What materials are used for diagonal bridging?
3. How far apart are rows of bridging generally placed?
4. Explain how metal strapping is used as bridging.
5. State the advantage and the disadvantage of using solid bridging.
6. If bridging is not used, describe the alternative method of aligning and preventing joist movement.
7. What two essential dimensions are necessary for the layout of diagonal bridging with the framing square?
8. How is the bridging cut to fit an odd-sized space?
9. (a) What sized nails are used for diagonal bridging?
   (b) Why are the lower ends of diagonal bridging not nailed until the house is almost completed?
10. How many lineal feet of bridging material would be required for three rows of bridging in a house 38′ long?

Subfloors
11. List the four functions of subfloors.
12. What advantage have tongue and grooved sheets over square-edged plywood for subflooring?
13. State the advantages and the disadvantages of the two methods of laying subfloors with solid lumber.
14. (a) At what angle should the boards of a diagonally laid subfloor be to the joists?
    (b) How and where is the first board to be nailed in place on the floor?

15. How are the ends of the boards that project over the edge of the floor cut?
16. Why is it very important that the 12″ or 16″ joist spacing be exactly correct when plywood subflooring is used?
17. Why should the surface grain of the plywood be at right angles to the joists?
18. (a) What sized nails should be used with plywood subfloors?
    (b) How far apart should the nails be placed?
19. How many sheets of 4′ x 8′ plywood would be required for a floor 28′ wide x 56′ long if the joists are spaced 16″ on centre?

Construction Safety (see pages 399-417)

20. State the first safety rule that should be observed by all building tradesmen.
21. How does the wearing of hard hats and safety shoes prevent accidents?
22. Why is it important to have first aid for even slight injuries?

Chapter 10

WALL FRAMING AND WALL OPENINGS

One of the most important operations in house construction – and probably the most impressive in proportion to the time involved – is the erection of the wall framework. The method of erecting the wall framework will depend on the type of construction being used. In Chapter 4, platform frame construction was described as being the type most extensively used. The wall framing that adapts itself best to platform frame construction will therefore be described here.

In platform frame construction the wall framework is built directly on the subfloor and spiked through it into the joists. The subfloor forms a solid, level base for the wall and also provides an excellent platform for the carpenter while he assembles and erects the wall. The framework of the wall for a frame or masonry veneer house generally consists of 2″ x 4″ upright studding. The single lower plate (sometimes called the *sole* plate) between the subfloor and lower end of the studding and the double top plate that is attached to the upper end of the studding tie the wall together. They also provide a base for

Fig. 10:1   One frame wall in place.

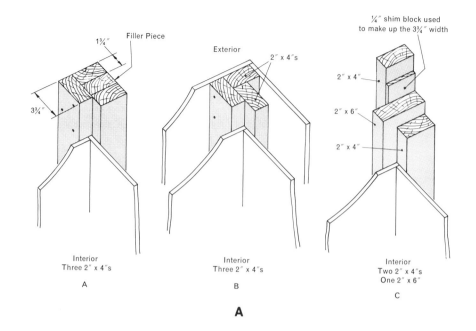

A

1¾″

Filler Piece

3¾″

Interior
Three 2″ x 4″s

A

Exterior

2″ x 4″s

Interior
Three 2″ x 4″s

B

¼″ shim block used
to make up the 3¾″ width

2″ x 4″

2″ x 6″

2″ x 4″

Interior
Two 2″ x 4″s
One 2″ x 6″

C

B

Fig. 10:2   (A) Three corner post arrangements; (B) Typical exterior corner wall framing.

114

the ceiling and second-storey floor joists, or the roof rafters, depending on the design of the house.

One of the most important factors in wall framing is the spacing of the studding, which may be 12″, 16″, 20″, or 24″ (centre to centre). The most common spacing is 16″. This will provide sufficient support for most frame walls and will accommodate most building materials, which are generally manufactured in 4′ modular widths.

Exterior walls and partition walls that support the ceilings must be made from 2″ x 4″ stock. Partition walls that act only as room dividers and do not support any other parts of the house may be made from 2″ x 3″ stock.

HOW TO LAY OUT A WALL SECTION

1. Determine the length of the wall.
2. Cut the lower and one of the upper plates to the exact wall length. A short wall may require only one length of stock for each plate. A long wall, on the other hand, may need two or three lengths for each plate.
3. Lay the pieces for the lower plate flat on the subfloor. Next to them place the pieces for the upper plate. Be careful to keep the ends even. See Figure 10:3. Before starting to lay out the location of the studding with a framing square, it must be decided which of the three methods of arranging the studding for the corner posts is to be used. Figure 10:2A illustrates these three methods. The method illustrated in Figure 10:2B is the one most often used.
4. Starting from one end, lay out the position of the first two studs, which will form part of the first corner posts as shown in Figure 10:3.
5. Using a framing square, lay out the position of the next stud by placing the end of the tongue of the square even with the line that marks the position of the second stud, as shown in Figure 10:3. Mark along the outer edge of the body of the square across both plates. Mark an X beside the line to indicate on which side of the line the stud should be placed.
6. Locate the position of any doors or windows that will be situated in the

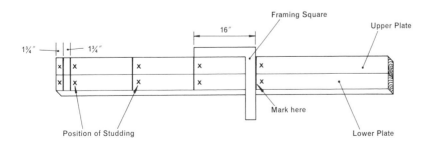

Fig. 10:3   Layout of studding position on plates.

115

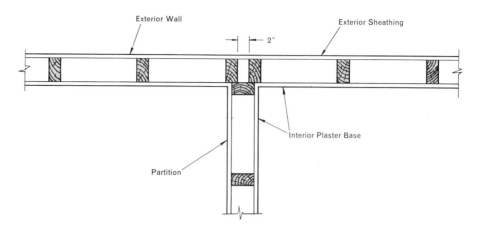

Fig. 10:4   Intersection of exterior wall and interior partition.

wall, and lay out the position of the double studding on each side of the opening. For small window openings, the studding may be continued at the regular 16″ spacing and the required studs or parts of studs cut out after the wall has been erected. (A detailed explanation of framing window openings is given in Chapter 25.) The standard 16″ spacing must be maintained above and below window or door openings regardless of the position of the double studding at either side of the openings, even though this may cause some studs to be very close together.

7. Locate the position of any partitions that intersect the wall and lay out the double studding, allowing 2″ between the studs as shown in Figure 10:4. These studs should be in addition to those placed at the regular 16″ spacing.

ASSEMBLY AND ERECTION OF WALL SECTIONS

1. Cut the required number of studs to the correct length. The length should be the clear ceiling height shown on the plan less the thickness of the three plates, plus the thickness of the finished floor and the lath and plaster or other ceiling material. There will be a saving of time if all the studs for the exterior walls are cut at the same time from the same pattern. This will also ensure that they will all be exactly the same length.

2. Place the plates on edge on the subfloor and set the studs in their correct position between the plates as shown in Figure 10:5.

3. Fasten the studding in place by driving 4″ spikes through the plates into the ends of the studs. Make sure the edge is on the line and the X is covered.

4. The window and door openings are generally framed in the wall while it is still lying on the subfloor.

   Builders often find it easier and faster to build the wall as an almost complete sub-assembly, as is done for a pre-fabricated house, where

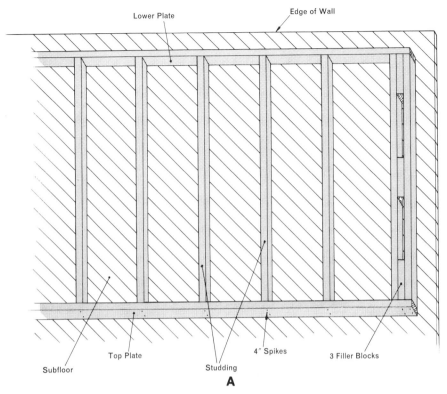

Lower Plate   Edge of Wall

Subfloor   Top Plate   Studding   4″ Spikes   3 Filler Blocks

A

B

Fig. 10:5   (A) Assembled wall lying on the subfloor before erection; (B) Assembled wall with rough window framing completed before it is erected.

117

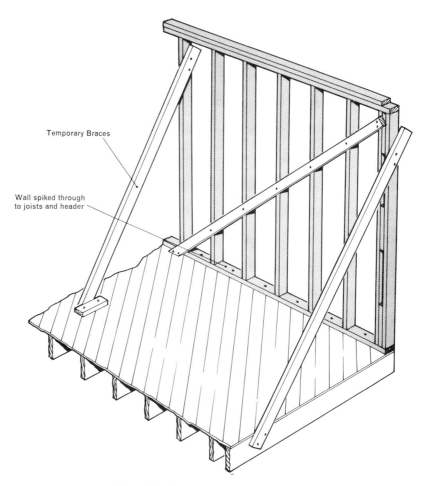

Fig. 10:6 (A) Wall frame set in place.

much of the material included in the finished wall is nailed on the frame while it is still lying on the subfloor. This material may include the diagonal sway bracing, exterior wall sheathing, and in some cases, the window and door frames as well as the exterior siding and trim. This practice, however, is generally restricted to one-storey homes.

5. Raise the top plate until the wall is in a vertical position. Shift the wall section until it is in the correct location and is flush with the edge of the subfloor. If the wall section is long, this operation will require two or more men.

6. Secure the wall by driving 4″ spikes through the lower plate into the subfloor, joists and header at 2′ intervals.

7. Nail temporary diagonal braces to the top of the wall and to the sub-floor to hold the wall in an upright position until all four walls have been erected. See Figure 10:6A.

8. Assemble and erect all exterior walls in the same manner.

9. Plumb all corners with a spirit level and straight edge and secure them

Fig. 10:6 (B) Frame wall for the gable end of a home with a low-pitched roof. The upper double plates are at the roof line and the studs are cut in individual lengths to fit.

by driving 4″ spikes through the corner posts.

10. Nail on the top double plate. Use long lengths and lap the corners as shown in Figure 10:7. Leave a 4″ space where partitions intersect the wall to allow the top plate of the partition to tie into the main exterior wall. See Figure 10:8.

Some exterior walls are built with masonry material from the footing up to, or slightly above, grade line and a frame wall from there to the first floor level. With this type of wall there is less foundation exposed; the exterior siding or brick is allowed to extend almost to grade. Such a wall is shown in Figure 10:9.

There are other methods of wall framing used in other types of frame construction, but the method described here is the one most extensively used in most parts of Canada.

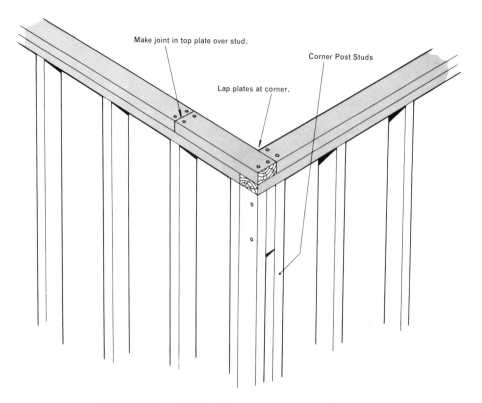

Make joint in top plate over stud.

Corner Post Studs

Lap plates at corner.

Fig. 10:7   Upper double plates at the corner of a building.

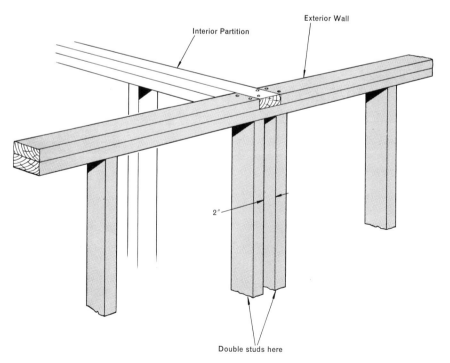

Exterior Wall

Interior Partition

2"

Double studs here

Fig. 10:8   Intersection exterior and interior wall partition.

120

A

B

Fig. 10:9 (A) A short frame wall running from the highest point of grade to the first floor level; (B) Wall framing for a house with a low-pitched roof. For low-pitched roofs the double top wall plate may fit directly under the roof joists, in which case the studs are cut in individual lengths to fit the sloping plate.

121

FRAMING THE WALL OPENINGS

In either frame or masonry veneer houses, special framework is required around the window and door openings. The openings must be framed so that the wall structure is not weakened in any way. The purpose of the framework is to strengthen the wall and to provide a solid structure to which the window and door frames, the exterior wall sheathing, the plaster base, and the interior trim can be nailed.

The rough frame opening should be 1″ wider and ½″ longer than the actual size of the window or door frame. This will allow some clearance for fitting the frames and will also provide sufficient space for rock wool insulation between the 2″ x 4″ framework and the window frame.

When laying out the rough window and door openings in a wall frame, we must know the location and size of the window and door frames to be used in the rough opening. This information will be shown on the plans. The dimensions are given to the centre line of the window or door.

The size of the window openings is generally determined by the size of the individual panes of glass (referred to as lights) in the sash. The sash is the wood or metal frame that holds the glass. The window frame is the larger part in which the sash fits. The size of the lights is given on the plans. The over-all width of the window frame can be found by adding to the combined width of the panes, the width of the side stiles of the sash, plus the thickness of the side members of the window frame (called the jambs) and the 1″ clearance between the frame and the rough framework. See Figure 10:10. The over-all height is found in a similar manner: to the combined length of the panes is added the width of the top, bottom, and meeting rails of the sash, as well as the thickness of the top jamb and the sill and the ½″ clearance between the top jamb and the framework. See Figure 10:10.

The wood allowance for the window sash and frame depends upon the type of window to be installed and whether the sash or glass is to slide, swing, or be permanently fixed. This information is also found on the plans.

Probably the most popular type of window in general use is the double hung window. It contains two sashes that slide up and down, by-passing each other. Double hung windows may contain any number of lights; however, in the example given here each sash contains one light measuring 24″ x 20″ (the width is always given first). The standard wood allowance used for calculating the length and width of a double hung window frame is given in Figures 10:10 and 10:11.

Some plans give the over-all dimensions of the window openings, particularly if special types of windows are to be used. A window schedule is generally included in the plans.

Window manufacturers list in their catalogues and data sheets the glass size, the corresponding size of the sash, the over-all size of the window frame, and the size of the rough stud opening or the brick opening into which the frame will fit. Carpenters often use these data sheets when they lay out and

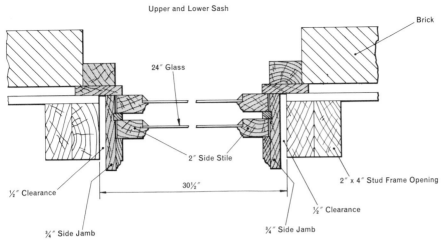

Upper and Lower Sash

Brick

24″ Glass

2″ Side Stile

2″ x 4″ Stud Frame Opening

½″ Clearance

30½″

½″ Clearance

¾″ Side Jamb

¾″ Side Jamb

Fig. 10:10   The allowance for wood members in calculating the width of the rough stud opening for a double hung window. Another method is to add 6½″ to the width of the glass.

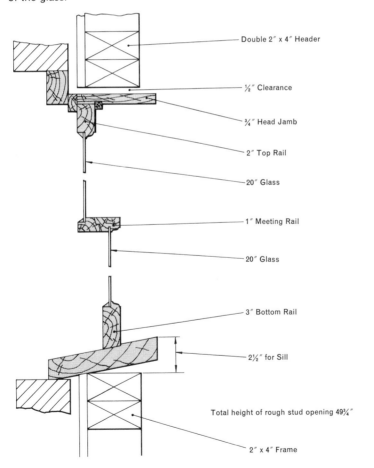

Double 2″ x 4″ Header

½″ Clearance

¾″ Head Jamb

2″ Top Rail

20″ Glass

1″ Meeting Rail

20″ Glass

3″ Bottom Rail

2½″ for Sill

Total height of rough stud opening 49¾″

2″ x 4″ Frame

Fig. 10:11   Allowance for wood members used in calculating the length of the opening for a double hung window. Another method of calculating the height of the window opening is to add 9¾″ to the glass size.

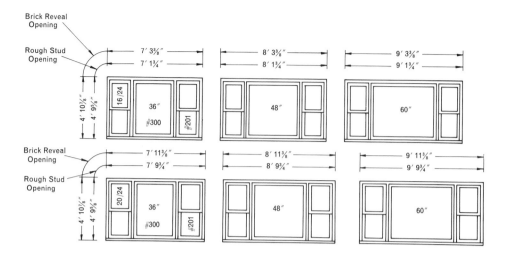

Fig. 10:12 Window catalogue data sheet information listing rough stud and brick openings for windows of a stated size.

frame window openings. This practice reduces the chance of error as the sheets provide the correct dimensions for newer and different types of windows whose over-all frame size is difficult to calculate from the glass size stated on the drawings. A portion of such a data sheet is shown in Figure 10:12.

The tops of all window frames in the house should be the same height from the floor regardless of the width or length of the windows. This height generally has a direct relation to the eaves, to some other trim member, or to a definite course of brick. This is necessary in order to maintain straight

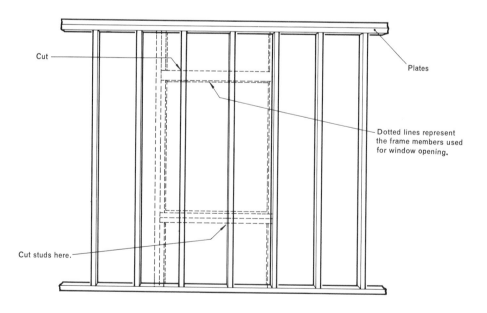

Fig. 10:13 Cutting in a window opening after frame wall has been erected.

lines, which are pleasing to the eye and are in good architectural form.

As has been stated, there are two methods of framing window openings. One method is to build the wall with the studding at its regular spacing. The window is then located on the plate, the studs cut or removed, and the opening framed as shown in Figure 10:13. However, this method is seldom used, and only for small windows.

The second method is to lay out and frame the openings when the regular studs are nailed in place, before the wall section is erected while it is lying on the subfloor. The procedure most often followed for this operation is described here.

TO LAY OUT THE WINDOW OPENING

1. From the dimensions given on the plan, locate the centre line of the window on the plate.
2. From the glass size, or from the manufacturer's data sheet, determine the width of the rough window opening.
3. From the centre line of the window, measure half the width of the rough opening plus 1¾″ (the thickness of the inner or trimmer studs). This will locate the position of the full-length studding.
4. The two outer vertical members can now be nailed in place. Make sure that the 1¾″ allowance has been made for the thickness of the trimmer studs.
5. Lay out the line for the bottom of the header and for the top of the rough sill. The height of the top of the opening from the floor can best be laid out by using a *window rod*, which is a narrow strip of wood with the height of the top and bottom of the window frames marked on it. The height of each window can easily be transferred from the rod to the wall. This is a much more accurate method than measuring the height of each opening individually.
6. Spike the double headers through the outer studding. Window and door headers are referred to as *lintels*. The 2″ materials used for lintels should always be placed on edge for greater strength. For openings that are less than 3′ 6″ wide, a double 2″ x 4″ lintel is strong enough; for larger openings, larger lintels are required. Table 2 taken from *Residential Standards* lists the lintel sizes required for various window spans.
7. Spike in place the inner double studs. These are called *trimmer studs.* Use 3½″ nails spaced 30″ apart and staggered.
8. Nail the two rough sill members in place. These pieces may be placed flat, as strength is not the important factor. Sometimes only a single 2″ x 4″ is used for this member.
9. Fasten the short cripple studs above and below the window. They must be placed at the 16″ locations originally laid out on the plates.
10. In large openings, a truss may be built between the header and the top plate for added support. Figure 10:15 illustrates such a truss.

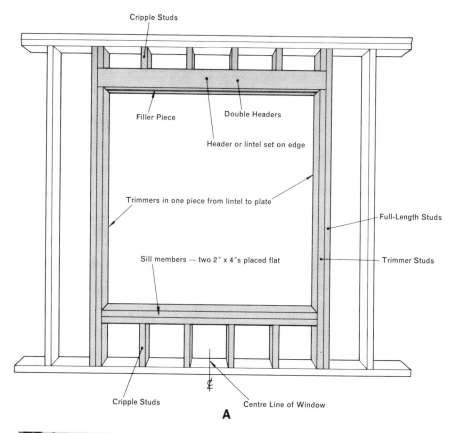

Cripple Studs

Filler Piece

Double Headers

Header or lintel set on edge

Trimmers in one piece from lintel to plate

Full-Length Studs

Sill members — two 2″ x 4″s placed flat

Trimmer Studs

¢

Cripple Studs

Centre Line of Window

A

B

Fig. 10:14   (A) Framing around window opening; (B) Large window opening with two 2″ x10″s used as lintels.

126

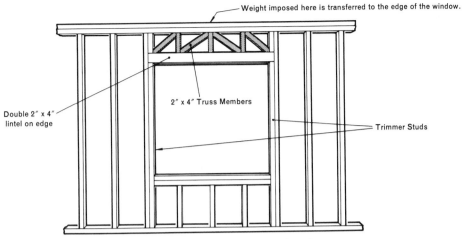

Fig. 10:15   Trussed Window Opening

TABLE 17C

SPANS FOR VARIOUS DEPTHS OF LINTELS MADE FROM NOMINAL 4-IN. THICK LUMBER OR TWO THICKNESSES OF NOMINAL 2-IN. LUMBER INSTALLED ON EDGE

Location of Lintels	Supported Loads Including Dead Loads and Ceiling	Nominal Depth of Lintels (in.)	Maximum Allowable Spans (ft. — in.)
Interior Partitions or Walls	Limited Attic storage	4 6 8 10 12	4 — 0 6 — 0 8 — 0 10 — 0 12 — 6
	Full attic storage, or roof load, or limited attic storage plus one floor	4 6 8 10 12	2 — 0 3 — 0 4 — 0 5 — 0 6 — 0
	Full attic storage plus one floor, or roof load plus one floor, or limited attic storage plus two floors	4 6 8 10 12	— 2 — 6 3 — 0 4 — 0 5 — 0
	Full attic storage plus two floors, or roof load plus two floors	4 6 8 10 12	— 2 — 0 3 — 0 3 — 6 4 — 0
Exterior Walls	Roof, with or without attic storage	4 6 8 10 12	4 — 0 6 — 0 8 — 0 10 — 0 12 — 0
	Roof, with or without attic storage plus one floor	4 6 8 10 12	2 — 0 5 — 0 7 — 0 8 — 0 9 — 0
	Roof with or without attic storage plus two floors	4 6 8 10 12	2 — 0 4 — 0 6 — 0 7 — 0 8 — 0

From Residential Standards. Supplement No. 5 to the National Building Code of Canada

Note: The size of lintel specified for a given span varies according to the position of the wall and to the weight to be imposed on the wall.

Because they require less labour to build, and because they are more convenient than trusses, solid lintels made from 2″ stock are more commonly used to bridge the span over large windows. Figure 10:16 illustrates a lintel made from two 2″ x 8″s set on edge.

Because two pieces of 2″ dressed stock are not as thick as the width of 2″ x 4″ dressed material, filler blocks must be used between the two lintel members that are placed on edge. See Figure 10:17.

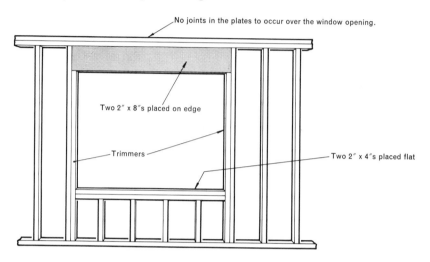

No joints in the plates to occur over the window opening.

Two 2″ x 8″s placed on edge

Trimmers

Two 2″ x 4″s placed flat

Fig. 10:16   Window opening with a solid lintel.

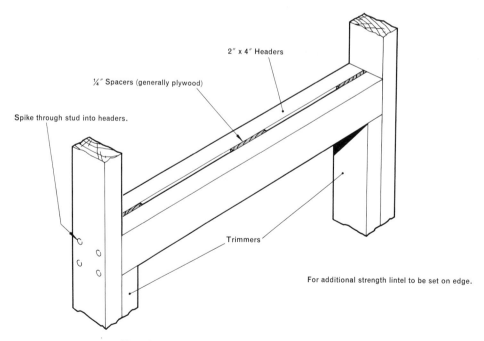

2″ x 4″ Headers

¼″ Spacers (generally plywood)

Spike through stud into headers.

Trimmers

For additional strength lintel to be set on edge.

Fig. 10:17   Spacers used between lintel members.

For smaller windows, whose openings are sometimes framed in after all the studding is in place, as illustrated in Figure 10:13, the layout is similar to that for larger windows, in that the width of the window is located on the plate from the centre line of the window given on the plan. Mark the heights of the lintel and sills on the studs and make allowances for the depth of these members. Cut the studs where marked. These will become the cripple studs above and below the window. For the width of the window, nail the side members in place

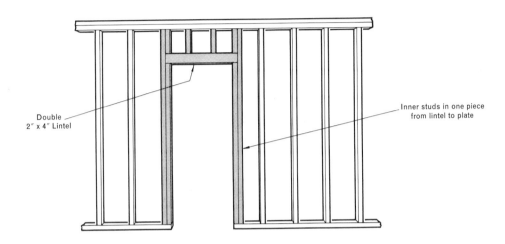

Double
2″ x 4″ Lintel

Inner studs in one piece
from lintel to plate

Fig. 10:18   Framing around a door opening.

Fig. 10:19   Framing around a garage door opening.

on the layout lines. The header and sill members can now be nailed in place and the cripple studs attached to them. The trimmer studs are spiked to the side members to complete the framing.

The procedure for framing door openings is almost the same as that for framing window openings. The one difference is that no sill supporting members are required. Figure 10:18 shows a typical door opening for a standard door frame. The top of the finished door sill should be from 1″ to 1½″ above the subfloor depending on the type of finished floor to be used.

The height of the rough exterior door opening can be calculated by adding to the door size 1″ or 1½″ for sill clearance, 1″ for head jamb, and 1″ for clearance and insulation. For the width of the door opening, add to the width of the door 1″ for jamb and ½″ for clearance and insulation on either side, or a total of 3″ plus the width of the door.

Care should be taken when framing the rough wall openings to ensure that the windows and doors will be in exactly the correct location and that the framework will properly support all the building materials that will be attached to it, or that will rest on it. All vertical members should be plumbed and all horizontal members levelled.

The same procedure should be followed when framing wall openings in either frame or brick veneer walls.

ASSIGNMENT
Wall Framing
1. What factor will govern the method used for building frame walls?
2. In platform frame construction, what does the wall frame rest on?
3. Make a drawing of a wall frame and name the framing members.
4. What is the purpose of the top member of the double plate?
5. At what spacings may studs be placed?
6. Which spacing is most often used? Why?
7. Make a drawing of three methods of arranging the studding at the corner where two exterior walls meet.
8. Describe the method of laying out the location of the studding on the plates.
9. Why is an X placed beside the layout lines used to locate the studding?
10. Why should the window or door openings not be allowed to interfere with the regular stud spacing?
11. How is the studding arranged where a partition intersects an exterior wall?
12. How is the length of the exterior wall studding calculated?
13. How is the wall frame assembled?
14. If the wall is to be built as a sub-assembly for a pre-fabricated house, what building materials may be attached to the wall before it is erected?
15. How is the wall secured to the floor assembly?
16. (a) How are the exterior walls held together and stiffened?

(b) How are the intersecting partition walls tied into the exterior walls?

17. Explain the meaning of *modular* construction (see glossary of terms).

Framing Wall Openings

18. Will a large window opening, if properly framed, affect the strength of the wall?

19. What building materials may be nailed to the framework around a rough window opening?

20. How much allowance should be left between the side of the window opening and the frame?

21. (a) What information must be known before the rough opening for a window frame can be laid out?

(b) Where can this information be found?

22. If a double hung window has eight lights (four in each sash) 14″ x 15″, what should the inside dimensions of the rough window opening be?

23. Where might the carpenter find the required rough opening size for a special type of window?

24. Why should the tops of all the window openings in the house be the same height?

25. What are the two general methods of framing window openings in a frame wall?

26. Make a drawing of a window opening in a frame wall and name all the parts.

27. Explain the purpose of a window rod.

28. What sized lintel should be used in a one-storey house over a window with a span of 9′ 6″?

29. Explain the principle of how a truss made from 2″ x 4″ over a long window span can support the weight imposed upon it.

30. Why must a filler block be used between the two lintel members when they are placed on edge?

31. What sized opening should be left in an exterior wall for a 2′ 8″ x 6′ 8″ door?

32. Why should a great deal of care be taken when framing wall openings?

Chapter 11

PARTITIONS AND CEILING FRAMING

PARTITIONS

Basically there are two main types of partitions:

(a) *Bearing Partitions* help to support the roof and the ceiling or, in some cases, the floor above by forming a direct bearing from the girder, or double joists, to the framing members above;

(b) *Non-Bearing Partitions* are used solely to divide one living area from another. They may or may not extend the full distance from the floor to the ceiling.

In a frame or brick veneer house, the partitions are usually built in two stages. The main bearing partitions are erected first to stiffen the framework of the building by tying the centre sections of the exterior walls together. This provides a rigid surface to which the exterior wall sheathing is nailed. The non-bearing partitions are built later when the house has been closed in by the walls and the roof. Some builders, however, prefer to build all the partitions at the same time.

Bearing Partitions

Bearing partitions must have girths which are short 2″ x 4″s nailed between the studs halfway up the wall to prevent the studs from bowing under the weight imposed on them by the floor or ceiling above. The levels of the pieces are staggered to facilitate nailing. See Figure 11:1B.

Arrangements must be made over doors and archways to support the load. A double 2″ header set on edge may be used for this purpose, or a truss may be made if there is enough room between the top of the door opening and the top of the wall. These two methods are shown in Figures 11:1B and 11:2A.

The studding for load bearing partitions should be made of 2″ x 4″s spaced at 16″ centres. These building standards also apply to the exterior walls.

Non-Bearing Partitions

For non-bearing partitions, 2″ x 3″s may be used, generally at 16″ centres, but under certain conditions, it is permissible to space them 24″ apart. It is also permissible to build non-bearing partitions with the 4″ side of the studs parallel to the wall provided there is no swinging door in the wall; this is often done in short walls around clothes closets in order to save space. This arrangement is not recommended for long walls as there is too much spring in the studs when they are used in the wall in this manner.

TO BUILD THE PARTITIONS

The dimensions on the plans should be checked and the positions of the partitions carefully laid out on the subfloor. The dimensions generally are from the outer edge of the exterior frame walls to the centre of the partitions. To locate one edge of the partition frame, measure from the outer edge of the building, at the starting point of the partition, the distance stated on the plans, less half the thickness of the partition wall frame (generally 1⅞"). Use the same dimension at the other end of the partition and strike a chalk line between the two points. See Figure 11:2B.

Cut the two plates to the exact length of the partition and lay out the position of the studding in the same manner as described for the exterior frame wall. There is one difference, however: there is only a single stud at each end of the partition where it intersects the exterior wall or another partition. The position of the door openings should be laid out on the plates by locating the centre of the opening as indicated on the plans. From this point, measure half the width of the door plus 1" for the side jamb of the frame and a further ½" for clearance. As the full-length studs should be installed first, allow another 1¾" for the thickness of the trimmer stud on each side of the opening. See Figure 11:3.

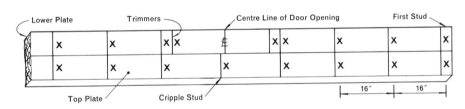

Fig. 11:3   Layout of stud positions on plates.

Locate on the plates the position of all intersecting partitions and mark the locations of the two studs to be used at these intersections, as shown in Figure 11:4.

While it is lying on the subfloor, assemble the partition in the same manner as the outside walls were assembled. The height of the door openings can be determined by adding to the door height 1" for the top jamb, plus the thickness of the finished floor material, plus ½" for clearance for the door to swing above the floor. It is best to complete the rough framing for all door openings before the partitions are erected.

After the partitions have been erected, they should be tied to the exterior walls by allowing the upper double plate to project over and nailing it to the exterior wall or another intersecting partition as shown in Figure 11:5.

In cases where partitions run parallel with the ceiling joists, short pieces of 2" x 4"s are placed between the joists, and the tops of the partitions are nailed to them. This holds the tops of the partitions secure and in the correct location. To provide a nailing support for the ceiling plaster base or dry-wall material, a 1″ x 6″ or a 2″ x 6″ is securely nailed to the top of the wall, as shown in Figure 11:6A.

Solid nailing must be provided for the plaster base and interior trim at all intersecting partitions.

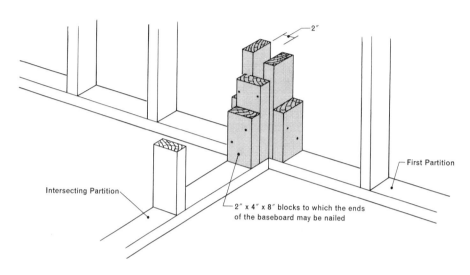

Fig. 11:4 Stud arrangement at partition wall intersections.

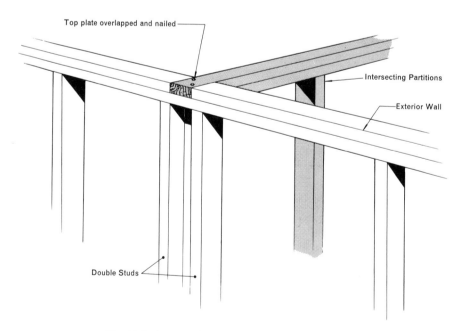

Fig. 11:5 Intersecting partition tied into exterior wall.

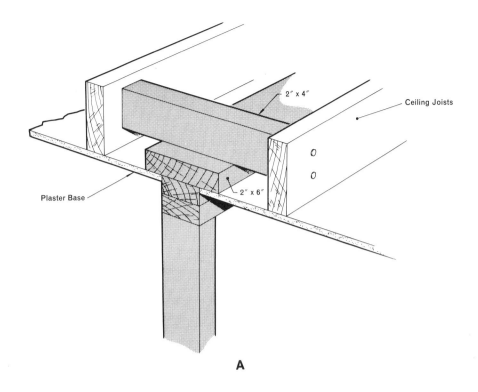

A

B

Fig. 11:6 (A) Blocking used at the top of partitions that run parallel to the ceiling joists; (B) 2″ x 6″ spiked to the top of a partition wall to provide nailing support for ceiling plaster base.

CEILING JOISTS

Ceilings are generally supported by ceiling joists made from 2″ material of varying widths, depending on the span and the type of ceiling they must support. Ceiling joists support only the ceiling, the insulation above, and, in some cases, a very limited storage weight. They are not to be confused with second-floor joists, which, because they must support all the weight imposed

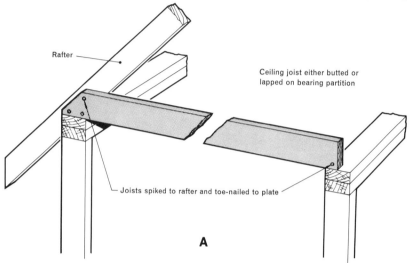

Rafter

Ceiling joist either butted or lapped on bearing partition

Joists spiked to rafter and toe-nailed to plate

A

B

Fig. 11:7   (A) Ceiling joists with one end resting on the exterior wall and the other end resting on a bearing partition; (B) Ceiling joists with one end supported by a girder. Note the use of joist hangers. A 1″ x 6″ is often run along the top of the ceiling joists near the centre of the span to align, stiffen, and space the joists.

138

on a living area, are necessarily larger and are subject to the same requirements as the first-floor joists.

Ceiling joists are usually spaced at 16″ intervals, which correspond with the stud spacing and allow them to be placed directly above the studs.

As a rule, the ceiling joists are nailed in place before the rafters are erected and sometimes before the exterior wall sheathing is applied. This stiffens the building greatly, and provides a substantial framework on which to build the roof.

In most cases one end of the ceiling joists rests on an exterior wall and the other on a bearing partition. In other cases, however, both ends rest on exterior walls or on bearing partitions.

Where it is feasible, the ceiling joists should run in the same direction as the rafters. The rafters can then be spiked to the ceiling joists as illustrated in Figure 11:7. However, to save material and to prevent spring or sag the ceiling joists should run in the direction that will give them the shortest span while still letting them rest on a bearing partition. This may mean that they will run at right angles to the rafters. Then short pieces of joist material are butted to the first joist and run at right angles to the plate and the rafters. The first joist, in effect, becomes a header. See Figure 11:8.

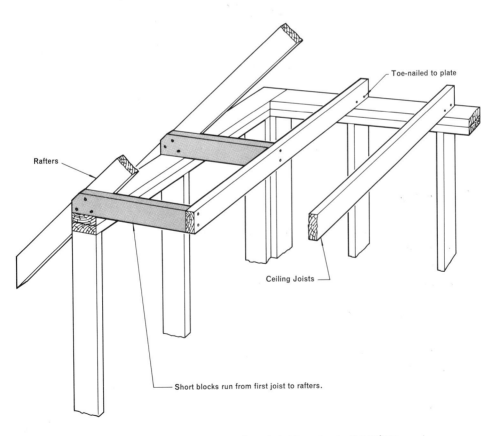

Fig. 11:8   Ceiling joists running at right angles to the rafters.

The ceiling joists may extend over the exterior wall to form a cantilever overhang where the joist forms the framing member to which the soffit is nailed. This type of construction raises the roof line slightly because the rafters rest on top of the joists rather than on the wall plate. See Figure 11:9. This provides a larger attic storage area, or, in a storey-and-a-half house, more living area. This type of framing, along with truss construction where the ceiling joists are built as part of the rafter unit, will be described more fully in a later chapter on roof framing.

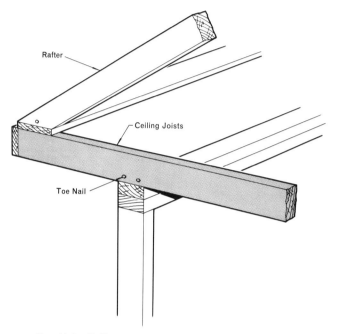

Fig. 11:9 Ceiling joists with a cantilever overhang.

ASSIGNMENT

Partitions

1. (a) List the two basic types of interior frame partitions.
   (b) Explain the difference between the two types.
2. Why should all main bearing partitions be erected before the wall sheathing is applied or the roof built?
3. (a) What are "girths"?
   (b) How are they held in place?
   (c) Why are they used?
4. Describe two methods of supporting the load over door or archway openings.
5. (a) What should be the size and spacing of studding for bearing partitions?
   (b) What is the minimum size of studs permissible for use in non-bearing partitions?

6. What is the disadvantage of building partitions with the 4″ side of the stud parallel with the wall?
7. How are the positions of the partitions located on the subfloor?
8. How does the stud layout for a partition differ from that of an exterior wall?
9. If an interior door is 2′ 6″ wide, what should be the distance between the two full-length studs on each side of the rough door opening?
10. Make a sectional drawing showing the arrangement of the studs at the intersection of two partition walls.
11. (a) How are the tops of the partitions tied to the exterior walls?
    (b) How are they tied to the ceiling joists that run parallel to the partition?
12. How is nailing support provided for the plaster base at the intersection of the top of the partition and the ceiling?

Ceiling Joists
13. List two factors that determine the width of ceiling joists.
14. At what spacing are ceiling joists generally placed?
15. Where feasible, why is it advantageous to have the ceiling joists run in the same direction as the rafters?
16. Where the ceiling joists do not run in the same direction as the rafters, what arrangement must be made to provide support for the ceiling?
17. What is the advantage of the type of construction in which the ceiling joists project over the exterior wall?

Chapter 12

WALL BRACING AND WALL SHEATHING

WALL BRACING

In frame construction it is necessary to stiffen and strengthen the walls by installing permanent diagonal braces that will keep the walls in a plumb or upright position. They are especially necessary if horizontal, one inch thick, solid sheathing is used. With this type of construction the vertical 2″ x 4″ studding and the horizontal sheathing form a rectangle, a shape that has very little strength when pressure is exerted from one corner towards the opposite corner. If you press together the opposite corners of an empty picture frame, you can easily change its shape. However, if a light brace is nailed diagonally across the frame, so that two triangles are formed, it is very difficult to distort the frame. A triangle is a much stronger geometric figure than a square or a rectangle. This principle is used where strength is required in buildings. Structural members are placed diagonally between vertical and horizontal members to form right-angled triangles.

Sway Bracing

The diagonal braces, or sway bracing, can be installed by two methods: 1. Cut-in; 2. Let-in.

The first method consists of cutting short pieces of 2″ x 4″, with a 45° angle on either end, to fit between the studding as shown in Figure 12:1.

Sway bracing should run at a 45° angle to the plates. This is not always possible, however, as door or window openings may be situated close to the corner of the building. Then short braces, referred to as knee braces or K braces, placed above and below a window opening as shown in Figure 12:2, serve to strengthen the structure, but not quite as effectively.

HOW TO INSTALL CUT-IN SWAY BRACING

1. If there are no wall openings near the corner that would interfere with a continuous diagonal brace, measure a distance equal to the height of the wall from the corner along the lower plate (point A, Figure 12:1).
2. From this point, stretch a chalk line to the top corner of the wall (point B, Figure 12:3).
3. Make a double 45° angle cut on one end of a 6′ length of 2″ x 4″. Fit the cut end into the corner as shown in Figure 12:3 and mark the piece of stock to length at the first stud from the corner.
4. Square a line at the point just marked and cut the stock to length. This

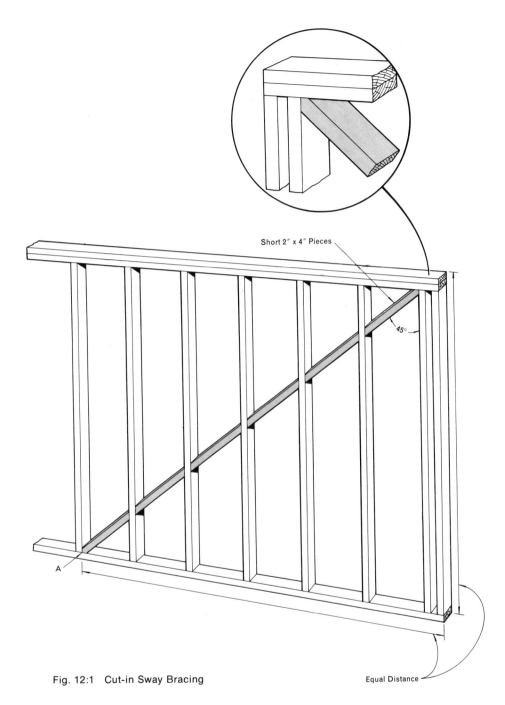

Short 2″ x 4″ Pieces

45°

A

Equal Distance

Fig. 12:1 Cut-in Sway Bracing

cut will also serve as the first cut for the second section of bracing.

5. Cut and fit the second and succeeding pieces in the same manner.
6. In each end of each piece start two 2½″ nails.
7. Nail the pieces in place. Take care to keep the edge even with the chalk line and flush with the edge of the studding. Take care also to see that the studs are not bowed or forced out of plumb when the sections are

143

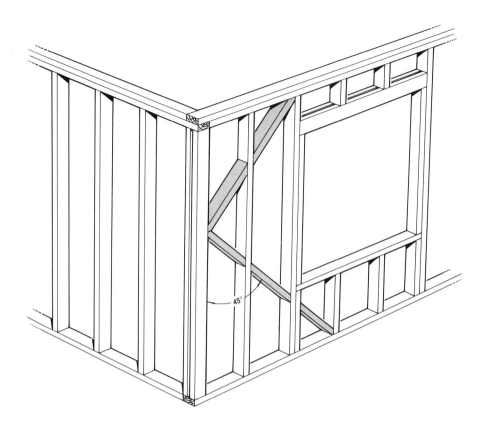

Fig. 12:2 Cut-in K Bracing

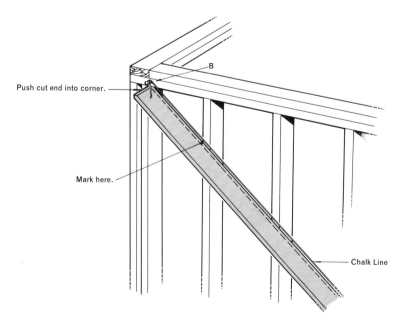

Fig. 12:3 Laying out the length of the first piece of cut-in sway bracing.

nailed in place. It is best to nail all pieces in place temporarily before driving the nails in tight.

8. Short knee or K braces are installed in the same manner as continuous braces, and are run, if possible, at a 45° angle to the plates as shown in Figure 12:2.

Although the cut-in type of sway bracing greatly strengthens the wall, the brace sections do interfere with the batt type insulation used in most homes. This, of course, is a disadvantage. The batts must be cut at the braces, which breaks the continuous insulation and the attached vapour barrier. The braces also make it more difficult to install water and sewer pipes, electric wiring, and heating ducts.

The let-in type of sway bracing does not have this disadvantage. It consists of a 1″ x 4″ let into the edge of the studding so that the outer face of the brace is flush with the outer edge of the studding as shown in Figure 12:4. The brace projects only 1″ into the wall and therefore does not affect the insulation or electrical, water, sewer, or heating services.

HOW TO INSTALL LET-IN SWAY BRACING

1. Nail the 1″ x 4″ brace temporarily in the correct position on the outside of the wall framework. The correct location and angle of the brace should

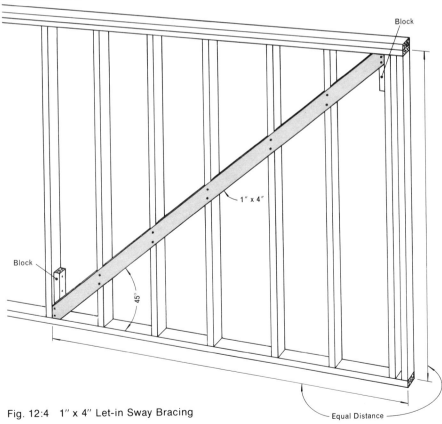

Fig. 12:4   1″ x 4″ Let-in Sway Bracing

be determined in the same way as described for the 2″ x 4″ cut-in sway bracing.

2. Mark a line against the upper and lower edges of the brace on each of the studs that it crosses.

3. Remove the brace, and lay out the depth of the cuts on the studs by setting an adjustable square to the thickness of the brace.

4. With a hand saw or an electric portable saw cut along the lines to the correct depth. Make two or three intermediate cuts to the correct depth between the outside lines.

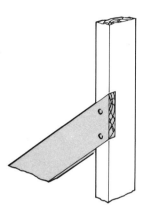

Fig. 12:5 1″ x 4″ let into the 2″ x 4″ stud.

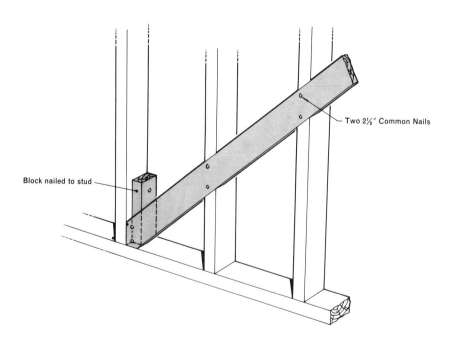

Fig. 12:6 Lower end on 1″ x 4″ sway brace.

5. Remove the waste wood between the saw cuts with a socket chisel and a mallet.
6. The brace can now be fitted into the cut-out recesses, and nailed with two 2½″ nails in each stud.

A block nailed to the stud at the lower end of the brace makes it unnecessary to cut the recess at the lower end of the stud. See Figure 12:6.

If you use an electric portable saw the depth of the cut can be regulated on the saw by adjusting the height of the blade, making it unnecessary to lay out the depth of the cuts mentioned in step 3.

EXTERIOR WALL SHEATHING

Wall sheathing is the base material attached directly to the studding. The finished siding and trim is nailed to the wall sheathing or brick or other masonry material is applied over it. As well as forming a base for these materials, wall sheathing also provides the structure with some degree of rigidity and insulation.

There are several types of materials used for wall sheathing. The type used may depend on the exterior finish of the house, that is, whether it is to be of vertical or horizontal wood, composition siding, or brick or stone veneer. The climatic conditions also affect the sheathing used. Some types have a greater insulating value than others.

In older homes the wall sheathing was made almost exclusively from ¾″ solid tongue and grooved shiplap or square-edged lumber. In some areas these materials are still used. However, in most places, other types of sheathing, particularly fibreboard, have replaced the solid wood variety.

Fibreboard Sheathing

This type of sheathing is made from compressed wood fibre or wood pulp. It comes in sheets that are 4′ wide, 8′, 9′, or 10′ long, and from ½″ to 1″ thick. Most types are treated on the outer face to make them water-resistant. Some are impregnated with an asphalt base material to make them still more impervious to water.

The main advantage of fibreboard sheathing is its high insulation quality. This is due to the fact that it is loosely compressed, porous, and made up, to a large extent, of miute air spaces. This also makes the sheets light in weight and easy to handle and cut. Another advantage of fibreboard sheathing is that it costs less per square foot than most other types of sheathing. There is also considerably less waste as the sheets can be purchased in lengths to correspond with the height of the wall. There is less labour involved, as most of the cutting required will be around the wall openings, if the studs are properly spaced. Since fibreboard is not affected by shrinkage, it makes a tighter job than solid wood sheathing.

Most fibreboard sheathing, however, does have the disadvantage of not providing as rigid a wall covering as wood. For this reason adequate sway bracing is necessary. Also, since fibreboard sheathing does not provide a sufficiently solid base on which to nail shingles, shakes, or vertical siding, it is most commonly used on houses that have brick and stone veneer or horizontal siding, which can be nailed directly into the studding. If exterior finish that must be nailed to the sheathing between the studs is to be used, furring strips must be provided.

A more rigid, ½ " fibreboard sheathing has been developed that will support nails and that is stiff enough to make sway braces unnecessary. It is not yet in general use, however, because of expense and because it has somewhat less insulation value than most other fibreboard sheathing.

Particle Board Sheathing

A material that is similar to fibreboard is a more tightly compressed composition board made from wood chips, referred to as *particle board*. It is somewhat heavier, with less insulation value.

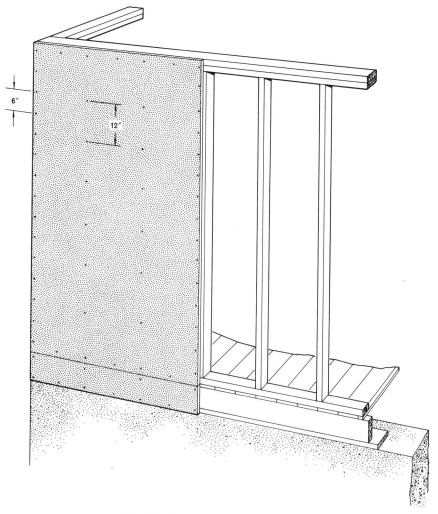

Fig. 12:7 Fibreboard sheathing applied vertically.

Gypsum Board Sheathing

Another type of sheathing made in sheet form is *gypsum board*, manufactured in sheets 2′ or 4′ wide, 8′ long, and ½″ thick. It consists of a gypsum core sandwiched between two heavy moisture-resistant layers of heavy paper. Gypsum board makes a rigid sheathing but has a much lower insulation value than fibreboard.

Plywood Sheathing

Plywood sheets are extensively used for sheathing and, when properly nailed, make a very rigid wall that does not require sway bracing. An unsanded sheathing grade plywood 5/16″ thick is generally used. It is extensively used for pre-fabricated homes. Plywood has the advantage of providing a surface strong enough to nail most types of siding to, while still being light in weight, easy to apply, and economical.

Sheathing that is made in sheets or panels can be applied either vertically, with the long side of the sheet parallel to the studding, as shown in Figure 12:7, or horizontally, with the long side of the sheet parallel to the plate. See

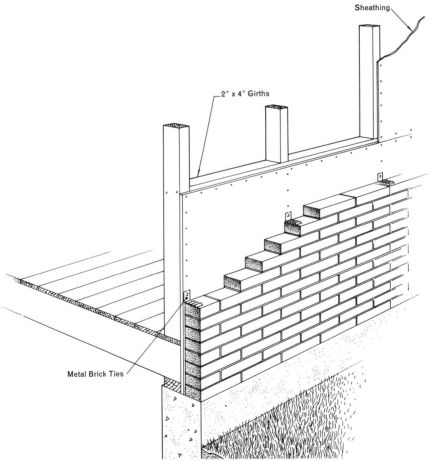

Fig. 12:8   Fibreboard sheathing applied horizontally (brick veneer construction).

Figure 12:8. When sheets are used horizontally, girths should be placed between the studding, as all edges should have nailing support. Gypsum board is the exception to this rule as the long edges have a groove on one edge and a V on the other, making it unnecessary to use short 2″ x 4″ girths between the studs at the joints. These sheets are always applied horizontally. Vertical joints should be staggered where possible.

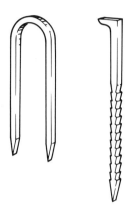

Fig. 12:9   Two types of staples used with a nailing device to hold plywood to solid wood.

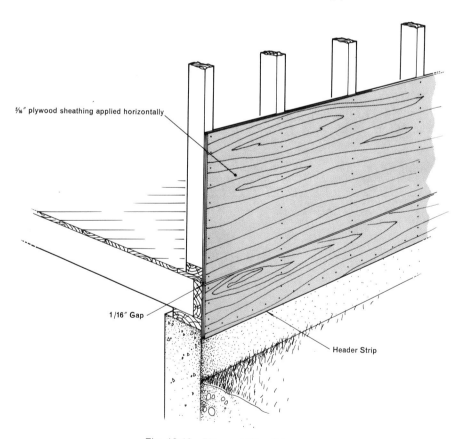

Fig. 12:10   Plywood Sheathing

150

The nail spacing should be at 6″ intervals on the edges of the sheets and at 12″ intervals along all intermediate supports. Rust-resistant, 1¾″ wire nails are often used, but spiral or ring barbed nails have greater holding power. For fibreboard or gypsum board the nails should have a 10-gauge shank and a 7/16″ diameter head. For a more efficient and speedy application, staples may be used in place of nails as fasteners. Staples are made in a variety of sizes and shapes; they fit into the magazine of a nailing device and are driven by an air-activated gun or by striking the head of the nailing device with a heavy rubber or cowhide mallet. Two types of staples are shown in Figure 12:9.

Plywood or fibreboard sheets must be applied with a 1/16″ space between the sheets, to allow for any swelling, which would cause the sheets to buckle if the joints were tight.

It is recommended by plywood manufacturers that when plywood sheathing is used the same sheet should not be nailed to both the bottom plate and the ends of the joists or the header. To prevent the joist shrinkage from affecting the wall frame, there should not be a solid tie between the main wall and the floor framing. For this reason a header strip of plywood sheathing is often used as shown in Figure 12:10.

Solid Wood Sheathing

When *solid lumber* is used as sheathing, the individual boards are generally ¾″ thick and 4″ to 8″ wide. They should never be less than ⅝″ thick nor more than 12″ wide. The wider the individual piece the more shrinkage will take place, and shrinkage will affect the appearance of the finished siding.

Solid wood sheathing is generally made from matched lumber with either a tongue and grooved or shiplap edge to make a tight, solid surface. When the exterior finish is of wooden shingles or shakes, open sheathing made from square-edged stock, generally 1″ x 4″, with the individual boards spaced 1″ to 2″ apart, may be used. The shingles bridge the gaps and are solidly nailed to the sheathing. See Figure 12:11.

Solid wood sheathing may be applied either at right angles to the studding or diagonally to it. When the sheathing is applied horizontally, the joints should be staggered and should always occur over studding for nailing support. Two 2½″ nails should be used in each stud, three nails if the boards are 6″ wide or wider. When the sheathing is applied diagonally, no sway bracing is needed as the diagonal sheathing provides the same bracing effect. The ends of all pieces must be cut at a 45° angle to be fully supported on the studding. In both methods the pieces may be allowed to project over the window or door openings, to be cut off later with a hand or electric portable saw. The application of diagonal sheathing is similar to that described for diagonal subflooring in Chapter 9. Diagonal sheathing entails a greater percentage of waste and requires more labour, as the carpenter must be continuously climbing up and down to nail the lower end of the pieces at the

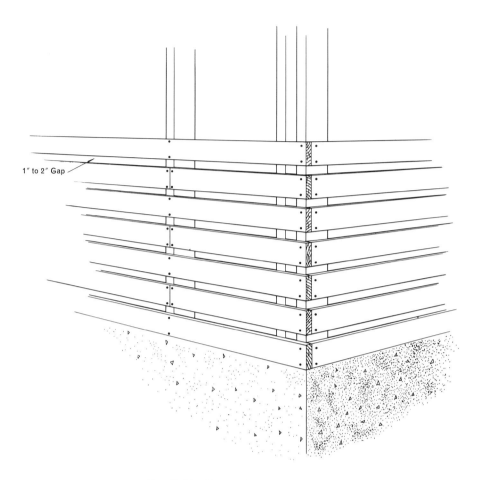

1" to 2" Gap

Fig. 12:11   1" x 4" Open Sheathing

foundation level and the top end at the top plate. However, the advantages of this type of sheathing make the expenditure of the extra material and labour worth-while in the interests of a much stronger wall.

The current trend among builders is to finish the wall framing completely, including the window openings, sway bracing, and sheathing, while the wall sections are still lying on the subfloor. This saves much time and labour as it is easier and faster to work on the wall when it is in a horizontal position and when it requires no scaffold.

In estimating the number of board feet required to cover a wall with matched-edge solid wood sheathing, an allowance must be made for waste and matching. Find the number of square feet in the wall area and deduct the areas of large openings (disregard small openings). For horizontal 1" x 6" matched sheathing, add thirty per cent for waste and matching; for 1" x 8" matched sheathing, add twenty-five per cent. If the sheathing is applied diagonally, add an additional six per cent. When sheet stock is used only a ten per cent allowance need be added for waste. Only the areas of very large

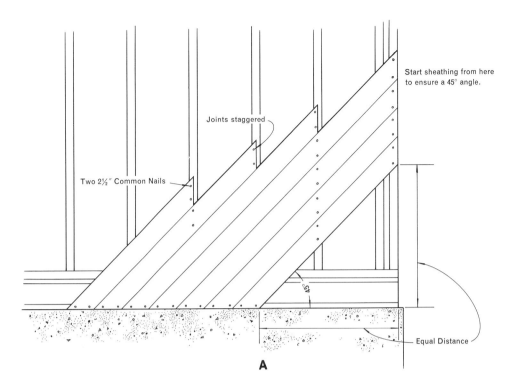

Start sheathing from here to ensure a 45° angle.

Joints staggered

Two 2½″ Common Nails

45°

Equal Distance

A

B

Fig. 12:12 (A) Solid Wood Diagonal Sheathing; (B) Exterior wall with plywood sheathing ready for erection.

153

openings are deducted in estimating the total number of sheets required.

Having described the relative values and advantages of the various types of wall sheathing, we must point out that it is permissible, under the National Building Code and its supplement No. 5, *Residential Standards,* which is used for all N.H.A. Loan Homes, to omit the sheathing when certain types of siding are used.

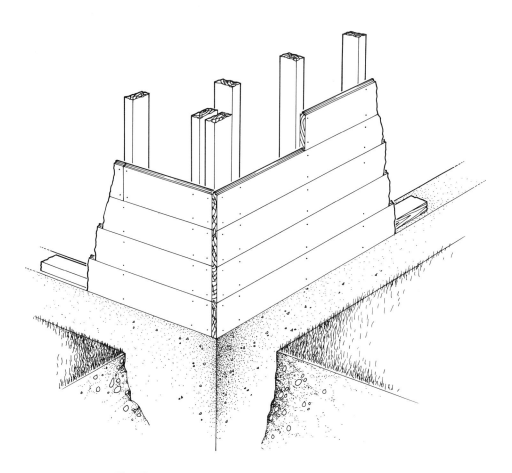

Fig. 12:13   Tongue and Grooved Horizontal Sheathing

Houses having plywood, hardboard, particle board, or brick or other masonry exterior finishes may be built with a double thickness of approved building paper instead of any type of solid sheathing. The paper is generally applied vertically, with the joints placed over the studs and lapped at least 4″. The paper should be fastened directly to the studding with large-headed roofing nails or staples that are not more than 3″ apart. Houses built with sheathing paper in lieu of solid sheathing, for the purpose of building homes at a competitive cost, comply only with the minimum building requirements. Many builders prefer to exceed these minimum requirements and use solid sheathing regardless of the type of exterior siding material used.

154

ASSIGNMENT

Sway Bracing

1. Why are sway braces used?
2. Which hollow frame is the strongest: a square, a rectangle, or a triangle?
3. Write a paragraph describing the two types of sway bracing:
   (a) the cut-in type
   (b) the let-in type.
4. (a) At what angle to the plate should sway bracing run?
   (b) Why?
5. What is meant by:
   (a) Knee braces?
   (b) K braces?
6. List the first three steps in installing cut-in sway bracing.
7. Why is it advisable to nail the individual pieces of cut-in sway bracing temporarily until all pieces have been fitted?
8. What is the disadvantage of cut-in sway bracing?
9. How are the positions of the individual cut-outs located on the studding when let-in sway bracing is being installed?
10. When is sway bracing unnecessary in building frame walls?

Sheathing

11. What is the purpose of wall sheathing?
12. What factors determine the type of wall sheathing material to be used on a house?
13. (a) What are the dimensions of fibreboard sheets used for sheathing?
    (b) List the advantages and disadvantages of fibreboard as a sheathing material.
14. How does particle board differ from fibreboard?
15. What is the composition of gypsum board sheathing?
16. List the advantages of plywood sheathing.
17. What are the two methods of applying sheet wall sheathing?
18. Why are girths used when applying sheet type sheathing?
19. (a) What sized nails should be used for sheet type sheathing?
    (b) How far apart should these nails be spaced?
20. Why is a 1/16″ space left between sheets of plywood or fibreboard?
21. What purpose does a header strip serve when plywood sheathing is used?
22. (a) When solid wood wall sheathing is used why should the board be no more than 8″ wide?
    (b) What condition could arise if wider boards are used?
23. Why is sway bracing not required when solid wood sheathing is applied diagonally?
24. List the advantages and disadvantages of the two methods of applying solid wood sheathing.

25. State the advantages of applying the wall sheathing to the wall frame before it is erected.
26. (a) How many board feet of 1″ x 6″ tongue and grooved sheathing would be required to cover a wall 40′ long and 9′ high, the wall to have three window openings 8′ wide and 5′ high, and the sheathing to be applied diagonally?
    (b) How many sheets of fibreboard sheathing would be required for the same wall?

Construction Safety (see pages 399-417)

27. Make a sketch of two types of wooden scaffold.
28. What are the advantages of using sectional metal scaffolding?

Chapter 13

ROOF TYPES AND ROOF TERMINOLOGY

Besides being an obviously essential part of a house, the roof, if it is architecturally well designed, properly proportioned, and well built, may also be the most distinctive feature of the home. Because of the functional and aesthetic importance of roofs, several chapters of this text will be devoted to roof framing.

The main purpose of a roof is to provide protection from rain, snow, and sun and to act as a barrier against the transmission of heat, either from inside or outside the building. The roof also serves as a structural support to tie the walls together, keep them upright, and help them resist wind pressure.

Probably the first structures made by men had flat shed-type roofs. Down through the centuries, as houses became larger and more complex, roofs were developed with different shapes and slopes; they had larger overhangs and were built of a wide range of different materials. All of these factors helped to make the roof an attractive and integral part of the house design.

ROOF TYPES

There are two basic types of roofs: *pitched* (sloped) and *flat.* All other types are variations of these two. Some of those we see most often will be described and illustrated here.

Pitched Roofs

Shed or Single-Slope Roof. This is a simple type of roof that slopes in one direction only. It is used mainly on small buildings, on additions to larger buildings, or over such parts of a house as door entrances and dormers.

One wall of the structure is built higher than the other to provide sufficient slope. A shed roof may have a slope from 2″ to 6″ for every 12″ of rafter length. The rafters usually rest on the plates of the two walls, as shown in Figure 13:2.

Gable Roof. The gable roof is the most common type of roof in use today and is basic to all other pitched roofs. It consists of rafters that meet in the centre with the roof sloping in two directions. The structural details of the gable roof are shown in Figures 13:3 and 13:4.

Hip Roof. In a hip roof – sometimes called a cottage roof – the rafters are so arranged that the roof slopes in four directions. The rafters rest on the plates

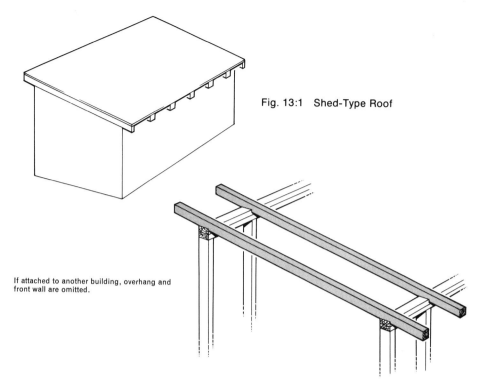

Fig. 13:1   Shed-Type Roof

If attached to another building, overhang and front wall are omitted.

Fig. 13:2   Framing Members of a Shed Roof

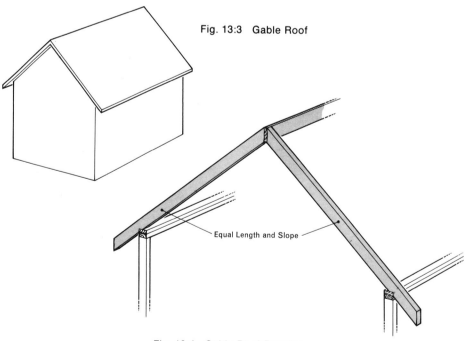

Fig. 13:3   Gable Roof

Equal Length and Slope

Fig. 13:4   Gable Roof Framing

of all four walls and slope towards the ridge. If the building is square they slope to a point or peak. Three types of rafters are required to frame a regular hip roof. See Figures 13:5 and 13:6.

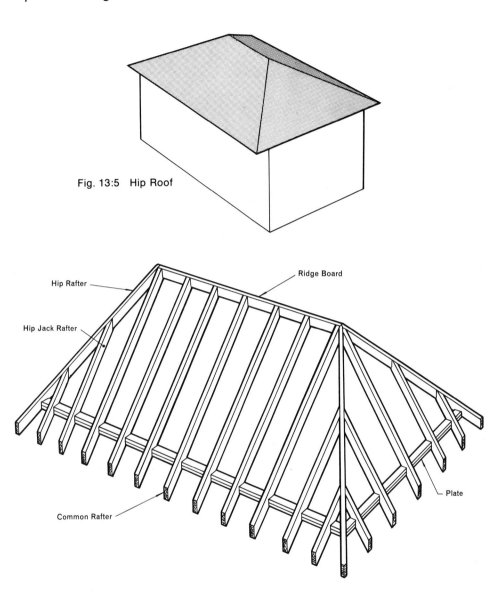

Fig. 13:5   Hip Roof

Fig. 13:6   Hip Rafter Framing

Hip and Valley Roof. The hip and valley roof is made up of two roof sections that intersect each other, generally at a 90° angle. There are many variations of this type of roof. The sections may have either a hip or a gable end. The slope or pitch may be the same in both sections, or the ridge of one may be of a higher elevation than the other. The five types of rafters used for this roof are shown in Figure 13:8.

159

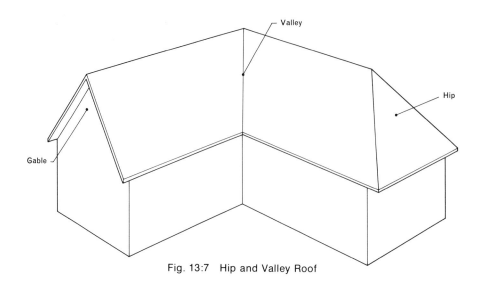

Fig. 13:7 Hip and Valley Roof

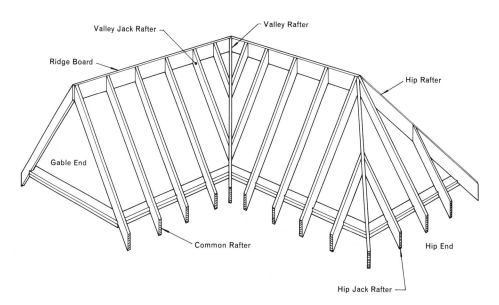

Fig. 13:8 Hip and Valley Rafter Framing

Gambrel Roof. This roof is similar to the hip roof except that each side has a double slope. The lower slope is generally the longer and the steeper of the two. The gambrel roof is used on Colonial-type houses. It is also often used on barns as there is more storage space under the roof.

Mansard Roof. The mansard roof combines the features of the hip and gambrel roofs in that each of the four sides has a double slope, the lower section longer and steeper than the upper section. In some cases the upper section is flat with a deck type roof on top.

160

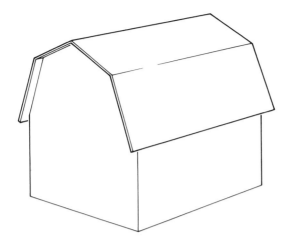

Fig. 13:9   Gambrel Roof

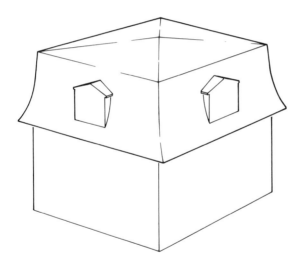

Fig. 13:10   Mansard Roof

Unequal Pitch Roof. The angle of the slope of the roof is referred to as the *pitch.* An equal pitch roof is one in which all sections of the roof areas have the same pitch, such as the roof shown in Figure 13:7. An *unequal* pitch roof is one in which the sections have a different slope or pitch: for instance, a gable roof, one side of which is longer than the other. See Figure 13:11A. A hip and valley roof has an unequal pitch if the spans (the widths of the roof sections) are different and the roof ridges are the same height (Figure 13:11B) or if the spans are the same and the roof ridges are different heights (Figure 13:11C).

161

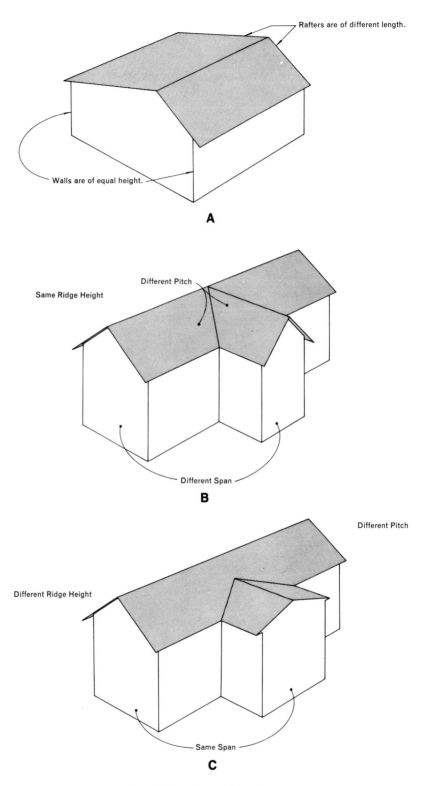

Fig. 13:11   Unequal Pitch Roofs

Flat Roofs

Flat roofs are extensively used in industrial and commercial building and to a lesser degree in residential building. Few of them are perfectly flat. They generally have a slight slope to one side for drainage, or they may slope towards one or more drainage outlets situated along the centre line of the roof.

For residential building, the sheathing and roofing are applied to the top of the roof joists, which serve as the rafters. The finished ceiling material is nailed to the underside of the roof joists. Insulation may be placed between the joists or between the sheathing and the roofing material. Flat roofs require larger framing members than pitch roofs because they must support not only the heavier roofing material, but also the weight of a greater water and snow load. The roof may overhang the walls on all sides as shown in Figure 13:12, or the walls may extend above the roof to form a parapet, as illustrated in Figure 13:13. If the roof has an overhang, lookout rafters are generally used

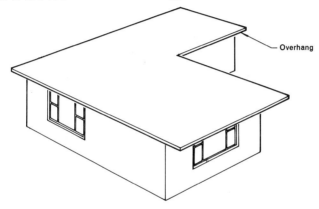

Fig. 13:12   Flat Roof

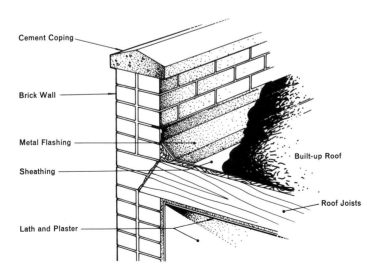

Fig. 13:13   Flat Roof with Parapet

163

that butt into double roof joists. The double joists must be set a greater distance in from the wall than the overhang of the roof, to give the overhang support. See Figure 13:14.

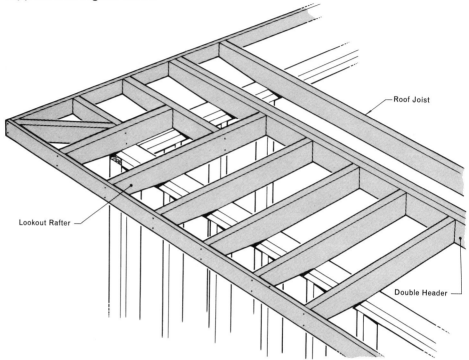

Fig. 13:14   Flat Roof Framing at Overhang

ROOF FRAMING TERMS

Before describing the layout, cutting, and erection of rafters and other roof framing members, we should define some of the roof framing terms, and also the mathematical formulas necessary in rafter layout.

The Span of a Building
The horizontal distance between the outer edge of the plate on one wall to the outer edge of the plate on the opposite wall.

The Run of the Roof
The distance from the outer edge of the plate on one wall to the centre of the building; one-half the span.

The Total Rise of the Roof
The vertical distance from the top of the wall plate to the top of the ridge board.

The Pitch of a Rafter
The slope or incline of the rafter determined by the angle formed between the rafter and the plate.

164

Common Rafters

The main structural supports of the roof, running from the plate to the ridge at right angles.

Hip Rafters

Rafters that form the intersection at an external roof angle, running from the plate to the ridge at a 45° angle, as shown in Figure 13:6.

Valley Rafters

Valley rafters are similar to hip rafters in that they also run at a 45° angle from the plate to the ridge, but differing in that they form the intersection of an internal roof angle between the main part of the building and an "ell" or other projection. See Figure 13:8.

Jack Rafters

There are two types of jack rafters, the hip jack rafter, which runs from the plate to the hip rafter, and the valley jack rafter, which runs from the valley rafter to the ridge. These two rafters are shown in Figure 13:8.

Cripple Rafters

These are short rafters extending from the valley rafter to the hip rafter.

Collar Ties

Sometimes called collar beams, these are generally made from 2″ x 4″ stock and run between two common rafters to keep them from sagging in the centre. They greatly strengthen the rafters and sometimes also serve as second-floor ceiling joists.

The Overhang of a Rafter

That portion of a common, hip, valley, or hip jack rafter that extends past the plate over the wall. Its two purposes are to protect the wall and to add to the appearance of the house.

Lookout or Tail Rafters

Short rafter sections, about twice the length of the overhang, spiked to the side of the common or hip jack rafters. They are used where there is an open cornice where the rafter ends are exposed to view and are therefore cut to an ornamental shape. It is much easier to cut these short pieces than to shape the ends of long rafters.

Ridge Board

1″ x 6″ or 2″ x 6″ member placed between the tops of the rafters. It makes a straight ridge line, ties the rafters together, correctly spaces the tops of the rafters, and makes it easier to erect the roof.

Most of the roof framing members and terms are shown in Figure 13:15.

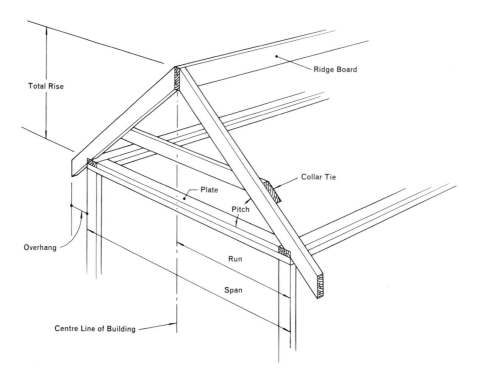

Fig. 13:15   Roof Framing Terms and Members

ROOF FRAMING MATHEMATICS

There are certain basic facts and simple mathematical formulas that you must know in order to understand the principle of roof framing.

The slope or pitch of a roof may be expressed in several different ways:

(a) as the number of inches of vertical rise per foot of horizontal run. This is sometimes called the *cut* of the rafter.

(b) as a fraction such as ¼, ⅜, or ½. The fraction is arrived at by computing the ratio of the total rise to the span.

EXAMPLE: To find the pitch of a roof when the width of the building (the span) is 32′ and the total rise (the distance from the top of the plate to the top edge of the ridge board) is 8′. The pitch would be the ratio of the rise

to the span $= \dfrac{\text{rise}}{\text{span}} = \dfrac{8}{32} = \dfrac{1}{4}$ pitch.

If the total rise on the same roof were 12′, the pitch would be:

$$\frac{12}{32} = \frac{3}{8} \text{ pitch.}$$

If the pitch is stated on the plans as a fraction, the total rise of the roof can be found by multiplying the pitch by the span.

EXAMPLE: To find the total rise of a roof that has a ⅓ pitch and a span of 24′. The total rise will be ⅓ x 24′ = 8′ total rise. If the pitch of the same

166

building were ¼, the total rise would be ¼ x 24′ = 6′ total rise.

Very often the pitch is stated as the number of inches rise per foot of horizontal run, and is illustrated on the plans as shown in Figure 13:16. Then the pitch, as a fraction, can be found by dividing the number of inches rise per foot of run by 24 (24 because the span is twice the run).

EXAMPLE: To find the pitch as stated in a fraction if the number of inches rise per foot of run is 9.

The pitch would be $\dfrac{9}{24} = \dfrac{3}{8}$ pitch.

If the rise per foot were 8″ the pitch would be $\dfrac{8}{24} = \dfrac{1}{3}$ pitch.

Conversely, to find the number of inches rise per foot of run if the pitch is stated as a fraction, simply multiply the pitch as stated in a fraction by 24.

EXAMPLE: To find the number of inches rise per foot of a roof:
If it has a ⅓ pitch

$$\frac{1}{3} \times 24 = 8″ \text{ rise per foot of run.}$$

If the roof has a ¼ pitch the rise would be ¼ x 24 = 6″.

The number of inches rise per foot for any given pitch will be the same regardless of the span of the building.

The basis of all rafter layout, when using the framing square, is the number of inches rise per foot of run. This is the figure that must be arrived at regardless of how the pitch is indicated on the working drawings or in the specifications.

To find the total rise when the pitch is stated as the number of inches rise per foot of run, multiply this number by the run of the building.

EXAMPLE: A roof has a 10″ rise per foot of run and a run of 18′.
The total rise would be 10 x 18 = 180″ or a 15′ total rise.

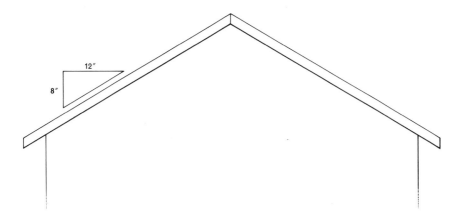

Fig. 13:16 The architectural symbol designating pitch by indicating the number of inches rise per foot of run of the roof.

There are three rules that can be relied upon to solve many roof framing problems.

1. To find the rise of a roof, multiply the pitch by the span.
2. To find the pitch of a roof, divide the rise by the span.
3. To find the number of inches rise per foot, multiply the pitch by 24.

ASSIGNMENT

Types of Roofs

1. List three functions performed by a well-constructed roof.
2. What are the two basic types of roof construction?
3. Where is a shed-type roof used?
4. Name the type of roof most often used in residential construction.
5. Describe a hip roof.
6. Make a sketch of a hip and valley roof and name the rafters used.
7. Why are gambrel-type roofs often used for barn construction?
8. Write a short description of a mansard roof.
9. List three examples of unequal pitch roofs.
10. Why are flat roofs built of heavier framing material than pitch roofs?
11. List four factors that will determine the type of roof to be built on a house.

Roof Framing Terms

12. Define the following terms:
    (a) The span of a roof;
    (b) The run of a roof;
    (c) The pitch of a rafter.
13. Name and describe four types of rafters.
14. State the purpose of:
    (a) A collar tie;
    (b) A lookout rafter;
    (c) The ridge board.
15. Make a drawing showing a sectional view of a gable roof and name four framing members and five roof framing terms.

Roof Framing Mathematics

16. State two ways in which the pitch of a roof may be expressed.
17. If the span of a roof is 36′ and the total rise is 12′, what is the pitch?
18. What would be the total rise of a roof with a ¼ pitch and a span of 40′?
19. What would be the pitch (stated as a fraction), if the roof has 8″ vertical rise per foot of horizontal run?
20. If a roof has a ½ pitch, how many inches rise per foot of run will the rafters have?
21. State the three rules used to solve many roof framing problems.

Chapter 14

LAYOUT OF COMMON RAFTERS

There are actually two problems involved in laying out the common rafter: (a) to determine the correct length of the rafter, so that the roof will have the desired slope and the ridge the specified height; (b) to lay out the rafter in such a way that, when it is cut on the layout lines, neat properly fitting joints will be formed at the ridge and the plate.

As the common rafters form the main bearing members that support the roof, it is important that they be the correct length and that they fit perfectly. There is nothing that indicates poor workmanship on the part of the carpenter more than unsightly, improperly fitting rafters. More important is the fact that incorrectly fitted rafters greatly affect the strength of the roof, because the weight of the roof cannot be properly transferred from one member to another.

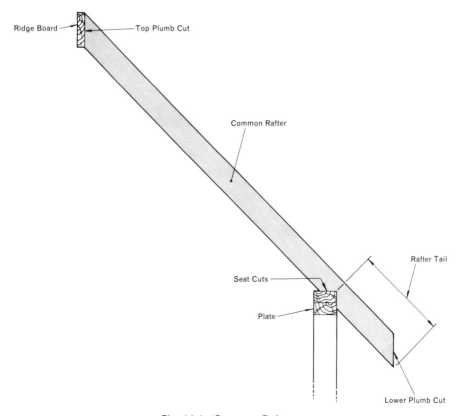

Fig. 14:1   Common Rafter

TO DETERMINE THE CORRECT LENGTH OF A COMMON RAFTER

There are several methods of determining the length of a common rafter:
1. by scaling the framing square;
2. by making a scale drawing (graphic method);
3. by mathematical calculation;
4. by the step-off method;
5. by using the rafter framing table on the framing square.

Scaling the Framing Square

The first method, that of scaling the framing square, is a fast method that should be used only for determining the rough length of the rafter, such as when one makes out the Bill of Material before ordering the stock.

The approximate rafter length can be easily determined by using the scale 1″ = 1′ and measuring diagonally from the inch figure on the tongue of the square that corresponds to the total rise of the roof to the number on the body of the square that corresponds to the run of the roof.

EXAMPLE: To find the length of a rafter for the roof of a building 26′ wide (a 13′ run) and a total rise of 7′ 6″.

With a rule, measure diagonally from the 7½ on the tongue of the square to the 13 on the body of the square. This distance will be found to be 15″, which means that the rafter will be approximately 15′ long plus the overhang. See Figure 14:2.

The Graphic Method

This method consists of making an accurate scale drawing of the roof in order to calculate the length of common rafters. This may be a convenient method for the architect or draftsman but it is seldom used by the carpenter because of the time involved, the chance of error, and the difficulty of transferring the exact length and the correct angles for the cuts from the drawing to the full-sized stock.

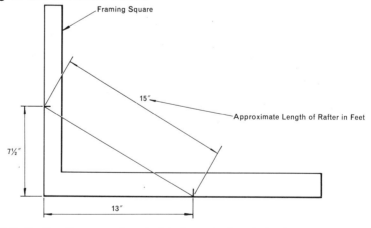

Fig. 14:2   Scaling the square to calculate the rafter length. 1″ on the square =1′ of rafter length.

The Mathematical Method

The length of a rafter can be readily found mathematically if you visualize the common rafter as the long side, or hypotenuse, of a right-angled triangle, and the rise and run of the roof as the other two sides. To find the length of the hypotenuse of a right-angled triangle use *Pythagoras's theorem,* which states that the square on the hypotenuse of a right-angled triangle equals the sum of the squares on the other two sides. See Figure 14.3.

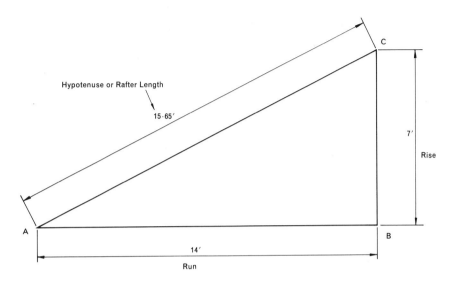

Fig. 14:3   Rafter length is equal to the hypotenuse of the triangle.

EXAMPLE: To find mathematically the length of a common rafter on a roof with a 14′ run and 7′ rise.

$$\text{Run } AB^2 = 14 \times 14 = 196$$
$$\text{Rise } BC^2 = 7 \times 7 = 49$$
$$AB^2 + BC^2 = 196 + 49 = 245$$
$$\text{Hypotenuse } AC = \sqrt{AB^2 + BC^2} = \sqrt{196 + 49} = \sqrt{245} = 15.65$$
or 15′ 7⅞″.

Length of the common rafter 15′ 7⅞″ + the overhang.

The two rafter layout methods considered to be the best from the carpenter's standpoint are the *step-off* method and the *rafter table* on the framing square. This is because all layout lines as well as the length of the rafter can be accurately determined. Let us consider first the step-off method.

Step-off Method

The principle of this method of rafter layout is that for every foot of horizontal run there is a definite number of inches rise to the roof. This is referred to as the unit of run. The amount of rise will, of course, depend on the pitch of the roof. If the pitch is known, the rise per foot can easily be found as was described in Chapter 13.

The basis of the step-off method for common rafter layout is that the 12″ mark on the outer edge of the body of the framing square is always used for the horizontal layout lines because it represents 1′ of run. The inch mark that represents the number of inches rise per foot of run is used on the outer edge of the tongue of the square for all vertical layout lines.

When these two numbers are used together, with the square set on the rafter as shown in Figure 14:4, it is referred to as *one step-off.*

If the square is placed on the rafter in the correct position the number of times that there are feet in the run of the roof, the exact length of the rafter will be determined. To understand this principle, you should be able to visualize the rafter in place with the framing square against the side of it, with the body parallel to the plate and the tongue in an upright or vertical position, as shown in Figure 14:5.

Rafter layout is an important and fairly complicated procedure. Care should be taken that the correct figures on the square are used, and that each step is carefully done. Any error in layout will greatly affect the length and fit of the rafters. The layout will be made simpler and more efficient if the following steps are carried out in a definite order.

Let us assume that a building has a span of 30′ and a ⅓ pitch (8″ rise per foot of run). A common rafter is to be laid out using the step-off method.

Procedure:

1. Set the rafter on a pair of saw horses.
2. Place the crowned edge of the rafter towards you. This is the edge of the rafter that should always be placed uppermost.
3. All length and layout lines are established from the measuring line of

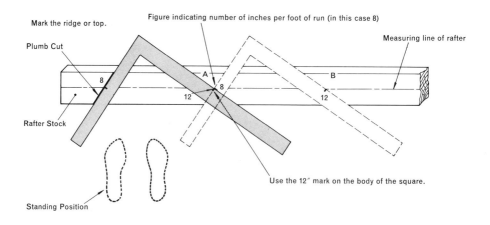

Fig. 14:4   First two step-offs in common rafter layout.

172

the rafter. This line should run the full length of the rafter. If 2″ x 4″ stock is used the line should be in the centre; if wider stock is used it should be 2″ in from the lower edge. The line can be drawn by setting the blade of an adjustable square at the correct distance and holding a pencil against the end of the blade as the square is drawn along the stock. The reason for using a measuring line is explained in Figure 14:5.

4. Start the layout from the extreme left end of the rafter as you face the stock with the body of the square to your right and the tongue to your left. Place the square on the rafter as shown in Figure 14:4 for the first step-off, using the figure 12 on the body of the square and 8 on the tongue. Make sure the numbers are directly over the measuring line of the rafter. Mark along the tongue of the square. This line will represent the top plumb cut of the rafter. Make a small mark where the body of the square crosses the measuring line at the 12″ mark (Point A on Figure 14:4).

5. Slide the square to the right along the rafter until the figure 8 on the tongue coincides with Point A, which was the 12″ point on the first layout. Make another mark where the figure 12 on the body of the square crosses the measuring line of the rafter at Point B. (Figure 14:4.) This completes the second step-off of the rafter layout.

6. Move the square along the rafter to the right as many successive posi-

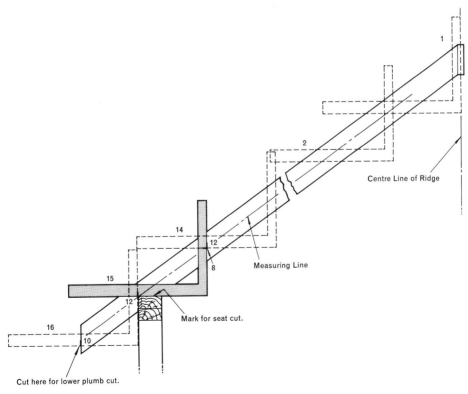

Centre Line of Ridge

Measuring Line

Mark for seat cut.

Cut here for lower plumb cut.

Fig. 14:5   Position of the framing square in succeeding step-off positions.

tions as there are feet of run — in this example 15', or fifteen step-offs as shown in Figure 14:5.

7. When the square is in the fifteenth position mark along the body to lay out the horizontal part of the seat cut.

8. Move the square to the sixteenth position and mark along the tongue. This will form the vertical part of the seat cut. See Figure 14:5.

9. If there is to be less than 12″ of horizontal overhang, it can be measured when the square is in the sixteenth position. If, for example, a 10″ over-

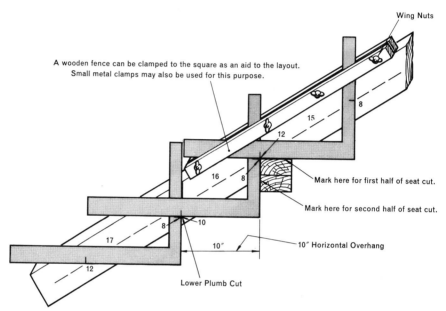

Fig. 14:6 Overhang Layout

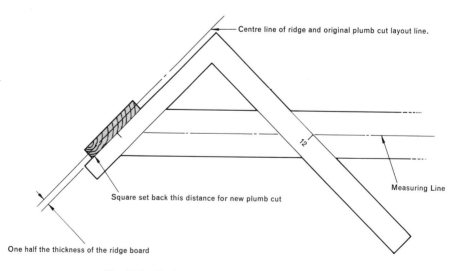

Fig. 14:7 Reduction of the rafter for ridge board.

hang is desired, a mark is made at the 10″ mark on the body of the square, as shown in Figure 14:6.

10. The lower plumb cut is laid out by placing the square on the rafter at the seventeenth position and marking along the tongue where it inter- sects the mark made for the desired overhang. If more than 12″ of overhang is required, the square will have to be placed on the rafter to one more position, but the same principle is used. See Figure 14:6.

11. A reduction in the length of the rafter must be made equal to one-half the thickness of the ridge board. This can best be accomplished by measuring this distance at a right angle to the plumb cut and then making a new plumb line parallel to the first by using the same two figures on the square as in Figure 14:7.

A problem arises when the span of the roof is in odd feet, for example, if the building were 27′ wide, the run would be 13′ 6″ and the layout of the common rafter would require thirteen and a half step-offs. The thirteen full step-offs would be laid out and the additional partial step-off made by placing the square on the rafter with the 12 and the 8 (for ⅓ pitch) on the edge of the rafter instead of on the measuring line. This allows more of the layout figures of the square to be over the rafter, making it possible to mark the length of the partial step-off directly on the rafter. The square should be slid along until the tongue of the square intersects the 12″ mark made on the measuring line of the last full step-off as shown in Figure 14:8. While the square is in this position, make a mark on the rafter at the 6″ figure on the body of the square. The square is again slid along the rafter until the tongue intersects this last mark. Now draw a line along the tongue which will form the first half of the seat cut. See Figure 14:8.

A partial step-off of any odd number of inches is made in the same manner. The width of the building should always be measured with a long tape at the top plate level before starting the rafter layout to determine what partial step-off, if any, is needed in laying out the common rafters to the exact length required for a perfect roof framing job.

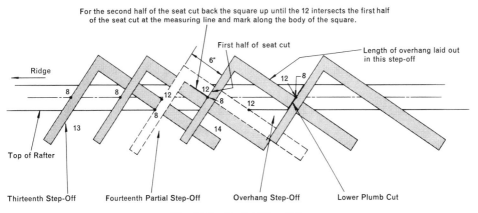

Fig. 14:8 Partial Step-Off

Some builders prefer to start the layout from the seat cut and make the succeeding step-offs toward the ridge, in which case, any partial step-off would be made at the ridge.

Rafter Table on the Framing Square

The method of finding the length of common rafters by using the rafter table on the framing square is fully described in Chapter 17.

After one common rafter has been laid out as a pattern, cut the top and bottom plumb cuts as well as the seat cut. Use a hand cross-cut saw or an electric portable saw. Care should be taken to make an accurate cut on the first rafter as it will serve as a pattern for all the other common rafters. After the second rafter has been cut out, it is a good idea to set the two rafters in place temporarily to see if they fit perfectly. Alterations should not be necessary; however, there is always a chance of error. If the first rafters fit, lay out and cut the required number of common rafters, using the same pattern for them all.

The crowned edge of all rafters must be placed uppermost. If a piece has an excessive amount of crown, or any other serious defect, it should not be used as a rafter.

If two short pieces of lumber are nailed to the edge of the pattern, one near each end, it will make it easier to line up the pattern with the rafter being marked. This will make a faster and more accurate layout. See Figure 14:9.

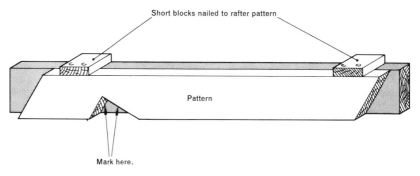

Short blocks nailed to rafter pattern

Pattern

Mark here.

Fig. 14:9   Rafters being laid out from a pattern.

ASSIGNMENT
Layout of Common Rafters
1. List the two problems in the layout of common rafters.
2. What are the effects of improperly fitted rafters?
3. For what specific purpose should a carpenter find the length of a common rafter by scaling the framing square?
4. Why do carpenters seldom use the graphic method of finding the length of the common rafter?
5. State the formula for finding the hypotenuse of a right-angled triangle.

6. By mathematical calculation, find the length of the common rafter for a roof with a 12' run and a 6' rise. (Show your calculations.)

7. What two methods of finding the rafter length are considered the best from the carpenter's standpoint?

8. What is the principle of the step-off method in rafter layout?

9. What determines the number of inches of rise per foot of run of the rafter?

10. Which two factors must be known before laying out a rafter by the step-off method?

11. What is meant by the unit of run?

12. If a roof has a ¼ pitch, how many inches rise per foot will the rafter have?

13. Why is the figure 12 always used on the body of the square when laying out common rafters?

14. In a roof with a 28' span and a ½ pitch, how many step-offs will be required for the rafter layout?

15. (a) What is the purpose of a measuring line on a rafter?
    (b) How is the line used?

16. Why should the crowned edge of a rafter always be placed uppermost?

17. Explain, using a sketch, how the first step-off is laid out and the top plumb cut marked on the rafter.

18. How are the two seat cut lines laid out where the rafter meets the plate?

19. Explain how an 8″ overhang would be laid out.
    (You may use a sketch to clarify your answer.)

20. How is the allowance for the thickness of the ridge board made?

21. If the span of a building is 29', how would the required partial step-off be made on the common rafter layout?

22. Why should the width of a building be measured with a steel tape at the top plate level before the rafters are laid out?

23. Why is it advisable to set the first two rafters that are cut in place on the roof before the other rafters are cut?

Practical Exercises

1. By scaling a framing square, find the approximate length of a common rafter for a roof with a 32' span and a ¼ pitch.

2. Using the step-off method, on a piece of 2″ x 4″ lay out the common rafter required for a roof with a 12' span, a ⅓ pitch, and a 1' overhang.

3. Lay out the common rafter for a roof with a 13' 8″ span, a 5/12 pitch, and an overhang of 9″.

Chapter 15

HIP AND VALLEY RAFTERS

The layout of hip and valley rafters is slightly more involved than the layout of common rafters, although a similar principle of layout is followed when the step-off method is used. The main difference is that the figure 17 replaces the figure 12 on the body of the square as the point of reference representing the unit of run. The number of inches rise per foot of run, however, is still represented by the corresponding figure on the tongue of the square.

If you look at Figure 15:2A you will note that the hip rafter is at a 45° angle to the plate and the ridge, whereas the common rafter is at a 90° angle to these members. If you visualize the square that is formed by the two common rafters and the end and side wall plates (see Figure 15:2A), the hip rafter will form the diagonal of this square. The unit of run of the common rafter is 12″, the unit of run of the hip rafter is the diagonal of a 12″ square, which is 16.97 or for rafter layout purposes, 17. In other words, the run of a hip rafter is greater than that of the common rafter although the total rise is the same. On a roof with a ⅓ pitch, each 12″ of run of the common rafter will rise 8″. The hip rafter will require 17″ of run to rise the same distance.

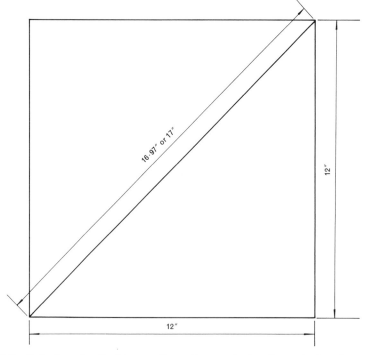

Fig. 15:1   Unit of run for the hip or valley rafter equals the diagonal of a 12″ square.

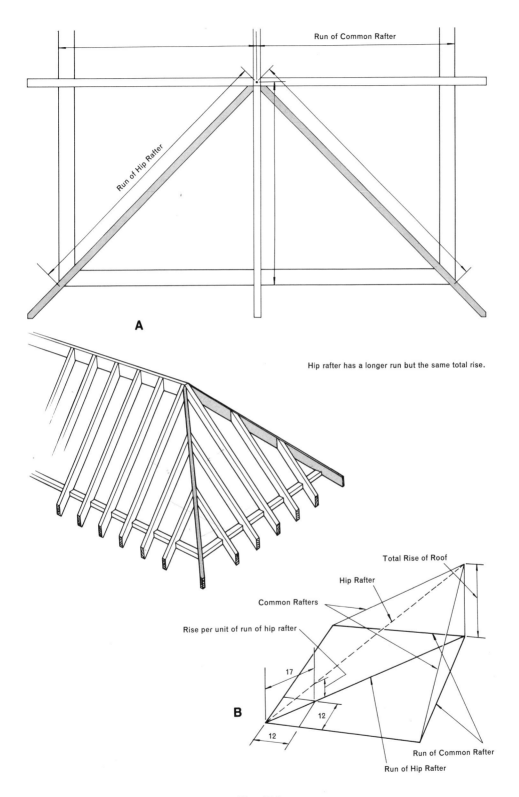

Run of Common Rafter

Run of Hip Rafter

A

Hip rafter has a longer run but the same total rise.

Total Rise of Roof

Hip Rafter

Common Rafters

Rise per unit of run of hip rafter

17

B

12

12

Run of Common Rafter

Run of Hip Rafter

Fig. 15:2

179

Study Figure 15:2B where this principle is illustrated. This, then, is the reason for using 17 instead of 12 as the unit of run on the body of the square.

The principle to remember in determining the length of a hip or valley rafter by the step-off method is to use 17 on the body of the square as the unit of run, and the figure corresponding to the rise per foot of run (as determined by the pitch) on the tongue of the square. (This, of course, is the same as would be used for the common rafter.) Make as many step-offs as there are feet in the run of the roof.

The step-offs will be laid out in the manner that was described in Chapter 14 for common rafters. Larger material is generally used for hip and valley rafters than for common rafters because they must support more of the

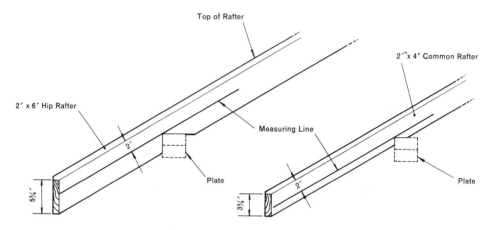

Fig. 15:3   Measuring line on hip and common rafters.

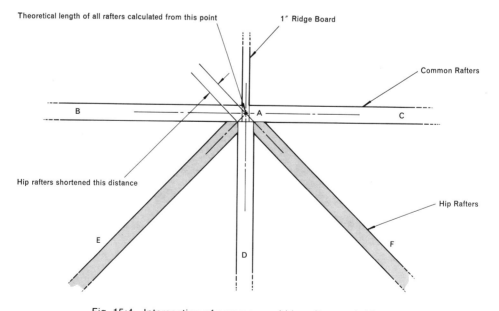

Fig. 15:4   Intersection of common and hip rafters and ridge board.

roof load. On many roofs, 2"x4" stock is used for common rafters, while 2" x 6" is used for hip or valley rafters.

The measuring line should be the same distance from the top of the hip or valley rafter as it was from the top of the common rafter. See Figure 15:3.

Most hip or cottage roofs will have three common rafters and two hip rafters meeting the ridge board at the same point. See A, Figure 15:4. You will notice that the common rafters B and C butt against the side of the ridge board and that the centre common rafter D rests on the end of the ridge board forming a ridge for the two hip rafters E and F. The hip rafters fit into the angles formed by the three common rafters.

The reduction in the length of the hip rafter to compensate for the ridge will be greater than was made for the common rafter, because the reduction here will be the diagonal distance from the end of the rafter to the peak of the roof (point A, Figure 15:4).

For a roof with a ¼ to ½ pitch, the allowance is approximately 1½" if 1" dressed stock is used for the ridge board. If a 2" ridge is used, an allowance of 2¼" is made. The reduction is marked back from the top plumb cut in the way that was explained in the last chapter for the ridge reduction for common rafters.

On some roofs, especially when the span is in odd feet, the two hip rafters are butted against the two common rafters and the side of the ridge, but have no common rafter between them. Therefore, a smaller reduction in the length of the hip rafter is needed. See Figure 15:5.

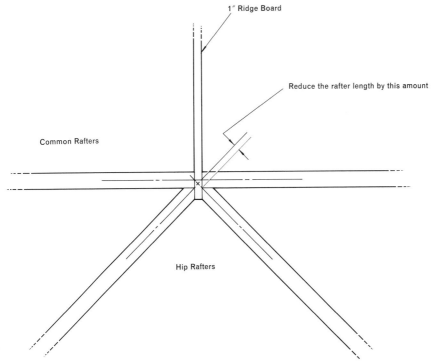

Fig. 15:5   Reduction for ridge board when no centre common rafter is used.

As well as having a plumb cut, hip rafters must have a side or *cheek cut* where they meet the ridge, as shown in Figures 15:4 and 15:5. The angle of this cut changes with the pitch of the roof. If the rafters were in a horizontal position, the cut would be 45°, but as the rafter is raised, the angle increases. The angle to be used can be determined by means of the framing square. First find the length of the hip rafter per foot of run, by measuring from the rise per foot of run on the tongue of the square to the unit of run for the hip rafter (17) on the body of the square. As an example: If the roof had a ⅓ pitch the length per foot of run would be found by measuring from the 8 on the tongue to the 17 on the body of the square — approximately 18¾". See Figure 15:6. This figure on the body of the square and the 17 on the tongue will form the correct angle for the side cut. Since the tongue of the square is only 16" long, however, it is impossible to make the layout with the figures 17 and 18¾. The same angle can be obtained by using one half of each figure, that is, 8½ on the tongue and 9⅜ on the body of the square.

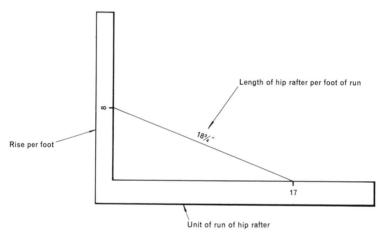

Fig. 15:6 To find the length of the hip rafter per foot of run.

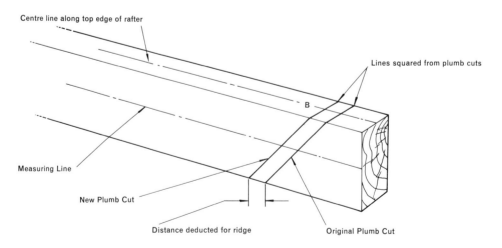

Fig. 15:7 Layout lines at the top end of the hip rafter.

Mark a line along the centre of the top edge of the rafter. Square a line across the top edge of the rafter at the top plumb cut to locate Point B where the two lines intersect. See Figure 15:7. Place the square on the edge of the rafter with the 8½ on the body of the square on the centre line of the rafter at the top of the plumb cut line. Place the 9⅜ mark on the tongue at **the** centre line of the top edge at Point B, as in Figure 15:8. Mark from the

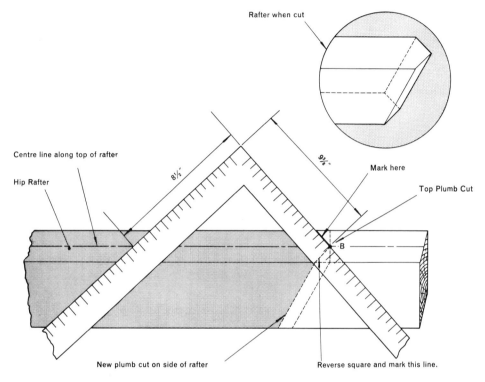

Fig. 15:8   Layout of side cut on hip rafter.

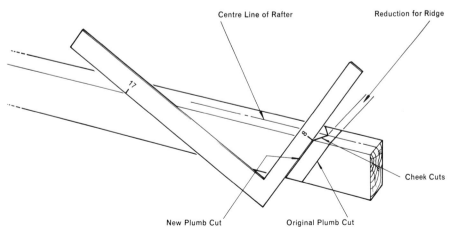

Fig. 15:9   Top plumb cut layout of hip rafter.

edge to the centre line. Reverse the square and do the same from the other edge of the rafter for the other cheek cut. It will be necessary to make a new top plumb cut on the side of the rafter as shown in Figure 15:9.

When a partial step-off is required for a roof whose span is an odd number of feet, the layout procedure is similar to that described for the common rafter. For example, for a roof with a span of 29' and a pitch of ⅓, the hip rafter would require fourteen full step-offs (the run being 14'6"), using 8 and 17 on the square. Since 17 is the unit of run of the hip rafter, the run for the half step-off required would be 6/12 of 17, or 8½". After the fourteenth step-off, move the square on the rafter to the fifteenth position and lay out the seat cut as shown in Figure 15:10.

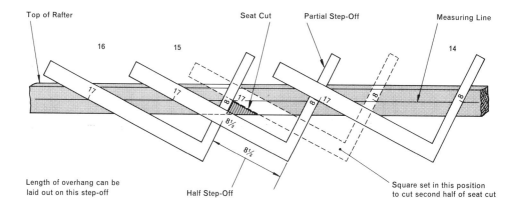

Fig. 15:10   Method of laying out a partial step-off.

It is generally necessary to make a partial step-off for the overhang of the hip rafter. However, if there is 12" of horizontal overhang on the common rafter, one step-off is made on the hip rafter using the number 17 as the unit of run. If, however, the overhang of the common rafter is 8", 8/12 of 17 or 11 5/16" would be used as the unit of run for the hip rafter.

The overhang of a hip or valley rafter must have side cuts as in Figure 15:11. These are laid out in the manner that was described for the side cuts at the top plumb cut.

Rather than lay out and cut the overhang before the hip and valley rafters are set in place, some builders leave two extra feet of rafter projecting past the plate. After all the rafters have been erected, a chalk line is stretched along the ends of the common rafters and over the hip or valley rafters. They are marked at this point and a line is drawn along the edge of a spirit level on the face of the rafter. The ends of the rafters can then be cut with a saw from the scaffold.

After one rafter has been laid out and cut in length, it is set in place to see that it fits properly. The other hip or valley rafters can be laid out from this pattern. It is a good idea to cut them in pairs so that the correct number are cut. Only sound, straight stock should be used for hip or valley rafters; they are the important framing members that carry much of the roof load. Make sure that the crowned side of the rafter is placed uppermost.

In order to give the roof sheathing an even bearing surface and to ensure that it lies flat when it is nailed to the hip rafters, the hip rafters should be bevelled along the length of both top edges. If this were not done, the hip rafters would project above the common and the jack rafters, and the sheathing would not lie flat. This operation is called *backing.* It may be done before the hip rafter is in place, or the edges may be bevelled with a hand axe after the rafter is in place. Figure 15:12 illustrates the principle of the backing operation.

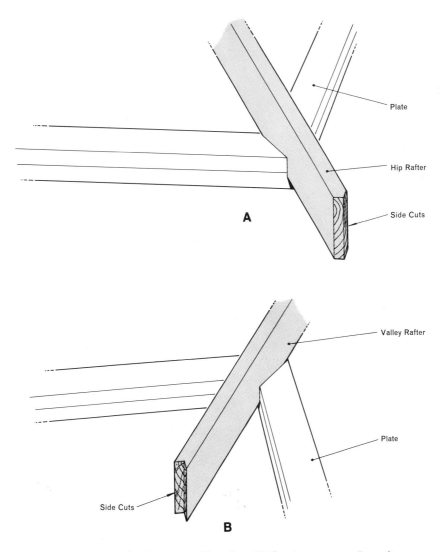

Fig. 15:11 (A) Overhang on a hip rafter; (B) Overhang on a valley rafter.

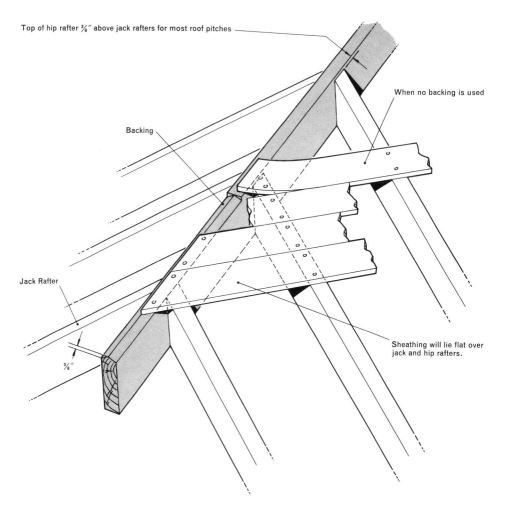

Top of hip rafter ⅜" above jack rafters for most roof pitches

When no backing is used

Backing

Jack Rafter

⅜"

Sheathing will lie flat over jack and hip rafters.

Fig. 15:12   Backing on hip rafter.

ASSIGNMENT

1. (a) What is the unit of run for a hip rafter?
   (b) Why is this figure used?
2. (a) At what angle does the common rafter meet the ridge?
   (b) At what angle does a hip rafter meet the ridge?
3. If in 12" of run, a common rafter rises 8", how many inches of run are required for the hip or valley rafter to rise the same distance?
4. When laying out a hip rafter for a roof with a ½ pitch, what figures would be used on the framing square?
5. How many step-offs are required to lay out the hip rafters for a house with a 31′ span?
6. What would be the length of the partial step-off for the hip rafter on a roof with a run of 14′8″?
7. Why is larger stock used for valley rafters than for common rafters?

186

8. Why should the measuring line be the same distance from the top of both the hip and the common rafter?

9. State the type and number of rafters that meet at the same point at the ridge of a hip roof.

10. How much reduction in the length of the hip rafter is generally made at the ridge?

11. How is the length per foot of run of the hip rafter found?

12. What is the purpose of the side or cheek cut of the hip rafter? How is the angle of this cut determined?

13. Using a sketch, describe how the side cuts of a hip rafter are laid out at the top plumb cut.

14. What would be the figure used as the unit of run on the square when making the layout for a 10″ overhang on a hip rafter?

15. Why must hip or valley rafters be cut from sound, straight stock?

..

Chapter 16

JACK RAFTERS

Jack rafters are short roof framing members that run between two longer members to tie the roof together. They provide nailing support for the sheathing and shingles and carry some of the weight of the roof.

The three types of jack rafters are:

(a) *hip jack rafters* – running from the plate to the hip rafters;
(b) *valley jack rafters* – running from the valley rafters to the ridge board;
(c) *cripple jack rafters* – the short rafters that do not reach either the plate or the ridge but go between the hip rafter and the valley rafter.

Jack rafters are shorter than common rafters and run parallel to them. They meet the ridge and plate at 90°, making the plumb and seat cut the same as for the common rafter. Jack rafters, however, meet the hip and valley rafters at a 45° angle which makes it necessary to make angle or cheek cuts where they intersect these rafters.

The length of the jack rafters will depend on the pitch of the roof and the position of the rafters on it. To determine the length and cuts of jack rafters, the same step-off method of layout is used as was used for the common rafters. The same figures are used on the square for the plumb and the seat cuts, since they are parallel to the common rafters and have the same rise per foot of run. The length is determined by the run of that particular rafter. The run of a jack rafter can be determined by its position on the roof. Let us assume that a hip roof has a ¼ pitch and a 14′ run, and the rafters are to be spaced at 24″ centres, as shown in Figure 16:2.

The location of hip jack rafters is generally laid out from the corner; the first jack rafter is located 24″ from the corner. This will mean that the run of the rafter will be 24″ because *the run of any jack rafter is equal to the distance it is from the corner of the plate of the building.* See Figure 16:2. Since the run of the first jack rafter is 2′, two full step-offs are required to lay out its length.

The second jack rafter is located 48″ from the corner. The run of this rafter, then, is 48″, which requires four full step-offs to lay it out. The run of each succeeding jack rafter will be 2′ longer than the preceding one.

If the rafters are placed at 16″ centres, as they generally are, it will be necessary to lay out partial step-offs in addition to the full ones. Since the first jack rafter would have a run of 16″, one full step-off and a partial step-off of 4″ would be required. The second rafter would require two full step-offs and a partial one of 8″ for the 32″ run of that rafter. The partial step-offs should be laid out in the manner that was described for the common rafter in Chapter 14.

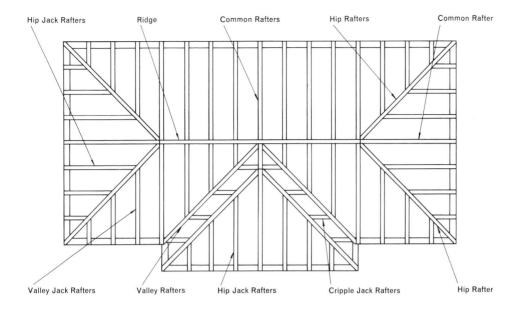

Fig. 16:1 Three Types of Jack Rafters

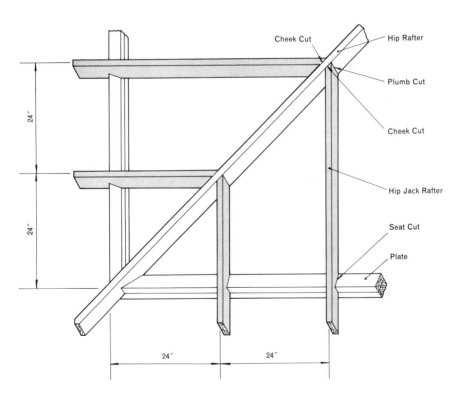

Fig. 16:2 Jack Rafter Spacing

189

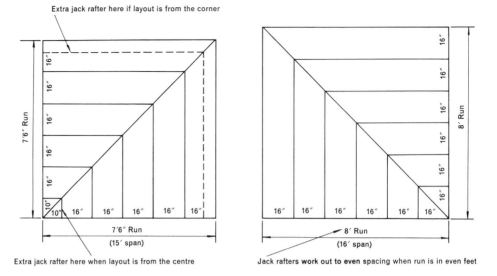

Extra jack rafter here when layout is from the centre

Jack rafters work out to even spacing when run is in even feet

Fig. 16:3   Jack rafter spacing when span is in odd feet.

Sometimes, especially when the run of the roof is in odd feet and there is a common rafter in the centre of the end section of a hip roof, the hip jack rafters are laid out from the centre common rafter towards the corner of the building. This makes the last space next to the corner smaller than the rest, which means the extra rafter required will be a short one rather than a long one which would be needed if the layout were started from the corner representing a saving of material. When the rafters are positioned in this way, the run of the longest jack rafter will be 16″ shorter (for rafters

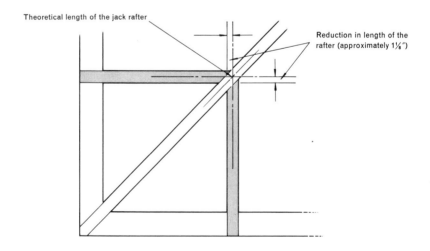

Theoretical length of the jack rafter

Reduction in length of the rafter (approximately 1⅛″)

Fig. 16:4   Reduction in length of the hip jack rafter for the thickness of the hip rafter.

190

spaced at 16″ centres) than the run of the common rafters. The run of each succeeding jack rafter would, in turn, be 16″ shorter. (The run of each, of course, still equals the distance from the rafter to the corner.)

To lay out the length of the jack rafters, start the step-offs at the top end of the rafter, just as was done for the common rafter. To lay out the second jack rafter for the roof shown in Figure 16:2, two step-offs would be required. The figure 8 would be used on the tongue of the square and the figure 12, as the unit of run, on the body of the square. Since the seat cut and the overhang plumb cut are the same for both jack and common rafters, the pattern that was used to lay out the common rafter should also be used for the seat and overhang portion of the jack rafter. This will ensure that the overhang portion of the jack rafters will be exactly the same as the rest of the rafters.

Hip jack rafters must be shortened in length a distance equal to one-half the diagonal thickness of the hip rafter, as shown in Figure 16:4. The reduction in length is made by measuring the required distance back from the top plumb cut and making a new layout line.

A double reduction in length must be made for valley jack rafters: one-half the thickness of the ridge board plus one-half the diagonal thickness of the valley rafter. See Figure 16:5.

A *cheek cut* must be made at the top of the hip jack rafters and at the lower end of the valley jack rafters. The cheek cut is required because the jack rafters meet the hip and valley rafters at a 45° angle. The angle of the cheek cut will vary slightly according to the pitch of the roof.

The correct angle can best be determined in a manner similar to that used

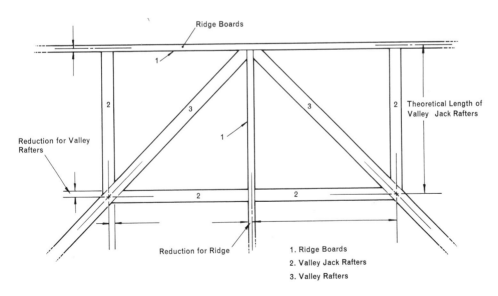

Fig. 16:5   Reduction in length necessary for valley jack rafters.

for laying out the cheek cut of the hip rafter; the length of the rafter per foot of run is used on the body of the square, but the figure 12 is used on the tongue of the square rather than the 17 that was used for the cheek cut of the hip rafter. The length of the jack rafter per foot of run is found by measuring from the figure on the tongue corresponding to the rise per foot (as determined by the pitch) to the 12 on the body of the square.

Square a line across the top edge of the rafter from the top plumb cut as it was marked after making the reduction for the hip rafter. Draw a line along the centre of the top edge of the rafter as in Figure 16:7.

Place the square on the edge of the rafter and lay out the cheek cut as shown in Figure 16:8. The length of the jack rafter per foot of run is used on the body of the square, and the figure 12 is used on the tongue. Mark along the body of the square.

You will observe in Figure 16:9 that one end of the cheek cut extends past the line squared from the plumb cut, and the other end of the cheek cut comes short of this line. This makes it necessary to make two new plumb cut layout lines, one on each face of the rafter. See Figure 16:9.

Unlike common rafters, no one pattern can be used to lay out all the jack rafters, as they differ in length. However, on a standard hip roof, there will be eight hip jack rafters that can be cut from one pattern, four of them right-handed and four left-handed. They should be cut in pairs to ensure that the correct number of each is made.

Cut the long jack rafters first. The pieces that are cut off may be used for the short rafters, and often, one top plumb cut can be used for two jack rafters.

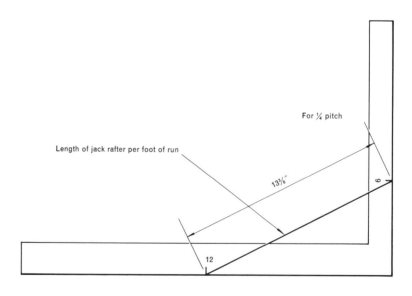

Fig. 16:6   To find the length of a jack rafter per foot of run.

192

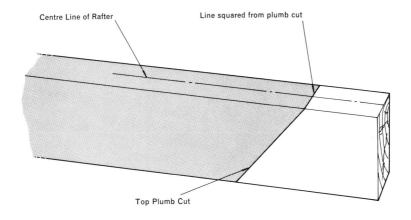

Centre Line of Rafter

Line squared from plumb cut

Top Plumb Cut

Fig. 16:7   Layout of jack rafter at top plumb cut.

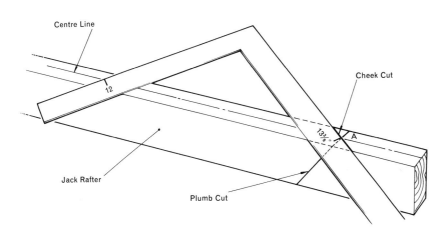

Centre Line

Cheek Cut

12

13⅜

A

Jack Rafter

Plumb Cut

Fig. 16:8   Layout of cheek of jack rafter.

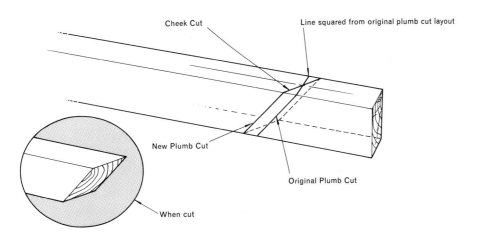

Cheek Cut

Line squared from original plumb cut layout

New Plumb Cut

Original Plumb Cut

When cut

Fig. 16:9   Layout of new plumb cut lines on jack rafter.

ASSIGNMENT

1. List three purposes served by jack rafters.
2. Explain the difference between a "hip jack rafter" and a "valley jack rafter".
3. A cripple jack rafter runs between which two roof framing members?
4. (a) Jack rafters meet the plate at what angle?
    (b) At what angle do they meet the hip rafter?
5. What is the unit of run of jack rafters?
6. What two factors must be known before attempting to lay out a jack rafter?
7. (a) If the jack rafters are spaced 24″ on centre, what is the run of the fifth jack rafter?
    (b) How many step-offs would be required to lay out this rafter?
8. (a) If the jack rafters are spaced at 16″ centres, what is the run of the fourth jack rafter?
    (b) In addition to the full step-offs, what partial step-off would be needed to lay out this rafter?
9. (a) Under what circumstances might the location of the hip jack rafters be spaced from the centre of the roof rather than from the corner?
    (b) What is the advantage of locating them in this manner?
10. Why is the common rafter used as a pattern for the overhang portion of the jack rafters?
11. How much allowance should be made in the length of the valley jack rafters to compensate for the ridge board and the valley rafter?
12. Why do hip or valley jack rafters require cheek cuts?
13. How would you find the length of a jack rafter per foot of run for a roof with a ⅓ pitch?
14. Explain, using a sketch, how the cheek cut is laid out on a hip jack rafter for a roof with a ¼ pitch.
15. On a standard hip roof, how many jack rafters of the same length will be required?

Chapter 17

RAFTER TABLE ON THE FRAMING SQUARE

Another method of determining the length of rafters is by using the *rafter table* that is to be found on most good makes of framing squares. Rafter tables are based on the same principle as the step-off method of layout; therefore, to be able to use the rafter table efficiently, it is necessary to understand the step-off method, which is described in the three preceding chapters. Not all makes of framing squares have identical tables, but they are all based on the length of the rafter per foot of run. Since our explanation will be clearer if we give examples from one specific rafter table, we have chosen the table that is stamped on the face of the Stanley Framing Square. This is one of the most commonly used makes in the building industry. If you understand the table on this square, you should have little difficulty in understanding the rafter table on any other make of square.

The rafter table is considered to be faster and more accurate than the step-off method, especially where it is necessary to make the many repetitive step-offs that are required to lay out a long rafter where there is a chance of a cumulative error. It must, however, be pointed out that the rafter table gives only the length of the rafter, not the angle of the top or lower plumb cut. When we use the rafter table, therefore, we must actually use a combination of the two systems of rafter layout.

The rafter framing table is stamped on the face of the body of the framing square. It consists of six lines, each line containing a row of figures and the type of rafter to which these figures pertain. The inch graduation figures on the outer edge of the square, just above the rafter figure, form a part of the table; they represent the number of inches rise per foot of run for any given pitch. Figure 17:1 shows a part of the rafter framing table.

Face of Steel Framing Square

	18	17	16
Length of common rafter per foot of run	21·63	20·81	20
Length of hip or valley per foot of run	24·74	24·02	23·32
Difference in length of jacks 16″ on centre	28⅛	27¾	26¹¹⁄₁₆
Difference in length of jacks 24″ on centre	43¼	41⅝	40
For side cut of jacks use	6¹¹⁄₁₆	6¹³⁄₁₆	7³⁄₁₆
For side cut of hip or valley use	8¼	8½	8¾

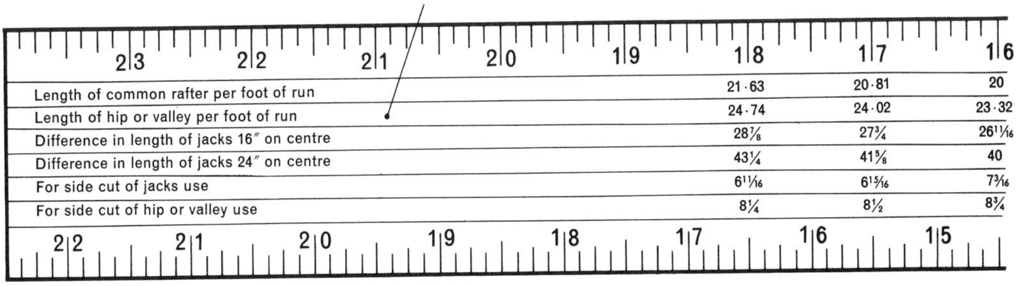

Fig. 17:1   Rafter Framing Table

The two factors that must be known before using the rafter framing table are:
(a) *the run of the rafter;*
(b) *the pitch, or the number of inches rise per foot of run.*
From this table the length of the rafter can be found for roofs with seventeen different pitches from 2″ to 18″ per foot of run.

COMMON RAFTERS

To find the length of common rafters look on the top line of the table which reads "Length of the common rafter per foot of run". As an example: we wish to find the length of a common rafter on a roof with a 14′ run and a ⅓ pitch, which is 8″ rise per foot of run. Look first along the outer edge of the square above the rafter table and locate the inch graduation that represents the number of inches rise per foot of run, in this example, 8. Directly below this on the first line will be found the number 14.42 which will be the length in inches of the common rafter per foot of run for a roof with a ⅓ pitch. See Figure 17:2. The length of this rafter, then, will be 14.42 x 14 = 201.88 inches or 16′ 9⅞″, the 14 being the number of feet in the run of the rafter.

The rule, then, to find the length of a common rafter using the rafter table, is to multiply the number stated in the table by the number of feet in the run of the rafter.

The length of any rafter, arrived at by using the rafter table, should be measured along the measuring line. This length must then be reduced by ½ the thickness of the ridge board. The length of the overhang must, of course, be added.

HIP AND VALLEY RAFTERS

The length of the hip and valley rafters is to be located on the second row on the table. Here again, we look under the number on the outer edge of the square which represents the rise per foot of run of the roof.

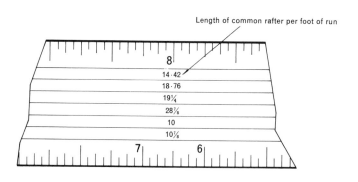

Fig. 17:2   Rafter framing table for ⅓ pitch.

Let us assume that a roof has a ¼ pitch and an 8′ run. To find the length of the hip rafter, locate the figure on the outer edge of the square that represents the number of inches rise per foot of run of the common rafter — in this case 6″. In the column directly below the 6, on the second line down labelled "Length of the hip or valley rafter per foot of run", will be found the number 18.00, which means that for every foot of the run of the building, the length of the hip or valley rafter will be exactly 18″. See Figure 17:4. Since, in this example, the run of the roof was 8′, the length of the hip rafter would be 8 x 18 = 144″ or 12 feet long, exclusive of overhang.

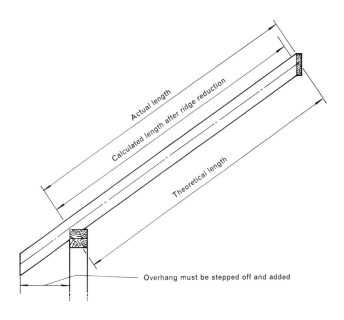

Fig. 17:3   Actual and theoretical length of the common rafter.

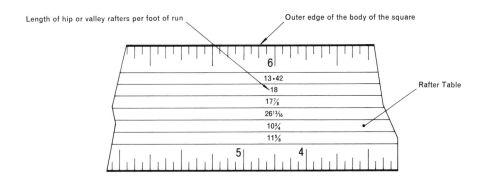

Fig. 17:4   Rafter framing table for a roof with a ¼ pitch.

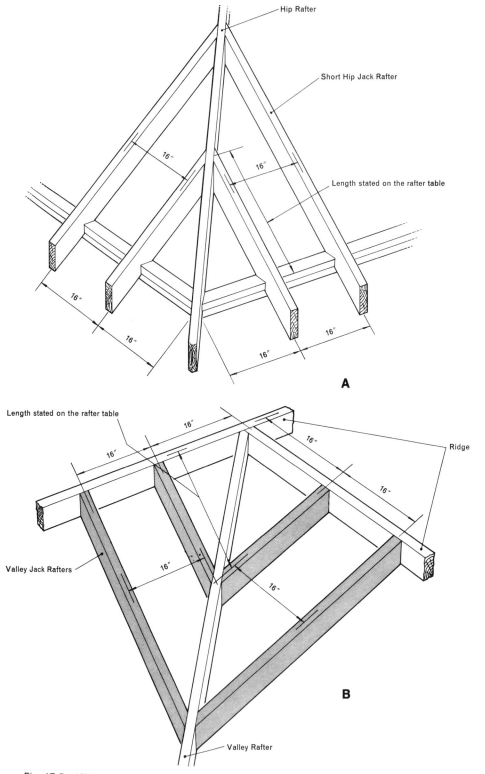

Fig. 17:5 (A) Location of short hip jack rafters laid out from the corner of the plate;
(B) Position of short valley jack rafters.

198

JACK RAFTERS

To find the length of a jack rafter we must know the pitch of the roof, the position of the jack rafter in relation to the corner of the building (first, second, third, and so on, from the corner), and the spacing of the rafters — whether at 16″ or 24″ centres. The run of the roof is of no concern: with the same pitch and the same spacing, the third hip jack rafter will be the same length whether the building is 20′ wide or 40′ wide.

The length of the shortest jack rafter for a roof of any given pitch can be found on the third or fourth line of the rafter table, depending on the rafter spacing. The value given in the table represents not only the length of the shortest jack rafter, but also the difference between the lengths of any two adjacent jack rafters. If the rafters are properly spaced, the second jack rafter is twice as long as the first, the third three times as long as the first, and so on, provided, of course, that the rafter locations are laid out from the corners of the building. If the jack rafter locations are laid out from the last common rafter, the longest jack rafter will be shorter than the common

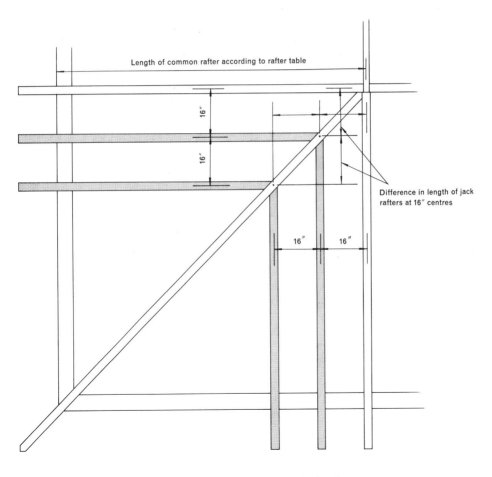

Fig. 17:6   Length of the long hip jack rafters.

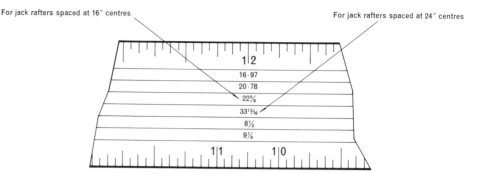

Fig. 17:7   Rafter framing table for ½ pitch.

rafter by the distance given on the table, and the second longest jack rafter will be shorter than the common rafter by twice this figure, and so on.

EXAMPLE: To find the length of the third jack rafter for a roof with a ½ pitch, the rafters to be spaced at 16″ centres.

On the outer edge of the square above the table locate the figure 12, which represents the number of inches rise per foot of run of the roof. Below the 12, on the third line down, is stamped the number 22⅝, as shown in Figure 17:7. This indicates that the first or shortest jack rafter for this roof will be 22⅝″ long, the third jack rafter will be 3 x 22⅝ = 67⅞″ = 5′ 7⅞″ long. From this length must be subtracted one-half the thickness of the hip rafter, and to it must be added the overhang.

If the jack rafters are spaced at 24″ centres, the same procedure is followed for determining their length, except that the fourth line of the rafter table is used.

Cheek or Side Cuts of Jack Rafters

The last two lines on the table deal with the angle of the cheek or side cuts of the jack, hip, and valley rafters. As was mentioned in the last chapter, the cheek cuts of the jack rafters are necessary where they meet the hip or valley rafters. The angle of this cut is to be found on the fifth line of the rafter table.

Since the angle of the cheek cut differs according to the pitch of the roof, the figure given in the table for any particular rafter is also based on the number of inches rise per foot of run. For example: Find the cheek cut for a jack rafter on a roof with a 5/12 pitch. On the outer edge of the body of the square find the figure that represents the number of inches rise per foot of run, in this case 10 (5/12 x 24). In the column directly below the 10, on the fifth line of the rafter table, which is labelled — "For Side Cut of Jacks Use", find 9¼. See Figure 17:8.

Using the 9¼ on the outer edge of the tongue of the square and the 12

200

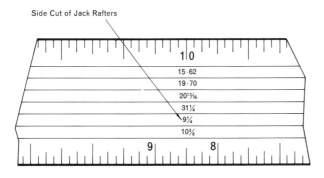

Fig. 17:8 Rafter framing table for a ⁵/₁₂ pitch.

on the body of the square, as in Figure 17:9, mark along the body or the 12″ side of the square for the cheek cut of the jack rafter.

The side or cheek cut of the hip or valley rafter can be found in a similar manner on the sixth line of the rafter table.

If you wish to lay out the cheek cut for a hip rafter on a roof with a ⅜ pitch, look on the sixth line of the table, in the column under the figure 9, and find the number 10⅝. See Figure 17:11. This number, when used on the tongue

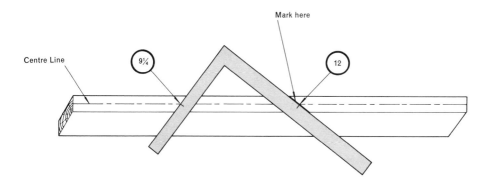

Fig. 17:9 Layout of side cut of jack rafter.

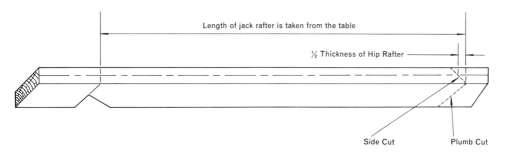

Fig. 17:10 Hip jack rafter layout.

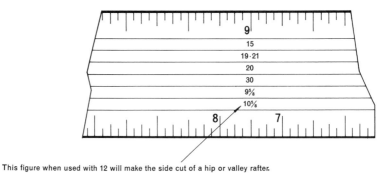

This figure when used with 12 will make the side cut of a hip or valley rafter.

Fig. 17:11   Rafter framing table for a roof with a ³⁄₈ pitch.

of the square with the figure 12 on the body of the square, will give correct side cut angle, as illustrated in Figure 17:12. Reverse the square and lay out the other half of the side cut. When using the rafter framing table, *always mark on the 12″ side of the square for the cheek cut of hip or valley rafters.*

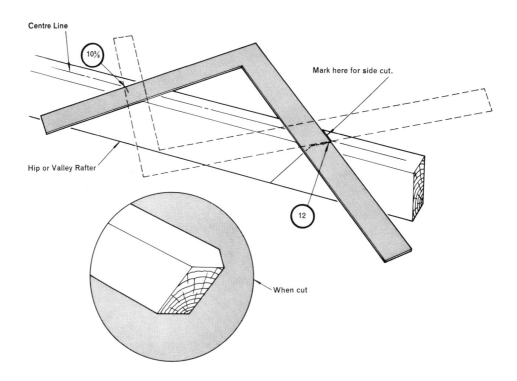

Fig. 17:12   Layout of side cut of hip or valley rafter.

ASSIGNMENT

1. List the advantages of using the rafter framing table to lay out the length of rafters.
2. On what principle is the rafter table based?
3. What information is necessary to determine the length of a rafter from the rafter framing table?
4. How many sets of rafter tables are provided on the square for different roof pitches?
5. From the sketch of the partial rafter table shown in Figure 17:1,
   - (a) determine the length of the common rafter for a roof with a 12′ run and a ⅔ pitch.
   - (b) determine the length of the hip rafter for a roof with a ¾ pitch and a 16′ run.
6. What would be the length of the fourth jack rafter on a roof with a ½ pitch, the rafters to be spaced at 16″ centres?
   Consult the sketch with the appropriate figures in this chapter in calculating the correct rafter length.
7. The fifth jack rafter is how much longer than the first?
8. (a) What additional length is generally added to the length of the hip jack rafters as determined from the rafter framing table?
   (b) What deduction must be made?
9. What is the purpose of the side cut on a jack rafter?
10. What figures would be used on the tongue and the body of the square to lay out the side cut of a hip rafter on a roof with a ½ pitch.
    Along which arm of the square should the line be drawn?

Chapter 18

ROOF ERECTION

Having laid out the rafters either by the step-off method or by using the rafter framing table on the framing square, and having cut the required number of rafters to length, the carpenter's next operation will be to frame the roof properly by correctly spacing the rafters and nailing them in place. The roof should be framed in such a way that it provides the maximum support for the material used. When designing a house, the architect will specify the size and spacing of the bearing members to be used in the roof. He will consider such factors as the dead load to be supported. This will include the weight of the roof, sheathing, and the shingles or other roof covering. For an average pitched roof, using plywood sheathing and asphalt shingles, the dead load is approximately ten pounds per square foot. The live load on the roof must also be considered. This refers to the pressure and weight exerted by wind and snow. This varies greatly from one geographical area to another. In most parts of Canada, for a moderately pitched roof this load is approximately forty pounds per square foot. These loads must be combined when calculating the size and spacing of the rafters. If the roof is to carry the load for which it was designed and still present a pleasing appearance, it must be well built; all members must fit properly and be well secured to each other.

HOW TO FRAME A GABLE ROOF

Let us first consider the gable roof, since it is basic to all other types of pitched roofs. The position of the rafters should first be located on the plates. The outer edge of the first rafter should be even with the end of the plate. With the framing square, lay out the position of the second and succeeding rafters at 16″ or 24″ centres in the manner that was described for floor joists and wall studding layout. If the ceiling joists run in the same direction as the rafters and are already properly positioned and nailed in place, one rafter should be placed beside each joist, as the spacing is generally the same. If the spacing does not work out evenly for the total length of the roof, an extra rafter may be required on each side, making the space between the last rafter and the one next to it less than the distance between the other rafters.

After the layout has been made on one plate, the rafter locations should be laid out on the ridge board. Two or more sections of ridge may be required for the full length of the roof. Place the ridge beside the plate as shown in Figure 18:1, so that the lines can be transferred from the plate to the ridge. The joints in the ridge should occur in the centre of a rafter location, so that both ridge sections will be nailed to the same rafter. After the layout is completed on the ridge board, it can be taken to the other side of the roof and set beside the plate so that the rafter positions can, in turn, be transferred to that plate. This ensures that the rafter locations will be exactly the same on both of the plates and the ridge.

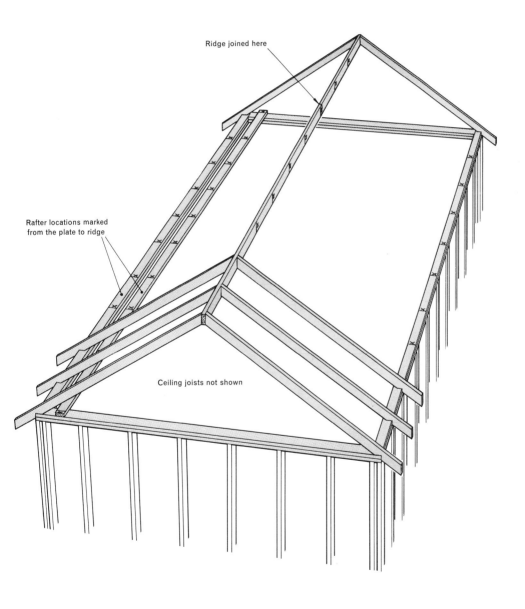

Fig. 18:1   Gable Roof

HOW TO ERECT A GABLE ROOF

For the erection of most roofs, a portable scaffold is required, to enable the carpenter to reach the ridge to nail the rafters in place. The scaffold usually rests on the ceiling joists. It should be approximately 4' wide and 8' or 10' long and it should extend to within 5' or 6' of the ridge. The scaffold platform can be moved along as the roof erection progresses. A scaffold is generally not required at the wall end of the rafters, since the carpenter can stand on the plate or on the ceiling joists.

To frame a roof of this type efficiently, two or more men are required because of the nature of the work and the length of the material used.

The procedure for erecting a gable roof may vary with the style of house, but in general it is as follows:

1. Select two straight rafters for the first pair, and lean them against the scaffold in the centre of the building with the top end of the rafter up.
2. Nail the first section of the ridge board to the top plumb cut of one of the rafters, using two 2½" common nails. Keep the end of the ridge flush with the outer edge of the rafter.
3. Nail another rafter to the same side of the ridge, about six or seven rafter spaces away from the first. Keep the top of the ridge even with the top of the plumb cut of the rafter.
4. Raise these two rafters and the section of ridge board to approximately the correct height — that is, to where the seat cut fits snugly at the plate — and prop the ridge up in that position. Nail the rafters securely on the correct location marks. If 2" x 4" rafters are used a 4" spike can be angled through the top of the rafters into the plate. If larger rafter stock is used, toe-nail them with two 2½" nails on each side because a 4" spike will not reach through the rafter into the plate when driven from the top.
5. Nail two rafters in place on the other side of the roof directly opposite the first two rafters. Nail them first to the plate at the seat cut, then adjust the height of the ridge until it is exactly even with the top of the rafters. Toe-nail them to the ridge using 2½" nails.
6. Plumb the first pair of rafters by using a spirit level and a straight 2" x 4" as shown in Figure 18:2.
7. To stiffen the roof and keep it plumb, it must be braced by nailing a diagonal brace from the top of the rafter to the plate. If the brace is attached to the underside of the rafter, as in Figure 18:2, it will not interfere with the application of the roof sheathing.
8. Nail in place the other rafters in the first roof section, nailing the seat cut first. Erect them in pairs, so that too much strain is not put against one side of the ridge.
9. Move the portable scaffold along and erect the other rafters and ridge board sections in the same manner.
10. When all rafters have been nailed in place, the gable end studding should be framed. The layout and spacing of these studs should be the

same as for the main wall framing. The layout is generally started from the centre of the building, as shown in Figure 18:3. This allows the studs to be cut in pairs and also leaves the area directly below the peak free of 2″ x 4″ framing. This makes it more convenient to install a ventilation louver, which often fits between the standard 16″ spaced gable end studding. If there are window openings in the gable ends, their locations and widths should be laid out on the plate and the studding located accordingly.

11. Mark the gable end studs to length by placing a piece of 2″ x 4″ on end on the layout line. Plumb it with a spirit level and mark it to length under the rafter as illustrated in Figure 18:3. If both gable ends are to be framed, four studs of the same length will be required, two right-hand and two left-hand.

12. Lay out and cut the other studs in the same fashion. It is more economical to cut the long studs first, because the short ends can then be used for the short studs.

13. Toe-nail the square end of the studs to the plate with four 2½″ common nails and the top end with two 2½″ nails as shown in Figure 18:3. Care should be taken not to force a bow in the rafter by driving the top of the stud too tight.

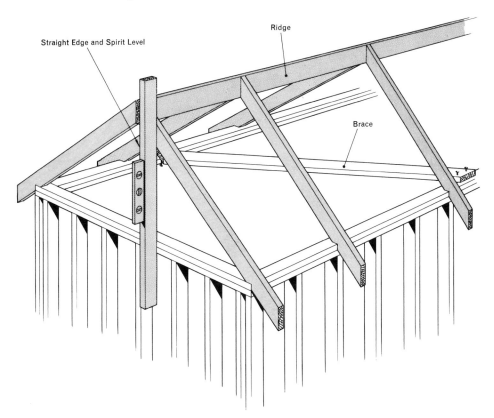

Fig. 18:2 Plumbing the gable end rafter.

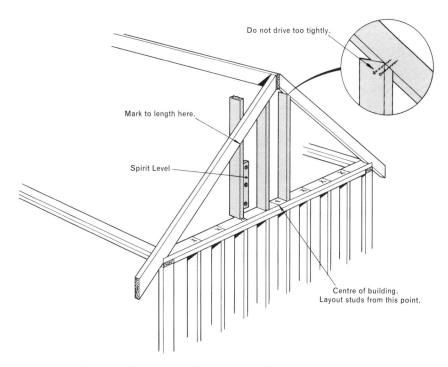

Do not drive too tightly.

Mark to length here.

Spirit Level

Centre of building.
Layout studs from this point.

Main wall studding not necessarily directly below gable studs

Fig. 18:3   Marking gable end studding to length.

HOW TO FRAME A HIP ROOF

It is particularly important when making the layout for a hip roof that the three common rafters that butt against the hip rafters be correctly positioned, or the hip and jack rafters, as laid out by the step-off method or from the rafter table, will not fit properly. In Figure 18:4 the distances A,B,C, and D are all exactly equal. They represent the distances from the corner of the plate to the centres of the three common rafters, 1, 2, and 3. These three common rafters, together with the plates, form the two perfect squares of which the hip rafters 7 and 8 are diagonals.

In a hip roof layout, the distance from the corner of the building to the centre of the first common rafter on the side or the end of the roof must be equal to the run of the roof.

To locate the centres of the six common rafters that butt against the hip rafters, measure along the plates, in both directions from all four corners, a distance equal to the run of the roof. To locate the outer edge of these rafters, measure, from their centre locations, a distance equal to one half the thickness of the rafter, as illustrated by lines E and F, Figure 18:4. With the framing square, lay out the other common rafters in the centre section of the roof at the regular spacing. An extra pair of rafters may be required if the spacings do not work out evenly.

When the span of the building is in odd feet, or when the regular spacings

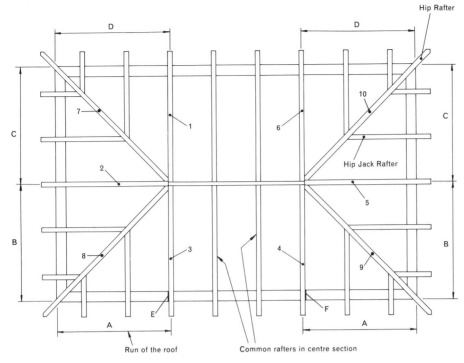

Fig. 18:4 Rafter layout on a hip roof.

of the rafters do not fit evenly into the run of the building, the jack rafter locations should be laid out from the first common rafter towards the corner of the roof. If an extra set of jack rafters is required, they will be the short ones closest to the corners.

HOW TO ERECT A HIP ROOF

1. Lay out the ridge board for the centre section of the roof by placing a piece of 1″ x 6″, or other ridge board stock, on the plate. Mark the length to extend from the outer edge of the common rafter at one end of the centre section of the roof to the outer edge of the common rafter at the other end (rafters 3 and 4, lines E and F, as shown in Figure 18:4).

2. Transfer the rafter location lines from the plate to the ridge. See Figure 18:4.

3. Erect the centre section, which consists of the common rafters and the ridge boards.

4. Nail the two end rafters in place (2 and 5 of Figure 18:4).

5. Set the hip rafters in place. Make sure that the top plumb cuts fit snugly between the two common rafters. Nail the rafters securely at both the plumb and seat cuts.

6. Nail the hip jack rafters in place, starting with the longest ones. Keep the tops of the rafters even with the backed edges of the hip rafters, as shown in Figure 18:5A. The backing operation was described in Chapter 15. If the hip rafters have not been backed off, the tops of the jack rafters should be kept slightly above the tops of the hip rafters as

in Figure 18:5B. The roof sheathing will then lie flat when it is nailed over the rafters. The same effect can be achieved by dropping the hip rafter slightly. Backing, however, is preferable.

Nail the jack rafters to the hip rafter with two 2½" common nails, as shown in Figure 18:5A, taking care not to force the hip rafter out of alignment by driving the nails in too tight. Installing the jack rafters in pairs will help greatly in keeping the hip rafter straight.

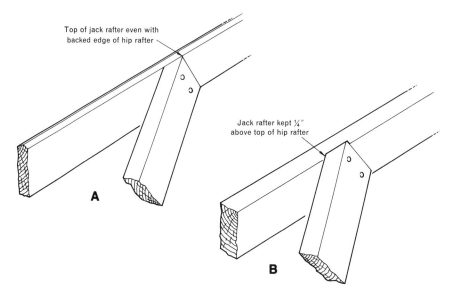

Fig. 18:5   Methods of attaching jack rafter to hip rafter.

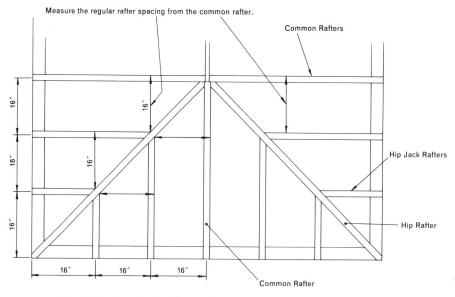

Fig. 18:6   Keep the hip jack rafters parallel to the common rafters.

210

The hip jack rafters must be kept parallel to the common rafters. This can be done by locating the point on the hip rafter where the longest jack rafter should intersect it and by measuring from the common rafter a distance equal to the rafter spacing. See Figure 18:6. After each jack rafter is nailed in place, measure this same distance from it to locate the position of the top of the next jack rafter.

HOW TO FRAME A VALLEY ROOF

The framing of a *valley roof* is similar to the framing of a hip roof, except that more of the layout must be made on the ridge board.

Figure 18:7 shows a plan view that is more or less typical of a valley roof. There are many variations of valley roofs: the pitch and/or span of one wing of the building may be different from the other roof sections of the house. The layout and framing steps described here for the roof shown in Figure 18:7, however, are applicable to most valley roofs.

The valley rafters run from the intersections of the plates to the ridge.

1. On plate A, lay out the rafter locations for the long, straight side of the roof made up of common rafters attached to the ridge board and the plate. Use the framing square to make the layout in the regular manner with the specified rafter spacing.

2. The combined length of the pieces that make up the ridge board for the long section of the roof must be exactly the same length as the plate. These can be set on the plate and the rafter locations transferred to the

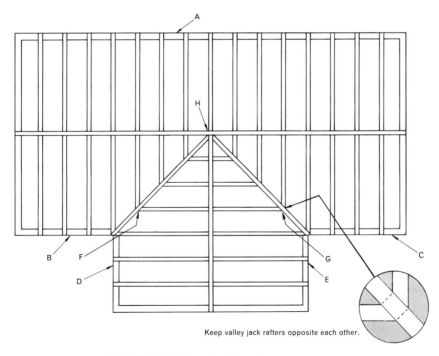

Keep valley jack rafters opposite each other.

Fig. 18:7 Gable and valley rafter arrangement.

211

ridge. A common rafter must be placed directly opposite point H where the valley rafters will intersect the ridge. If the regular rafter spacings do not correspond with the ridge intersection, an extra common rafter must be placed at point H.

3. The layout for plates B and C can be made by transferring the rafter location lines from the ridge. If the ridge is too awkward for this purpose, use the framing square, making sure that the lines correspond with those on plate A.

4. Lay out plates D and E, starting from the outer corners of the building and working towards the valley rafters. It may require an extra pair of rafters with a smaller spacing at points G and F to make the valley jack rafters of the two sections of the roof come opposite each other.

5. Cut and lay out the ridge board for the valley section of the roof. It should extend from the outer edge of the plate to the centre of the main roof section. Then subtract one-half the thickness of the other ridge board.

6. The common rafter locations can be marked on the ridge by laying it on plate D and transferring the lines from the plate to the ridge.

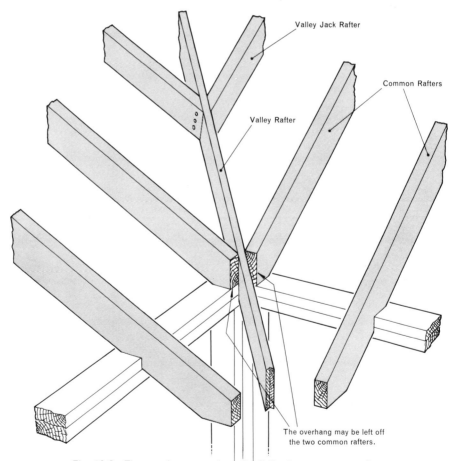

Fig. 18:8 The overhang may be left off the two common rafters.

7. Lay out the valley jack rafter position on the ridge board with the framing square, using the regular spacing where possible, but making sure these valley rafters will come opposite the valley jack rafters on the other section of the roof.

8. Erect the sections of the roof that consist of only the common rafters and the ridge.

9. Nail the two ridge boards together temporarily at point H.

10. Set the two valley rafters in place and adjust the position of the ridge board intersections until the tops of the two valley rafters fit properly. Nail the seat cut first by toe-nailing into the plate. Then fasten the top by driving 2½″ nails through the ridge as well as toe-nailing.

11. Nail the valley jack rafters in place starting with the longest. Drive nails through the ridge into the top plumb cut of the rafters where they meet the valley rafter. To locate the position of the longest valley jack rafter, measure over the correct spacing distance from the last common rafter. In turn, measure from the longest jack rafter the correct spacing to the next longest, to locate the spot where it should meet the valley rafter. Install valley jack rafters in pairs and make sure they come opposite each other at the valley rafter. See Figures 18:7 and 18:8.

12. Brace the roof by nailing 1″ x 4″s diagonally from the underside of the top of the rafters to the plates.

ASSIGNMENT

1. Who generally specifies the size and spacing of the bearing roof members?

2. (a) What is meant by the dead load on a roof?
   (b) What is meant by the live load that is imposed on a roof?

3. If a roof with a ⅓ pitch is built to suit our Canadian climate, what is the combined live and dead load per square foot that it must withstand?

4. If the ceiling joists and the rafters of a house run in the same direction, where should the rafters be placed on the plate in relation to the ceiling joists?

5. How are the rafter location lines laid out on the ridge board of a gable roof?

6. Where should the joints in the ridge board of a gable roof occur?

7. How can you make certain that the rafter location will be the same on both the plates and the ridge board of a gable roof?

8. Why does it require at least two men to frame a roof?

9. Describe how the first section of a gable is erected.

10. How are the rafters braced until the roof sheathing is applied?

11. Why should rafters be nailed in place in pairs?

12. Why are the studding locations for the gable end of a roof laid out from the centre of the building?

13. How is the gable end studding marked to length?
14. Why should care be taken when nailing the top of the gable end studs in place?
15. On a hip roof, what should be the distance from the corner of the plate to the centre of the first common rafter?
16. In your notebook make a scale drawing of the plan view of a hip roof, 20′ x 28′, showing the location of all rafters (rafters to be spaced at 16″ centres).
17. The hip rafter is the diagonal of a square formed by which other framing members?
18. State the rule that governs the position of the first common rafter on a hip roof.
19. In what situation should the hip jack rafters be laid out from the first common rafter toward the corners of the building?
20. If the hip rafter has *not* been backed off, how does this affect the manner in which the hip jack rafters are attached to it?
21. How can you be assured that the hip jack rafters will be parallel to the common rafters?
22. Why should a common rafter be placed directly opposite the point where the valley rafters intersect each other and the ridge board?
23. Why are the valley jack rafter positions laid out only on the ridge board?
24. Which valley jack rafters should be nailed in place first?

Construction Safety (see pages 399-417)

25. How are the upright sections of the steel scaffold held together?
26. List five safety precautions that must be observed when building or using scaffolds.

Chapter 19

ROOF TRUSSES

In the last several chapters we have been describing the conventional method of roof framing in which the supporting members such as rafters, ceiling joists, and collar ties are individually cut, erected, and nailed in place to form a sturdy roof framework. An alternative to this method of roof construction and one that is considered superior, in many respects, is the use of *roof trusses*, sometimes referred to simply as "trussed rafters".

A *truss* is a structural framework composed of several members, so arranged and joined together that they form a series of triangles, thus transferring the load imposed at any point on the framework along the members to the walls, columns, or other vertical supports at the ends of the truss. No intermediate partitions, columns, or other centre vertical supports are necessary in a standard roof truss arrangement.

Trusses are extensively used as framework of roofs, as floor joists, over large wall openings, and in other places where structural support is necessary to carry the load over a long span. Trusses are pre-assembled and set in place as pre-fabricated units.

Although roof trusses have been in use for many years, it is only recently that they have been extensively accepted and incorporated in residential home construction. This is due to the current trend of a shift-over from conventional framing to truss construction. There are several valid reasons for the increased acceptance of roof trusses.
They are:
1. *efficiency.* A single unit roof truss often involves less lumber for a given span than does conventional framing that includes a number of members such as rafters, ridge, ceiling joists, and collar ties. Also contributing to the efficiency of roof trusses is the fact that they are spaced at 24" centres instead of the 16" spacing of conventional framing members.
2. *speed of erection.* Since trusses are pre-assembled, they can be set in place, the roof covering applied, and the roof completed in much less time than it takes to build a comparable roof in the conventional manner. The fact that no bearing partitions need be built before the roof is framed also speeds this operation.
3. *lower cost.* This may well be the deciding factor when the two roof systems are being considered.
4. *flexibility.* The use of roof trusses allows the partitions to be placed independent of the rafter or ceiling joist. They may even be movable. This

can only be accomplished by providing ceiling framing that requires no centre support.

5. *better and more efficiently designed trusses.* In an effort to provide better and more efficiently designed homes in keeping with the current trend for more open and flexible room arrangements at reasonable cost, architects and builders have made significant improvements in the structural design of houses. One of these major design improvements has been in the field of roof trusses, both in the size and arrangement of the members, and in the fastening devices used to form a positive connection at the joints. The efficient and speedy method of pre-fabrication, transportation, and erection of roof trusses in large quantities has caused a great reduction in the number of man-hours required to frame a trussed roof and a corresponding reduction in cost, thus making their use much more economical than it was formerly.

An example of a roof truss is shown in Figure 19:1.

Trusses, however, have their limitations and are not the answer to all roof framing situations. They lend themselves to mass-produced homes whose roofs have a minimum number of hips and/or valleys. For larger, custom-built homes with individual roof lines, varied pitches, and different hip and valley arrangements, the conventional piece-by-piece roof framing method will best serve the purpose. Also, for smaller, individually built homes, where the floor plan provides for a permanent centre partition wall that can serve as a roof framing support, the builder will doubtless find the conventional roof framing method more convenient.

Although trusses can be used for storey-and-a-half houses, it is generally found to be more economical to use conventional type rafter framing for these. The use of trusses restricts the attic storage space because of their diagonal braces. Both roof framing methods have their place; very often either method can be used to equal advantage.

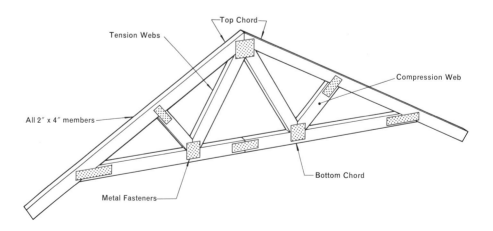

Fig. 19:1 Standard Gable Roof Truss

You will note from Figure 19:1 that the terminology used for roof trusses is not the same as that used for conventional roof framing. The *top chord* corresponds to the rafter, the *bottom chord* to the ceiling joist, and the *web members* to collar ties and braces.

Much of the strength of trusses depends on the secure positive joints at the intersection of the members. If there is any movement at the joints when pressure is applied to the top chord there will be a deflection or sag in either or both the top and bottom chord. This is because the downward pressure will not immediately be transferred along the other members until any slack in the joints has been taken up.

There are several methods of attaching the members at the joints. The first method used is to lap the lumber at the intersection and nail it securely. This, however, permits some movement at the point of nailing. It has been found that a more positive lapped joint can be obtained by using a metal ring connector and bolt as shown in Figure 19:2. The bolt holes are bored through the two lapped members at each joint. The pieces are then separated and a circular groove is cut around all the holes with the special tool shown in Figure 19:2C. The special tapered expansion rings can then be inserted in the grooves in one side of each joint, the top members placed over them and the bolts inserted and tightened.

In most truss ring joints, a 2½″ x ¾″ ring is used. The grooves are cut ⅜″ deep in each member so that the surface of the two pieces touch when the ring is installed between them. The split ring transfers the load and the ½″ machine bolt holds the members in contact with each other and the ring.

Many light trusses used in residential construction have butt joints instead of lapped joints and are sometimes referred to as *monoplane truss* rafters. With this arrangement all the members lie flat in the same plane. Monoplane truss construction provides symmetrical balancing of stresses both within the truss and from one member to another.

The joints can be made secure with the use of ½″ *plywood gussets* nailed and glued to both sides of the butt joints. The gussets must be large enough to cover the entire joint and must be well nailed. A monoplane roof truss with plywood gussets is shown in Figure 19:4.

The same method of truss construction can be followed with metal plate connectors used in place of plywood gussets. The metal plates may be perforated with drilled holes through which nails are driven into the truss members, or they may be stamped in such a way that a series of rectangular shaped holes are punched out and the displaced metal, which is still attached to the plate at one end, is bent into sharp, toothlike spikes. See Figure 19:5. When this plate, called a Gang-Nail®* truss connector plate, is driven or pressed into the wood over the joint, it forms an excellent connector. These plates are made from 14, 18, and 20 gauge metal in a wide range of sizes to suit the joints over which they are placed. A Gang-Nail® truss connector plate made from 14 gauge galvanized steel is shown in Figure 19:5.

* Gang-Nail® is the registered trademark of Automated Building Components, Inc.

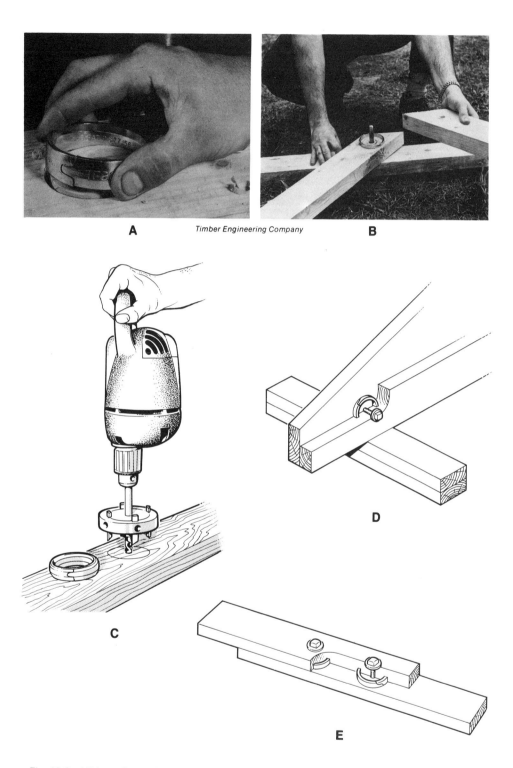

Timber Engineering Company

A

B

C

D

E

Fig. 19:2 (A) Inserting split rings into conforming grooves; (B) Split rings automatically align truss members; (C) Electric drill and combination cutter and drill used for installing the split ring and bolt; (D) Cut-away view of split ring used between top and bottom cord; (E) Cut-away view of split ring used for a lapped joint.

218

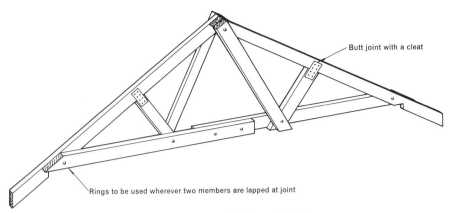

Butt joint with a cleat

Rings to be used wherever two members are lapped at joint

Fig. 19:3   Truss with Lapped Joints

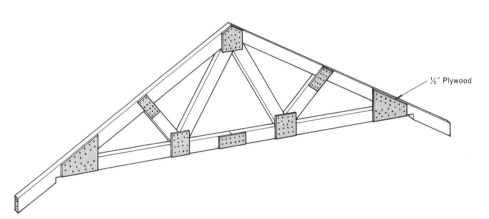

½″ Plywood

Fig. 19:4   Monoplane Roof Truss with Plywood Gussets

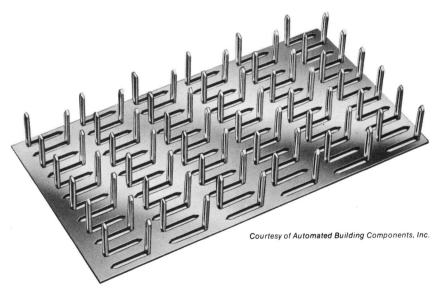

Courtesy of *Automated Building Components, Inc.*

Fig. 19:5   Gang-Nail® Truss Connector Plate

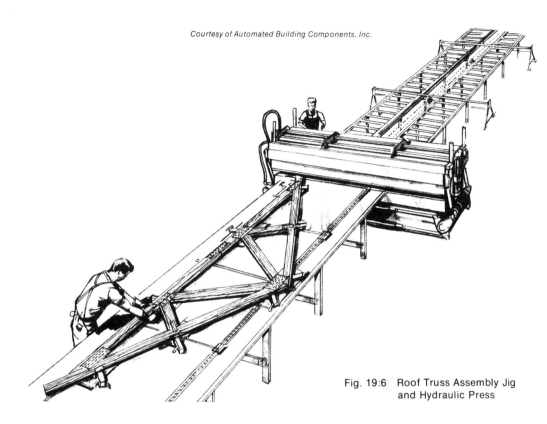

Fig. 19:6   Roof Truss Assembly Jig
and Hydraulic Press

Roof trusses can be made at the building site as the house is being erected, but more often they are pre-fabricated at a central location, trucked to the site, and erected as a completed component, especially if metal Gang-Nail® truss connector plates are to be used. These plates should be pressed into the wood by a large hydraulic press.

For trusses to be efficiently made they should be built in an adjustable metal jig in which all members are clamped in their relative positions while all joints are securely fastened. Since this equipment is both expensive and difficult to move from job to job, many builders find it more economical to purchase roof trusses from firms who specialize in pre-fabricated building units. A roof truss jig and press is shown in Figure 19:6.

For trusses that do not require a press for their assembly, a temporary jig can be made on the subfloor or on an improvised platform by laying out the shape and size of the required truss and nailing blocks around the outline which will accurately locate each member. This arrangement works well, especially when plywood gussets are used over the joints.

Roof trusses are made in many designs, each used for a different roof framing situation. Some of the most frequently used designs are shown in Figure 19:7.

For some time, truss roofs were restricted to gable, flat, or arched roofs. Due to recent developments of improved fastening devices and connector

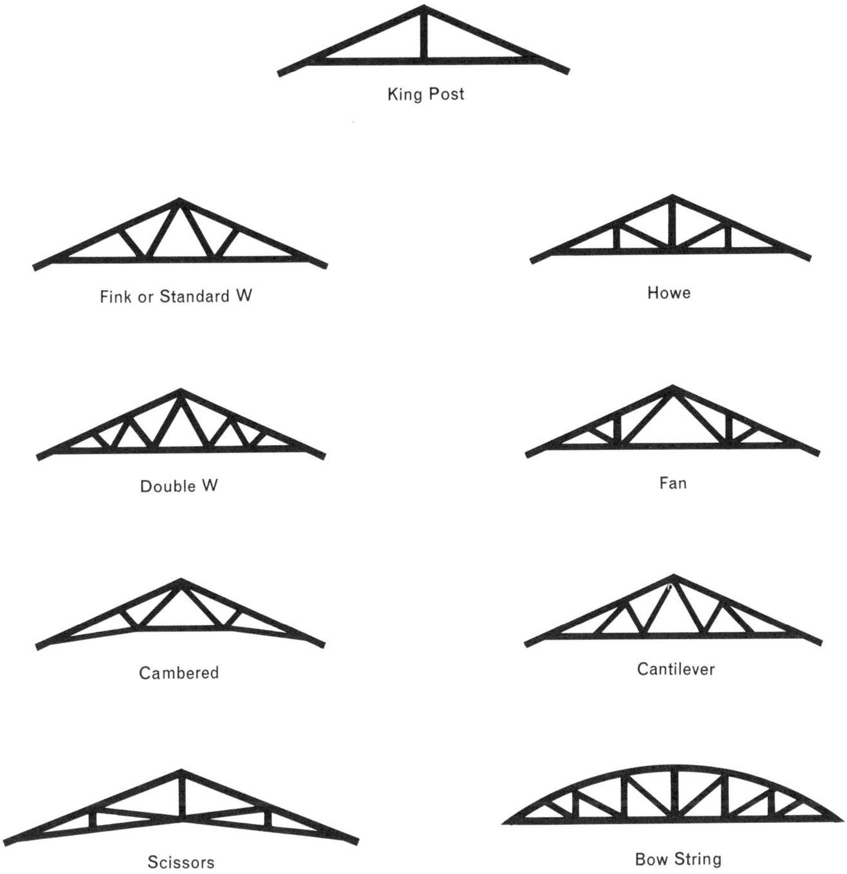

King Post

Fink or Standard W

Howe

Double W

Fan

Cambered

Cantilever

Scissors

Bow String

Fig. 19:7   Truss Designs

Courtesy of Automated Building Components, Inc.

Fig. 19:8   Standard "W" Roof Trusses in Place

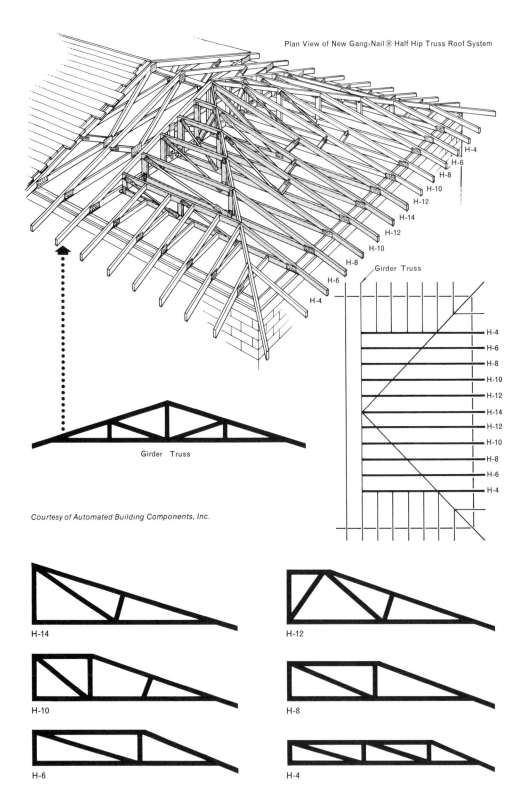

Plan View of New Gang-Nail® Half Hip Truss Roof System

H-4
H-6
H-8
H-10
H-12
H-14
H-12
H-10
H-8
H-6
H-4

Girder Truss

Girder Truss

H-4
H-6
H-8
H-10
H-12
H-14
H-12
H-10
H-8
H-6
H-4

Courtesy of Automated Building Components, Inc.

H-14

H-12

H-10

H-8

H-6

H-4

Fig. 19:9 Hip Truss Roof System

222

Courtesy of Automated Building Components, Inc.

Fig. 19:10   Steel Web Truss

plates, however, several types of hip roof trusses have been designed. One of these, designed for a 28' span, is shown in Figure 19:9. Several basic shapes of trusses are required to form the hip roof framework.

Steel web members with punched metal projections at the ends, similar to those used for the Gang-Nail® plates, are used on hip, flat roof, and floor trusses. They add the required strength but are not as heavy or bulky as wooden braces. A metal web brace is shown in Figure 19:10.

For both residential and industrial construction *floor trusses* can be used to advantage for long clear spans, such as for the recreational area shown in Figure 19:11.

Flat roof trusses are extensively used, especially for commercial and industrial building where a clear unsupported span of 50' or more is required with no posts or load-bearing walls. These trusses may be built with lumber or metal diagonal braces. Both types are illustrated in Figure 19:12.

Some of the other roof designs for which roof trusses are often used are shown in Figures 19:13-19:17.

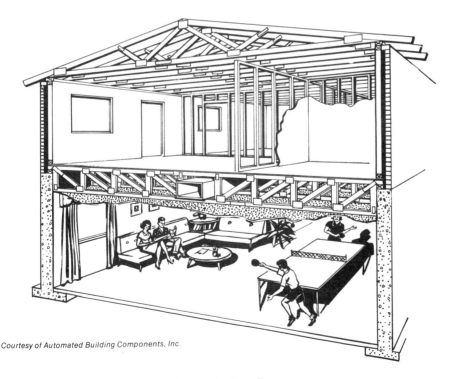

Courtesy of Automated Building Components, Inc.

Fig. 19:11   Floor Trusses

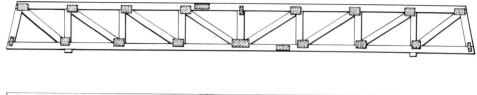

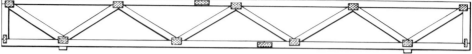

Courtesy of Automated Building Components, Inc.

Fig. 19:12   Flat Roof Trusses

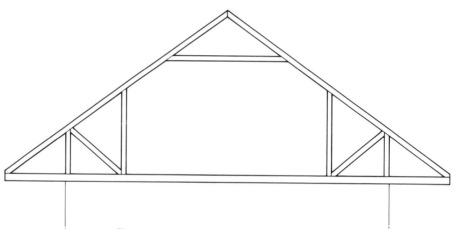

Fig. 19:13   Truss for storey-and-a-half house.

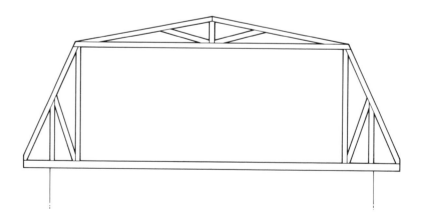

Fig. 19:14   Gambrel-type roof truss used on southern colonial homes.

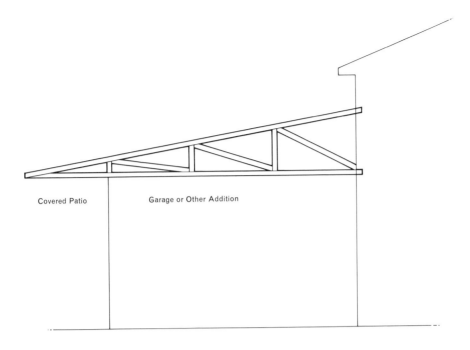

Fig. 19:15 Monopitch truss to be used against the side of the main house.

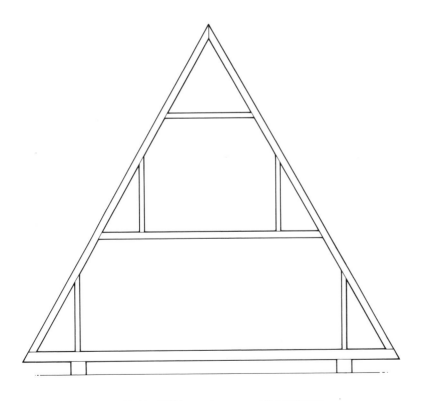

Fig. 19:16 "A"-frame truss used for cottages.

225

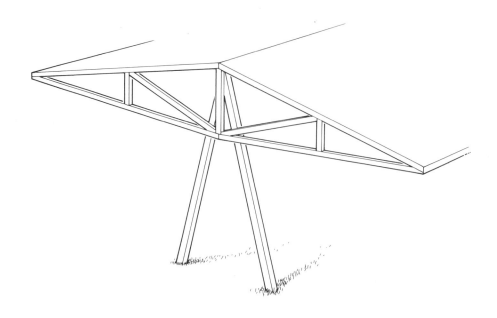

Fig. 19:17   Umbrella truss used for form shelters or in picnic and recreational areas.

The size and the spacing of the truss members can be determined by truss specification tables that are made available through truss manufacturers and other sources. If the span and the pitch are known, the other information can readily be found on the appropriate truss specification table. Such a table is shown in Figure 19:18. This information has been calculated by engineers who have taken into account the span of the building, the pitch of the roof, and the spacing of the trusses. The major factor to be considered, of course, in the design of any truss, is the load to be supported, which is governed by the live and dead load on the top of the roof and the weight of the finished ceiling material attached to the lower chord.

The erection of the light truss used for one-storey houses with spans up to 30′ does not present a problem since no special lifting equipment is necessary. Two men can lift up one end of the truss at a time and rest it on the plate in an inverted position. The truss can then be swung right side up, slid into place, braced, and nailed.

Roofs with greater spans and heavier trusses require some type of lifting device. A truck or other type of portable crane is often used to set the trusses in place. This operation is shown in Figure 19:19.

Trussed rafters can be toe-nailed to the plates with two 4″ spikes in each side of the truss. A better method, however, is the use of metal connectors or anchors, formed and drilled in such a way that nails can be driven through the metal into both the face and the edge of the plate as well as into the chord of the truss, thus making a positive joint between the truss and the wall framework. One type of metal connector is illustrated in Figure 19:20.

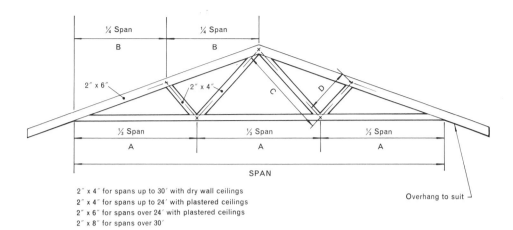

2″ x 4″ for spans up to 30′ with dry wall ceilings
2″ x 4″ for spans up to 24′ with plastered ceilings
2″ x 6″ for spans over 24′ with plastered ceilings
2″ x 8″ for spans over 30′

PITCH	SPAN	A	B	C	D
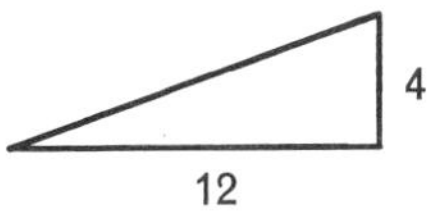 4 / 12	20′	6′8″	5″	4′8″	2′4″
	22′	7′4″	5′6″	5′1⅞″	2′6¾″
	24′	8′	6′	5′7½″	2′9½″
	26′	8′8″	6′6″	6′1¼″	3′½″
	28′	9′4″	7′	6′6¾″	3′3¼″
	30′	10′	7′6″	7′½″	3′6″
	32′	10′8″	8′	7′6¼″	3′8⅞″
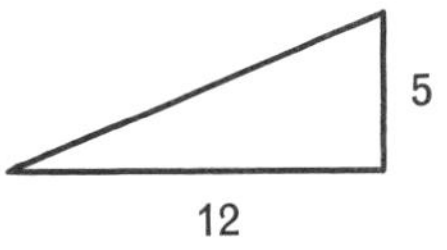 5 / 12	20′	6′8″	5″	5′5⅜″	2′7⅝″
	22′	7′4″	5′6″	5′10″	2′10¾″
	24′	8′	6′	6′4½″	3′2″
	26′	8′8″	6′6″	6′10⅞″	3′5¼″
	28′	9′4″	7′	7′5¼″	3′8½″
	30′	10′	7′6″	7′11¾″	3′11⅝″
	32′	10′8″	8′	8′6″	4′2¾″
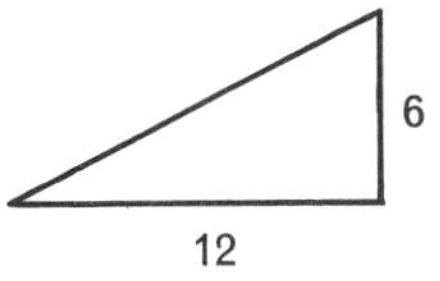 6 / 12	20′	6′8″	5″	5′11¾″	2′11⅝″
	22′	7′4″	5′6″	6′6⅞″	3′3¼″
	24′	8′	6′	7′2⅛″	3′6⅞″
	26′	8′8″	6′6″	7′9¼″	3′10½″
	28′	9′4″	7′	8′4½″	4′2″
	30′	10′	7′6″	8′11¾″	4′5¾″
	32′	10′8″	8′	9′7″	4′9¼″
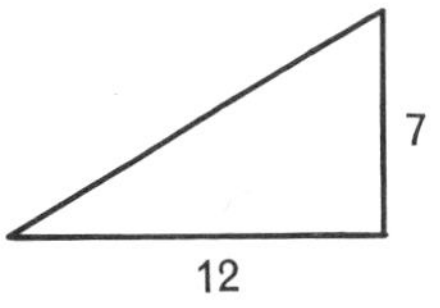 7 / 12	20′	6′8″	5″	6′8¼″	3′3⅞″
	22′	7′4″	5′6″	7′4¼″	3′8″
	24′	8′	6′	8′¼″	4′
	26′	8′8″	6′6″	8′8¾″	4′4″
	28′	9′4″	7′	9′4½″	4′8″
	30′	10′	7′6″	10′½″	5′
	32′	10′8″	8′	10′8½″	5′4″

Fig. 19:18   Truss Rafter Specification Table

Fig. 19:19   Erecting large roof truss with a crane.

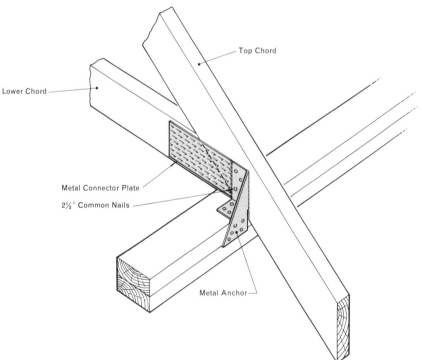

Fig. 19:20   Method of attaching truss to plate using pre-formed metal anchors.

228

LAMINATED BEAMS AND ARCHES

Another type of roof construction that is similar to trusses is *laminated beams and arches,* which are in wide use in commercial, church, and recreational buildings and to a lesser extent in residential construction. Many of the combination wall and roof arches are commonly referred to as trusses, although the principle is quite different. Roof-supporting laminated arches rely for their strength on their size and shape and on the fact that they are made up of layers of quality lumber glued together and shaped in such a way that the load imposed on them is transferred to the walls or to the foundation piers or abutments, the stress travelling through one single member. Trusses, on the other hand, have several members with counteracting stresses working as a series of triangles to carry the load.

The use of solid beams for roof support is not new. They are to be found in some of our oldest buildings, and have proved, over the years, to be an efficient type of construction. It has been only in recent years, however, that engineers have developed reliable adhesives for use in the laminating processes. They have also developed techniques for the economical manufacture of large arches or beams through the use of jigs and forms, on which 1″ or 2″ thicknesses of kiln-dried douglas fir or other lumber are laminated and shaped to any desired size or design. By bonding together many pieces of lumber to form an arch frame that will spring from the foundation or concrete abutment and act as the supporting wall and roof framework, lumber is utilized to its maximum capacity. Such a laminated arch is shown in Figure 19:21A. These arches are stronger than if they were made from sawn solid timbers. It would, of course, be impossible to fabricate many of these shapes from solid timbers. These arches can be successfully manufactured only with the use of expensive special equipment and under controlled conditions. All end joints in individual pieces have scarf joints and no joints in adjacent pieces are placed close to each other. After the arches have been laminated, they are planed to the required thickness. See Figure 19:21 B. They are then sanded and wrapped in plastic. They should not be unwrapped until just before the stain or varnish is applied.

Other designs of laminated roof and wall sections are shown in Figure 19:22.

Many laminated curved or straight roof beams are made to be independent of the side walls. They are attached to the upright supports by bolts, mechanical fasteners, or plywood gussets, thus making solid independent frames. They are set in place to form the structural skeleton of the building. A good example of this type of construction is the arena arch in Figure 19:23.

Rigid Frame Construction

A simpler adaptation of laminated beams and arches is called rigid frame construction. See Figure 19:24A. It is used for farm and light warehouse buildings in which utility and economy are the prime factors to be considered. Solid 2″ stock lumber is used to make rigid pre-assembled wall and roof frames for

229

Engineering Timber Products

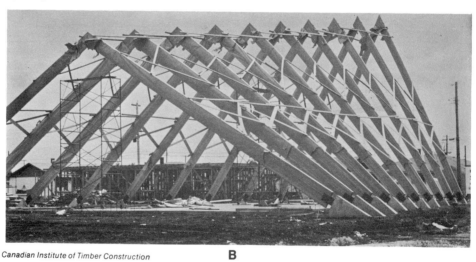

Canadian Institute of Timber Construction **B**

Fig. 19:21 (A) **Laminated Roof** Beams and Supporting Posts; (B) Long Laminated Roof Beams and Supporting Abutments.

230

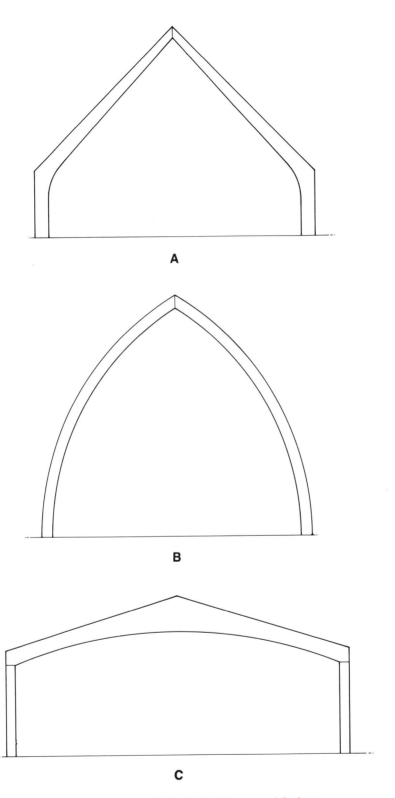

Fig. 19:22   (A), (B), and (C) Laminated Beams and Arches

231

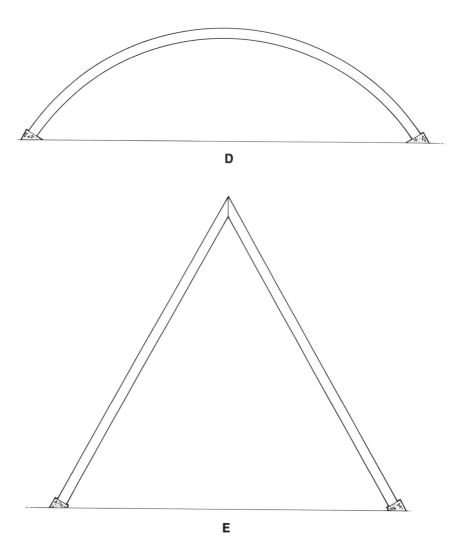

D

E

Fig. 19:22 (D) and (E) Laminated Beams and Arches

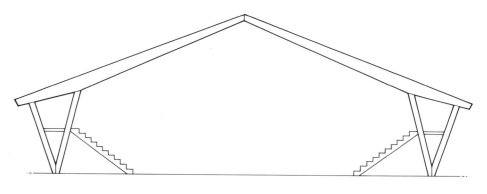

Fig. 19:23 Arena Arch

buildings with a clear span of from 20' to 40'. The span to be supported will govern the width of the lumber and the spacing of the frames. The butt joints at the ridge and between the rafter and wall members are secured by ½" plywood gussets securely nailed on both sides of the frame.

Another type of rigid frame construction which is becoming quite popular for farm storage building is shown in Figure 19:24B.

Straight beams used as horizontal roof supports may be made from solid stock or from several pieces of 2" material bonded together either flat or on edge. The beams may span the width of the house to form a flat roof, which generally extends over the walls to provide an overhang. See Figure 19:25.

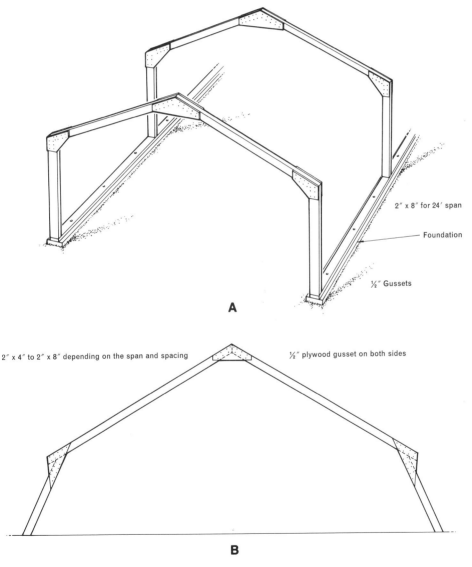

2" x 8" for 24' span

Foundation

½" Gussets

A

2" x 4" to 2" x 8" depending on the span and spacing

½" plywood gusset on both sides

B

Fig. 19:24   (A) Rigid Frame Design Construction for Storage Building;
(B) Rigid Construction Frame.

Fig. 19:25   Transverse beams supporting a flat roof.

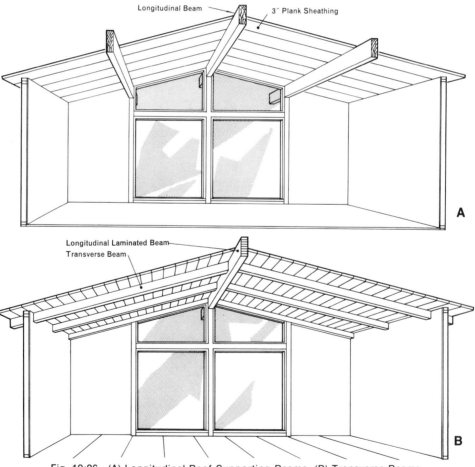

Longitudinal Beam   3˝ Plank Sheathing

A

Longitudinal Laminated Beam
Transverse Beam

B

Fig. 19:26   (A) Longitudinal Roof-Supporting Beams; (B) Transverse Beams.

On a pitched roof, the straight beams may run in a transverse or a longitudinal direction with 2″ or 3″ planking as sheathing. This construction is used for post and beam construction and is illustrated in Figures 19:26A and B.

In modern construction, roof trusses and laminated arches, built in a wide range of styles and configurations that will provide clear spans of from 50′ to 250′, give the architect and the engineer greater scope in design concepts. They enable the builder to erect buildings with increased speed, economy, and efficiency and permit the home owner to utilize the space available to the best advantage.

ASSIGNMENT

1. Define the term *truss* as used in roof construction.
2. Where are trusses used?
3. List five advantages of roof truss construction in residential building.
4. List three limitations in the use of roof trusses.
5. Make a drawing of a standard roof truss and name the parts.
6. Why is it very important that there be no movement at the joints of the truss members?
7. What is the disadvantage of the lapped nailed joint when used in trusses?
8. Describe the metal ring joint used in truss construction.
9. What is meant by a monoplane truss?
10. What material is used for gussets that secure the joints of monoplane trusses?
11. Describe the two types of metal plate connectors used on monoplane trusses.
12. Why are many roof trusses fabricated at a central location and transported to the building site as a completed building component?
13. What arrangement is used if the trusses are to be assembled at the building site?
14. Make a sketch of six truss designs and label them.
15. How many basic truss shapes are required to form the 28′ span hip roof truss arrangement shown in Figure 19:9?
16. Make a drawing of a truss that would be used for the following type of building:
    (a) flat roof; (b) storey-and-a-half; (c) A-frame;
    (d) shelter type (umbrella truss).
17. Make a sketch of a truss for a 26′ roof span with a 5/12 slope, indicating the dimensions and location of the members.
18. What factors must be considered in the design and spacing of roof trusses?
19. (a) How are light trusses for spans up to 30′ erected?
    (b) How are larger trusses erected?
20. How are roof trusses attached to the wall framework?

21. Explain the principle of transferring the roof load to the walls or foundation by:
    (a) trusses;
    (b) laminated arches.
22. What developments have made the manufacture of large laminated arches possible?
23. Make a drawing of four types of laminated arches and label each.
24. Explain the difference between a transverse and a longitudinal beam.

Chapter 20

ROOF SHEATHING

When all the rafters are securely nailed in place and the roof framework is squared and braced, the sheathing can be applied. The type of sheathing used will depend on the following:

(a) the finished roof covering to be used;

(b) the pitch of the roof;

(c) the spacing of the roof-supporting members.

Thicker sheathing must be used with post and beam construction in which the rafters are placed farther apart than in conventionally framed houses.

The type of sheathing most extensively used for modern home construction is ⅜" *fir plywood* in 4' x 8' sheets. Plywood provides a strong, even base on which the finished roof covering can be applied. Although the ⅜" plywood has some tendency to spring between the rafters, it is strong enough to

Plywood Manufacturers of B.C.

Fig. 20:1 Plywood roof sheathing being applied.

support the live and dead load of the roof, when used on standard spaced rafters. Its strength in relation to its thickness is due to the cross-lamination of plies. Some of the other advantages of plywood as a roof sheathing material are (a) its rigidity, which provides bracing and a resistance to racking; (b) its nailing strength: it will adequately hold the shingle nails driven through it, even though they protrude through the underside of the plywood; (c) its economy: cutting waste is minimized because the length of the sheets corresponds with the standard rafter spacing. The use of large sheets not only closes in the building rapidly but represents a saving in labour compared with other types of roof sheathing. Its smooth, flat surface, which is not affected by shrinkage, allows asphalt shingles to lie flat and smooth with no unsightly buckles or raised edges.

The plywood used for roof sheathing should be the exterior type made with waterproof glue. Douglas fir, other western softwoods, and poplar are most often used.

The surface grain of the plywood sheets must be at right angles to the rafters. The end joints of the sheets must be staggered; that is, no joints on adjacent sheets should be on the same rafter. These joints should have at least 1/16" gap to take care of possible swelling or expansion of the sheets.

TABLE 17E
MINIMUM THICKNESSES OF PLYWOOD ROOF SHEATHING

Joist or Rafter Spacing (in.)	Minimum Plywood Thickness	
	With Edges Supported (in.)	With Edges Unsupported (in.)
12	$5/16$	$5/16$
16	$5/16$	$3/8$
20	$3/8$	$1/2$
24	$3/8$	$1/2$

From Residential Standards. Supplement No. 5 to the National Building Code of Canada

The above table indicates the thickness of plywood required for various rafter spacings. It can be noted that some thicknesses of plywood, when used with certain rafter spacings, require edge support to stiffen them. This may be provided by nailing 2" x 2" pieces between the rafters to which the edges of the sheathing can be nailed; or tongue and grooved plywood may be used where the two sheets support each other. Another method of providing edge support is the use of H-clips. These are shown in Figure 20:2.

The plywood sheets should be held in place with 2" common nails spaced 6" apart along the edges and 12" apart along intermediate bearing supports.

Another material used extensively as roof sheathing is *1" lumber*. The individual boards should not be more than 12" wide, as wide stock has a tendency to cup and warp and thus prevents the shingles from lying flat. Square-edged 1" x 6" stock is most often used. The minimum thickness

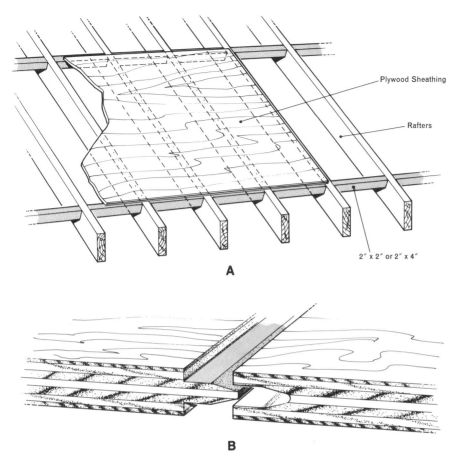

Plywood Sheathing

Rafters

2" x 2" or 2" x 4"

A

B

C

Plywood Manufacturers of B.C.

Fig. 20:2   (A) 2" x 2" used for edge support; (B) Tongue and Grooved Plywood Sheathing;
(C) Plywood must fit snugly into the H-clip.

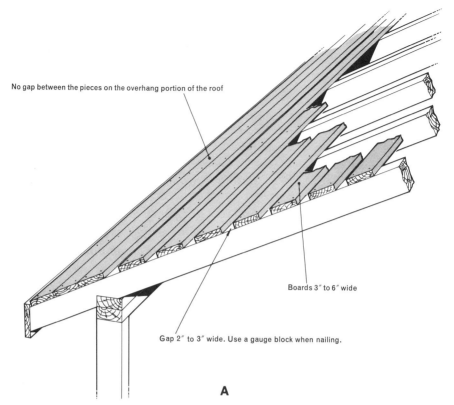

No gap between the pieces on the overhang portion of the roof

Boards 3″ to 6″ wide

Gap 2″ to 3″ wide. Use a gauge block when nailing.

A

Red Cedar Shingle & Handsplit Shake Bureau (B.C.)

B

Fig. 20:3   (A) Open Roof Sheathing; (B) Open Sheathing and Wood Shingles. Closed sheathing used at the overhang.

should be 11/16''; 3/4'' material is generally used. Green lumber of any width should never be used as it will warp and distort the shingles.

When wooden shingles are to be applied, *open sheathing* may be used where boards 1'' x 3'' to 1'' x 6'' are spaced 2'' to 3'' apart. This arrangement is sometimes called a slat deck. Leaving the space between the individual pieces is permissible because wooden shingles are stiff enough to bridge the gaps. This type of sheathing affords a considerable saving of material. The shingle nails must be so placed that they miss the gaps and are driven into the solid wood.

Either plywood or solid lumber sheathing should be started from the bottom of the roof. If the roof is steep, the sheathing should be started from a scaffold; on lower-pitched roofs it is possible to start the sheathing without the aid of a scaffold. When solid lumber is used, pick straight boards for the first row and keep the lower edge up from the top of the plumb cut of the rafter when nailing, as shown in Figure 20:4. In this way, the sheathing will not interfere with the fascia board trim. Drive two 2½'' common nails into each rafter. If the boards are more than 8'' wide use three nails. Let the sheathing project over the gable ends to be cut off later to the desired overhang.

If open sheathing is to be used, a spacer block can be cut to the desired width and used as a gauge when nailing the boards in place.

If the roof is steep, some arrangement must be made to provide footholds for the carpenter while he applies the sheathing. One method is to nail a 2'' x 4'' along the full length of the roof on top of the sheathing every 7' or 8' up the roof as the sheathing progresses. Another method, when solid lumber sheathing is used, is to leave out one row of sheathing board every 6' or 8', nailing these boards temporarily on top of the other sheathing just below the open space. See Figure 20:5. When the roof is completed the boards can be quickly set in the open spaces and securely nailed.

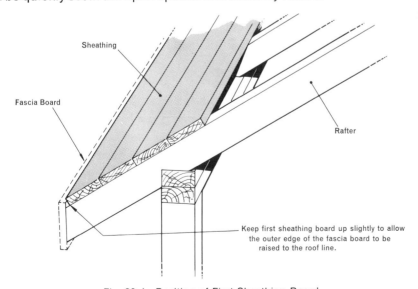

Sheathing

Fascia Board

Rafter

Keep first sheathing board up slightly to allow the outer edge of the fascia board to be raised to the roof line.

Fig. 20:4   Position of First Sheathing Board

241

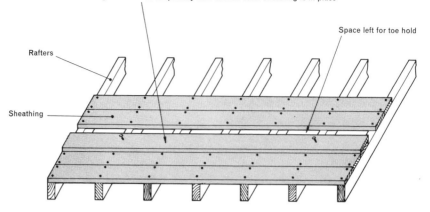

Sheathing board nailed temporarily here until all other sheathing is in place

Space left for toe hold

Rafters

Sheathing

Fig. 20:5   Method of providing a toe-hold when applying sheathing.

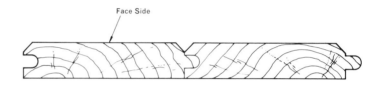

Face Side

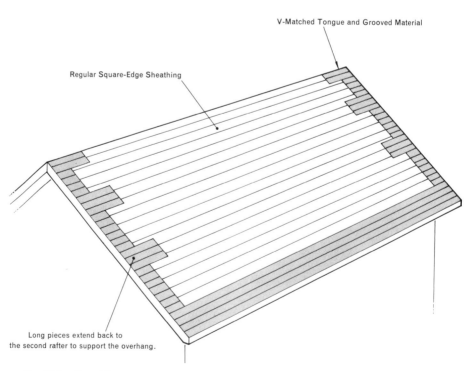

V-Matched Tongue and Grooved Material

Regular Square-Edge Sheathing

Long pieces extend back to
the second rafter to support the overhang.

Fig. 20:6   Sheathing arrangement for an open cornice when V-matched material is used.

242

On houses that have open cornices where the underside of the roof sheathing is exposed to view, a better type or grade of lumber is often used on the overhang portion of the roof, as shown in Figure 20:6. For this purpose tongue and grooved, V-matched material is generally used. The sheathing at the gable overhang is staggered, with some of the pieces extending in to the second set of rafters, in order to support the overhang portion of the roof. (See Figure 20:6.)

In post and beam construction, where the supporting roof rafters are spaced from 4′ to 8′ apart the sheathing material must be heavier than that used in conventional construction with its 16″ to 24″ spacing. Solid cedar 2″ or 3″ thick and 5½″ wide is generally used. Material that is 2″ thick or thicker, when used as roof covering, is generally referred to as "roof decking" and is used mainly on low-pitched or flat roofs.

In many modern homes the roof covering serves the dual purpose of sheathing and exposed ceiling material; the underside of the roof decking may have a finished dressed surface with V-grooved joints. Sometimes grooves are cut in the pieces, as shown in Figure 20:7, to give a combed or serrated surface. This surface, along with the rafters, is generally treated with a stain or varnish finish to make an attractive, natural wood ceiling.

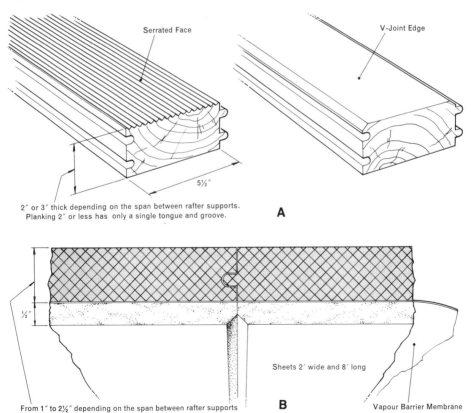

Fig. 20:7 (A) Double Tongue and Grooved Roof Deck Planking; (B) Two-layer combination roof deck and finished ceiling.

There are several ways of adding insulation in this type of roof construction. A rigid type of insulation may be placed between the sheathing and the shingles or other roofing material, as in Figure 20:9. It may also be placed between the rafters and the finished ceiling material which is attached to the underside of the rafter supports.

Another method is to use a heavy, stiff fibreboard roof decking material from 2″ to 3″ thick. This material is manufactured in sheets 2′ x 8′ with tongue and grooved edges. On the underside, a ½″ layer of finely textured white fibreboard is laminated to the main body of the sheet. Between the two layers is a vapour barrier membrane that prevents the transmission of moisture. This roof decking thus combines in one material the triple functions of providing a good insulation, a firm deck to which the waterproof roofing material can be applied, and a finished interior ceiling that is applied in one operation. The rafters and the underside of the roof decking are exposed to view in the same manner as the 2″ cedar decking. A ceiling of this type is illustrated in Figure 20:8.

Two-inch solid wood roof decking should be toe-nailed through the tongue edge of the pieces into the rafters with 4″ spikes. If the decking is 3″ or 4″ thick, 6″ spikes should be used. The toe nails will help to draw the pieces tight, as well as holding them down. The decking should be face-nailed as well as toe-nailed. The decking may be spiked through the width of the piece, with an 8″ spike driven from the tongue edge of one row of planks into the pre-

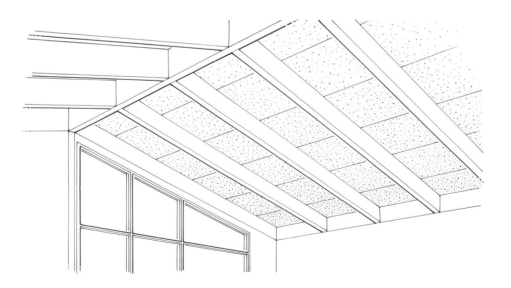

Fig. 20:8   Combination fibreboard roof deck and finished ceiling used in post and beam construction.

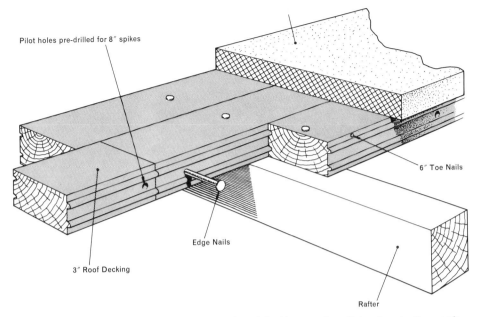

Pilot holes pre-drilled for 8″ spikes

6″ Toe Nails

Edge Nails

3″ Roof Decking

Rafter

Fig. 20:9   Edge-nailed tongue and grooved roof decking used on flat or low-incline roofs.

ceding row as shown in Figure 20:9. The holes must be pre-drilled to prevent the planks from splitting. The spikes should be no more than 30″ apart and no more than 10″ from the ends of the piece; in this way the joints need not be over the rafters.

After the sheathing or roof decking is completed, the material that was allowed to project beyond the required overhang at the ends of the roof must be removed. Mark it to a chalk line and cut it off with a hand or a portable electric saw.

The next operation is to nail the *fascia boards* in place. The fascia boards are the trim members of the roof, extending along the eaves and up the gable ends. They are nailed to the lower plumb cut of the rafters and to the ends of the sheathing at the gables, as shown in Figure 20:10. For pitched roofs with 1″ sheathing the fascia boards usually consist of 1″ x 6″ dressed pine stock as they form a part of the exterior trim, and also provide a sound base to which the eavestrough can be attached. Normally the gable end fascia boards have a shingle mould nailed along their top edge. This adds to their appearance and permits the shingles to extend beyond the fascia, which keeps the water from dripping down the fascia.

Good builders back the finished fascia board up with a sub-fascia, which consists of a 2″ x 4″ spiked directly to the ends of the rafters. This forms a solid straight base to which a finished wood or aluminum fascia can in turn be nailed. The subfascia at the gable end is secured by nails that are driven into it through the sheathing as in Figure 20:10.

If the roof is to have a valley, it should be prepared with a flashing or gutter before shingling is commenced. There are two methods of providing valley

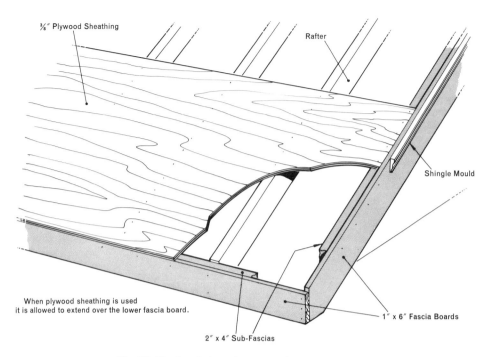

⅜″ Plywood Sheathing

Rafter

Shingle Mould

When plywood sheathing is used
it is allowed to extend over the lower fascia board.

2″ x 4″ Sub-Fascias

1″ x 6″ Fascia Boards

Fig. 20:10   Fascia board construction on gable roof.

flashing; the first is the use of 24 or 26 gauge galvanized metal. See Figure 20:11A. The metal valley flashing can be purchased already cut to width and bent to shape, to fit the valley, or it can be cut from standard sheets, 30″ wide. If the latter, the sheets can be cut lengthwise down the centre making two 15″ strips. To make a straight valley line, the metal should be bent in a sheet metal break. If there is not one available, a fairly straight bend can be made by drawing a line down the centre of the strip and placing the metal between two pieces of 2″ x 4″ and bending on the line. The greater the pitch of the roof, the sharper the bend should be.

Place the metal in the valley starting at the bottom of the roof. Cut the end of the sheet to fit the angle formed by the intersecting fascia boards. Allow the metal to project ½″ past the fascia boards. The strip of metal should be lapped at least 4″ at the joints with a thin layer of caulking compound between them. Nail the strip along the edges at 6″ intervals. It will increase the life of galvanized metal valley flashing if it is painted on both sides before it is installed. If the valley flashing is made of copper, however, there is no need to paint it.

The second method of preparing the valley is to use two layers of heavy, smooth or rock-faced rolled asphalt roofing material. Set the first layer, 18″ wide, in the valley and nail it along the outer edge. Place the second layer, 36″ wide, on top of the first layer, with a coat of asphalt liquid cement between the two. Nail the top layer along the two edges with sufficient nails to hold it in place until the shingles have been applied. As a guide for the shingles,

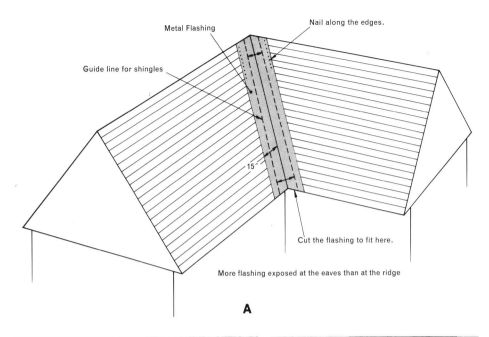

Metal Flashing

Nail along the edges.

Guide line for shingles

15″

Cut the flashing to fit here.

More flashing exposed at the eaves than at the ridge

A

B

Fig. 20:11   (A) Sheet Metal Valley Flashing; (B) Metal formed with a V-shaped ridge in the centre to prevent water running down one slope and under the shingles on the opposite slope.

strike a chalk line at least 4″ from the angle of the valley. The longer the valley, the farther away the line should be from the angle. It is a good idea to make the valley wider at the eaves than at the ridge as there is a greater flow of water over the lower portion of the roof. The valley should taper ⅛″ for every foot of its length. Such a valley flashing is illustrated in Figure 20:12.

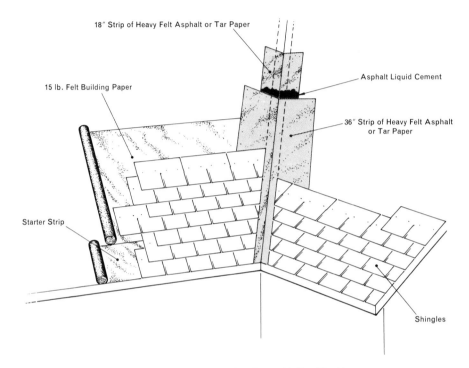

Fig. 20:12   Two-Layer Felt Paper Valley Flashing

ASSIGNMENT

1. List the three factors that will determine the type of roof sheathing to be used on a house.
2. State the advantages of using plywood as a roof sheathing material.
3. Name the wood most often used for sheathing-grade plywood.
4. (a) Why are the end joints of the plywood staggered so that they occur on different rafters?
   (b) Why should a 1/16″ gap be left between the sheets at the end joints?
5. What thickness of plywood should be used on a roof if the rafters are to be spaced on 24″ centres? (The edge joints of the plywood are to be unsupported.)
6. How can edge supports for plywood sheathing be provided?
7. (a) What size nails are used to hold the plywood sheathing in place?
   (b) How are they spaced?

8. (a) What is the usual width and thickness of solid lumber used for roof sheathing?

   (b) Why should very wide or green lumber not be used as roof sheathing?

9. Explain what is meant by open sheathing.

10. How can a foothold be provided to enable the carpenter to nail sheathing on a steep roof?

11. By using a drawing, show how the sheathing is arranged when solid lumber is used on a roof with an open cornice.

12. (a) Describe the type of roof sheathing that is generally used in post and beam construction.

   (b) Why is this type used?

13. List the three methods of providing insulation for a flat roof where 2″ roof decking is used.

14. List the advantages of using heavy fibreboard sheathing on low-pitched roofs.

15. Describe how plank decking is held in place.

16. (a) What are fascia boards?

   (b) How are they held in place?

17. Make a sectional drawing of a gable roof showing the fascia, rafter, and sheathing in their correct locations.

18. Describe the procedure that is followed to install heavy felt paper valley flashing on a roof that is to be shingled.

19. If the exposed portion of the valley is 8″ wide at the ridge, how wide should it be at the eaves if the valley is 18′ long?

20. (a) What should be the width of the metal strips used for valley flashing?

   (b) What metals are used for valley flashing?

Construction Safety (see pages 399-417)

21. (a) What is meant by a rolling scaffold?

   (b) What is meant by a scaffold trap?

Chapter 21

ROOF COVERING

SHINGLES

The roof sheathing, or decking, provides a strong, even surface to which some form of waterproofing material must be added to complete the roof.

Asphalt Shingles

In most parts of our country the popular material used for this purpose on residential homes is composition asphalt shingles.

Standard Asphalt Shingle. Asphalt shingles are manufactured in many sizes, shapes, weights, and colours, the most common type being the 3 in 1, 12" x 36" strip shingle shown in Figure 21:1. This type of shingle has a heavy felt base in which is embedded fire-resistant rock granules. The shingles are made in a wide range of colours that may be solid or two-tone.

The location of the nails is indicated on the sketch below.

The standard weight of these shingles is 210 lbs. per *square* (enough shingles to cover 100 square feet).

These 3 in 1 shingles provide a double thickness of shingle on the complete surface of the roof, which is considered sufficient covering for roofs with 1/6 pitch (4" in 12") or steeper.

Low-Slope Asphalt Shingle. For roofs with pitches as low as 1/12 (2" in 12"), special low-slope shingles measuring 18" x 36" are manufactured. Since the amount of shingle (usually 5") exposed to the weather is the same as with the

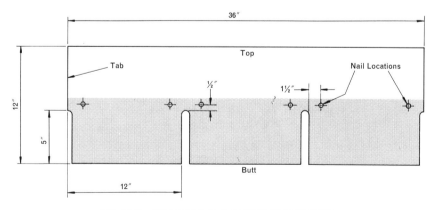

Fig. 21:1   Standard 3 in 1 Asphalt Strip Shingle

12″ x 36″ standard shingle, low-slope shingles will provide three thicknesses of shingle over the entire roof. The butts of both types of shingles are sealed down to prevent the shingles from being blown up in wind storms. Standard shingles have patches of asphalt adhesive, just above the slots, which adheres to the butt of the shingle put over it. The butts of the low-slope shingles must be cemented down as shown in Figures 21:2A and B. The first row of standard shingles must also be cemented down.

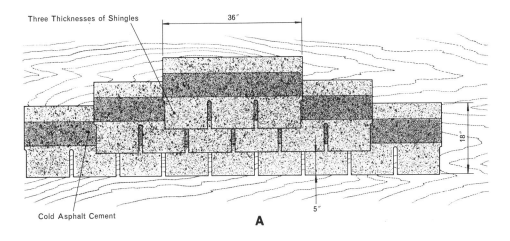

Fig. 21:2   (A) 3 in 1 Low-Slope Strip Asphalt Shingle (cemented down); (B) Standard 3 in 1 Strip Asphalt Shingles.

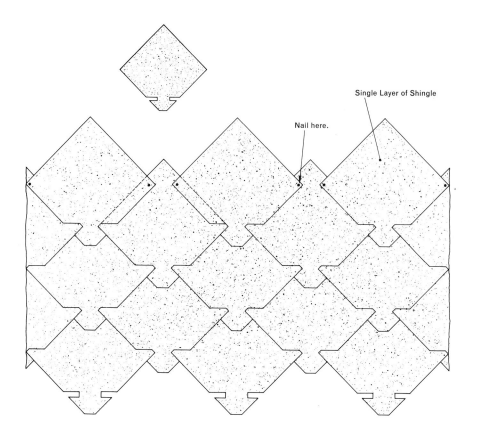

Fig. 21:3   Interlocking asphalt shingles.

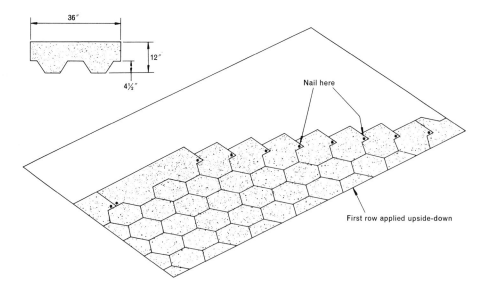

Fig. 21:4   Two-tab hexagon strip shingles.

Interlocking Asphalt Shingle. An interlocking shingle is manufactured that has a tab that fits under the shingle below it, thus holding the lower edge of the shingle down tight. An example of interlocking shingles is shown in Figure 21:3.

A lighter type of shingle is the two- or three-tab hexagon shingle, which is shown in Figure 21:4.

HOW TO ESTIMATE THE QUANTITY OF ASPHALT SHINGLES REQUIRED

1. Determine the area of the roof in square feet. (For a hip and valley roof this calculation can best be done by breaking the roof area up into rectangles and triangles.) To this area add:
   (a) ½ square foot per running foot of eave for the double starter row.
   (b) 1 square foot per running foot of ridge and hip for the cap shingles.
   (c) ½ square foot per running foot of valley for the shingles wasted in cutting.
2. Divide the total by 100 to arrive at the number of squares required. Make your calculations to the nearest bundle (there are three bundles to the square in most types of asphalt shingles).

HOW TO APPLY ASPHALT SHINGLES

Before shingling, be sure that all the sheathing has been well nailed and that the roof is dry, clean, and free from loose material. It is recommended that before the shingles are applied, a layer of asphalt waterproof 15 lb. felt paper be laid in horizontal strips over the entire roof with a 2″ lap at the joints. This is an added protection and provides some degree of extra insulation.

A 6″ starter strip of galvanized metal, painted on both sides, is attached to the lower edge of the roof. This serves as a drip edge and also as a stiff base to support the overhang portion of the shingles. It should project ½″ out past the fascia board. A second starter strip, at least 18″ wide and made of rock-faced 90 lb. "rolled roofing", is placed on top of the first starter strip. It should be laid along the eaves with its lower edge flush with the metal drip edge.

Another method of starting the shingles at the eaves is to lay a double course of shingles: the first thickness laid upside-down and the top shingles laid in the regular manner. See Figure 21:5B.

On a straight roof that has no valleys, start the shingling by snapping a chalk line from the ridge to the eaves in the exact centre of the roof. To lay the first shingle, place it on the starter strip with one of the cut-outs directly over the line layout and with the butt even with the lower edge of the starter strip. See Figure 21:5A. If a double thickness of shingles is to be used rather than a starter strip, proceed as shown in Figure 21:5B. Place the succeeding shingles with the cut-outs down and the ends barely touching one another. The shingle cut-outs on alternate rows or *courses* should be over the line. On

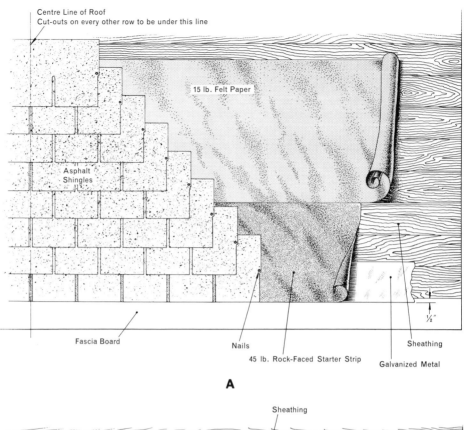

Centre Line of Roof
Cut-outs on every other row to be under this line

15 lb. Felt Paper

Asphalt
Shingles

½"

Fascia Board

Nails

Sheathing

45 lb. Rock-Faced Starter Strip

Galvanized Metal

A

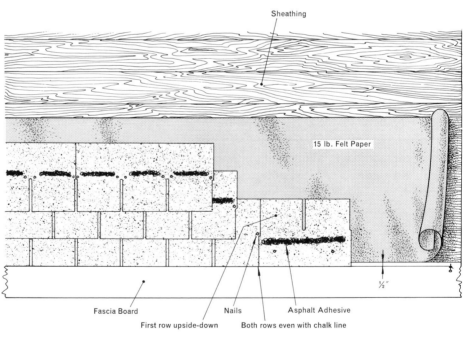

Sheathing

15 lb. Felt Paper

½"

Fascia Board

Nails

Asphalt Adhesive

First row upside-down

Both rows even with chalk line

B

Fig. 21:5   (A) Asphalt shingle roof; (B) A method often used for starting asphalt shingles at the eaves.

254

A

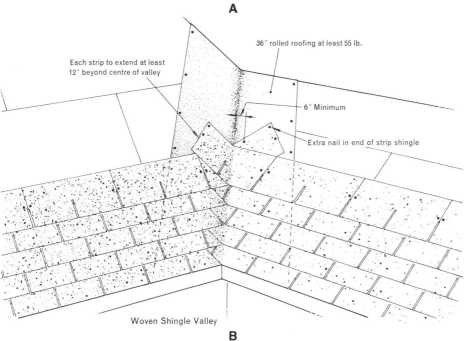

36″ rolled roofing at least 55 lb.

Each strip to extend at least
12″ beyond centre of valley

6″ Minimum

Extra nail in end of strip shingle

Woven Shingle Valley

B

Fig. 21:6 (A) Felt Roofing Paper and Sheet Metal Valley Flashing (one section of the roof
shingled); (B) The method shown above is sometimes used where the asphalt
strip shingles are bent around the valley. Heavy roofing felt must be placed in
the valley first. All shingle joints and nails must be kept well away from the
centre of the valley.

255

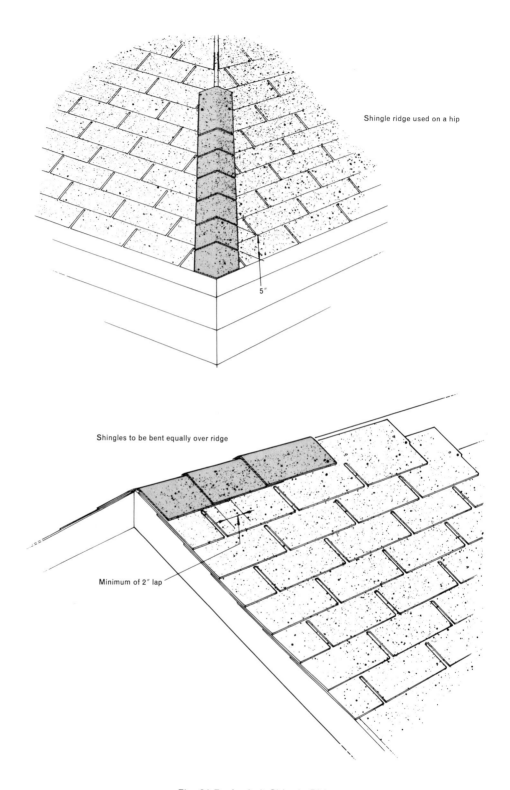

Shingle ridge used on a hip

5″

Shingles to be bent equally over ridge

Minimum of 2″ lap

Fig. 21:7   Asphalt Shingle Ridge

256

the other rows the line should be exactly in the centre of one of the shingle sections. It is important for the sake of appearance that cut-outs be kept exactly in line from the eaves to the peak. It is a good idea to put a spot of asphalt cement under each section of the first course of shingles to cement them to the starter strip. Most asphalt shingles are self-aligning. When starting a new course, keep the lower edge of the butt even with the tops of the cut-outs of the course below it. To check this alignment and to make sure that the rows are kept straight, snap a chalk line every six or eight courses, and run the shingles to this line. Nail the shingles as shown in Figure 21:5A. Start from the centre of the shingle and work towards the ends to prevent buckling. For a new roof use large-headed 1″ galvanized nails.

On a roof that has a valley, start the shingles from the outer edge of the roof. Never start the rows of shingles from a valley or a hip. Figure 21:6A shows the shingles that have been cut to a line at the valley flashing. Figure 21:6B illustrates an alternate shingle arrangement sometimes used at the valley.

When the ridge is reached, the top of the last row of shingles can either be cut or bent over the peak. When the other side of the roof has been shingled, an asphalt shingle ridge is generally applied. The individual sections are cut from the complete 3 in 1 shingle and nailed to the ridge, as shown in Figure 21:7.

There are other types of asphalt shingles that require somewhat different methods of application from the method described here. However, the manufacturer always gives explicit instructions, and these should be followed closely.

Wood Shingles

The first type of shingles that was used in this country to keep roofs weathertight dates back to pioneer times, when hand-split wooden shingles, though rough, uneven, and of varying thickness, served to keep the weather out of the log cabin.

Wooden shingles are still extensively used today to provide tight, long-wearing roofs, presenting an attractive natural wood appearance that blends well with many types of architecture. Shingles are now machine sawn to a uniform thickness in varying widths with parallel edges. The standard lengths are 16″, 18″, and 24″; the thickness tapers from 7/16″ at the butt to 1/16″ at the top. Most wood shingles are sawn from red cedar.

The length of the shingle exposed to the weather depends on:
(a) the pitch of the roof;
(b) the length of the shingles.

The recommended maximum exposure to the weather for wood shingles on roofs with a ¼ pitch and steeper is:
16″ shingles 5″;
18″ shingles 5½″;
24″ shingles 7½″.

Fig. 21:8   An Attractive Wood Shingle Application

In general the flatter the roof the less shingle exposure is permitted; however, wood shingles are seldom used on roofs with less than ¼ pitch, because the water does not run off the roof fast enough.

Wood shingles are packed in bundles, four of which will cover one square. There are various grades of shingles. The top grades are made from clear edge-grained stock; the lower grades, while they may contain knots, are clear for 6″ from the butt.

Shakes

Shakes are similar to wood shingles but they are thicker and usually longer. Instead of being sawn they are split so that they have a rough or serrated surface, which gives the house a rustic appearance. They may be the same thickness throughout or they may be tapered. Shakes generally have a greater area exposed to the weather than shingles. A split shake is shown in Figure 21:9A.

258

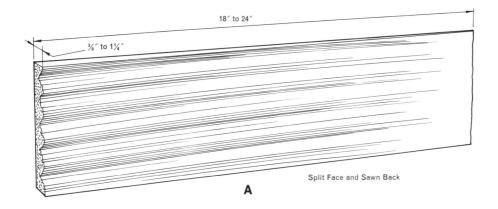

18″ to 24″

³⁄₈″ to 1¼″

Split Face and Sawn Back

A

B

Red Cedar Shingle & Handsplit Shake Bureau (B.C.)

Fig. 21:9   (A) Cedar Shake; (B) An example of an application of cedar shakes.

259

HOW TO APPLY WOOD SHINGLES

1. Stretch a chalk line the full length of the roof, parallel with the fascia, ¾″ out from the surface.
2. Lay the first row of shingles with the butt ends just touching the line. Nail as shown in Figure 21:10.
3. Lay another row of shingles directly on top of the first row, making sure that the side joints in the second row are at least 1½″ away from those below it.
4. Nail a strip of wood ½″ thick temporarily to the fascia board or shingle moulding at the gable end to serve as a guide for the overhang of the shingles here.
5. Lay the succeeding rows as shown. The correct amount of shingle exposure can be gauged by laying the shingles to a straight board of the same width as the required exposure or to a struck chalk line. Some roofers use a shingle hatchet to gauge this distance, but this is not considered as accurate a method as the use of a straight-edge or chalk line. A shingle hatchet is shown in Figure 21:11.
6. Continue laying the courses of shingles up the roof to the ridge. Nail the shingles with 1¼″ galvanized, rust-resistant shingle nails in the manner illustrated in Figure 21:10. The butt of the top course should be within 10″ of the ridge.
7. The ridge covering is usually made with narrow wood shingles as shown in Figure 21:12A and B. Sometimes, however, a solid wood or metal ridge is used as in Figure 21:12C and D.

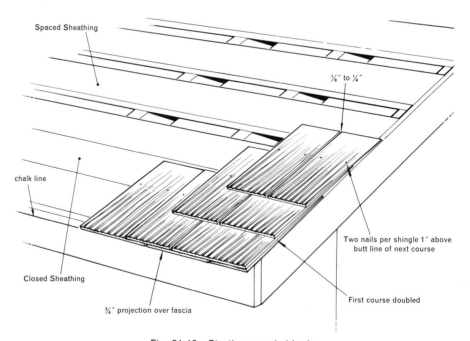

Spaced Sheathing

⅛″ to ¼″

chalk line

Two nails per shingle 1″ above butt line of next course

Closed Sheathing

¾″ projection over fascia

First course doubled

Fig. 21:10 Starting wood shingles.

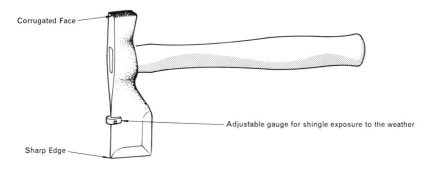

Corrugated Face

Adjustable gauge for shingle exposure to the weather

Sharp Edge

Fig. 21:11   The sharp edges are used for splitting and fitting the shingles. The gauge on the side of the blade can be placed against the butt of the shingle on one course to locate the height of the shingles in the next course.

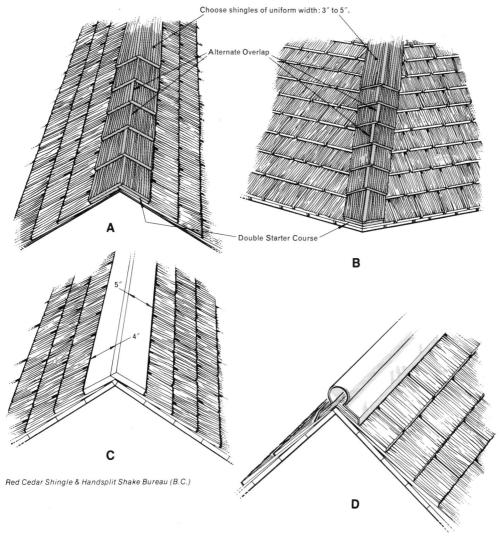

Choose shingles of uniform width: 3″ to 5″.

Alternate Overlap

Double Starter Course

A

B

5″

4″

C

Red Cedar Shingle & Handsplit Shake Bureau (B.C.)

D

Fig. 21:12   (A) Ridge shingle covering; (B) Hip shingle covering; (C) 1″ Lumber Ridge; (D) Galvanized metal ridge.

261

Composition shingles made from asbestos cement are often used as roof covering. Asbestos shingles, often referred to as imitation slate, are made as a hard, stiff slab, in several colours, with pre-punched nail holes. Any cutting done on the job must be done with a special guillotine cutter obtainable from the supplier. These shingles are heavier and more expensive per square than other shingles, but they have the advantage of being more fire-resistant and longer-wearing.

ROOF FLASHING

Where a shingled roof area meets a vertical surface such as a wall or a chimney, sheet metal "flashing" is required. It is generally made of 20 gauge galvanized iron or, on better homes, of copper. Flashing causes the water to flow from a vertical surface onto the roof surface instead of running under the shingles. Flashing is also required around dormer windows and at other places on the roof where the ordinary process of shingling will not make the roof completely waterproof.

Base Flashing

Where a sloping roof intersects a chimney or a wall, two types of flashing are required. The first is a *base flashing* that consists of pieces of metal, approximately 6" x 8", bent to the correct angle. One piece is used under each course of shingles, as illustrated in Figure 21:13.

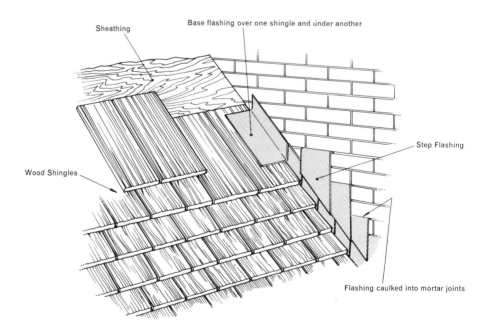

Fig. 21:13   Roof flashing at the intersection of a sloping roof and a vertical brick wall.

Step Flashing

The second type, called *step flashing*, consists of individual pieces cut to suit the brick courses and bent to fit into the mortar joints, in which each piece is embedded in caulking compound. It laps over the base flashing at the lower end of the wall or chimney, to form a neat, weather-tight roof and wall or chimney intersection.

Saddles

The area around the chimney that is most vulnerable to water leakage and that requires the greatest care in flashing is the upper portion. To prevent water or snow from collecting between the roof and the chimney, a saddle is used. A saddle is especially necessary if the chimney is situated on the lower part of a sloping roof. On a small chimney a one-piece saddle is used to deflect the water in two directions around the chimney. It can be laid out with a framing square, cut, and bent to shape before it is placed on the roof. The developed shape is shown in Figure 21:14, and the saddle in place, in Figure 21:15.

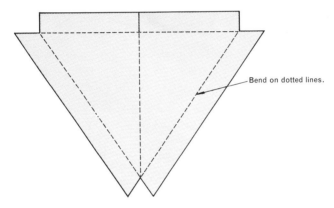

Bend on dotted lines.

Fig. 21:14 Developed shape of saddle, sometimes called a cricket.

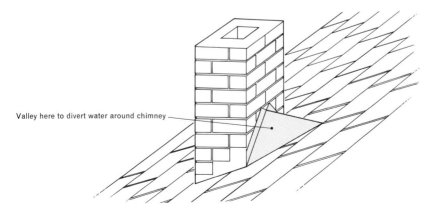

Valley here to divert water around chimney

Fig. 21:15 Saddle in place.

A saddle for a large chimney may consist of a wooden frame covered with metal, with soldered joints, or it may be shingled with two short valleys to divert the water around the chimney.

A piece of apron flashing used at the lower side of the chimney is shown in Figure 21:16.

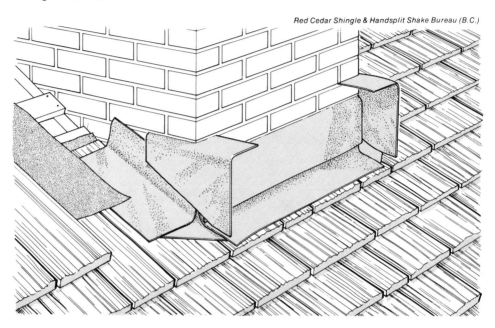

Fig. 21:16   Double flashing used at the lower part of a chimney on a cedar shake roof.

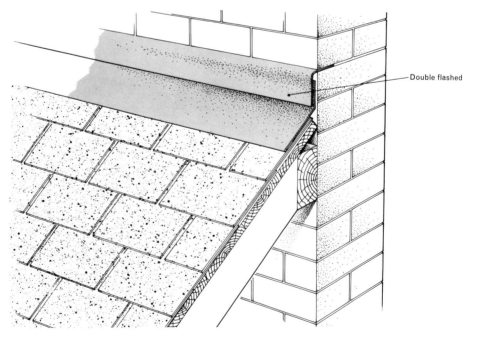

Double flashed

Fig. 21:17   Flashing between a sloping roof and a vertical wall.

264

Where a shed roof meets a vertical wall double flashing is usually used. See Figure 21:17.

Figure 21:18 shows a dormer window sill that rests directly on the roof. With such a window the flashing is often run under the sill and bent up on the inside to prevent water from blowing under it.

These are only some of the applications of flashing that are used on modern roofs. Others follow the same principles.

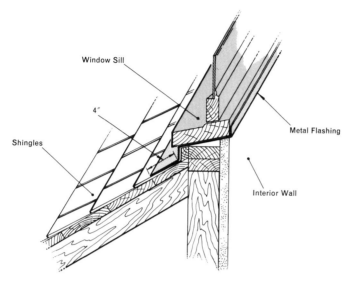

Fig. 21:18   Dormer Window Sill Flashing

BUILT-UP ROOFS

A built-up roof consists of several layers of water-resistant building material other than shingles that are used on flat or low-pitched roofs. They may include such materials as:
(a) rolled rock-faced heavy felt paper;
(b) several layers of felt paper alternated with layers of hot tar or asphalt. The top layer should be of tar or asphalt;
(c) heavy felt paper base with tar and gravel or finely crushed stone on top;
(d) metal roof covering consisting of galvanized metal or copper with soldered joints.

Rolled Rock-Faced Roofing
This type of roofing is similar to the material from which asphalt shingles are made, except that it is lighter and is made in a continuous roll, generally 36″ wide. It is manufactured in several colours. A similar roof can be made by using a heavy black tar paper, which may vary in weight from 50 to 150 lbs. per square. This material is often used on more or less semi-permanent buildings, as the cost is considerably less per square than for the other types of roof covering.

The single-thickness rolled roofing may be used on roofs with a 2″ in 12″ pitch or greater. The strips may be run either parallel to the ridge or at right angles to it. All joints should be lapped at least 2″, with a thin layer of semi-liquid asphalt or tar between the two layers. Use 1″ large-headed galvanized or other rust-resistant nails at 2″ intervals along the seams. Start nailing from the centre of the strip and work the wrinkles toward the ends. An application of rolled roofing is shown in Figure 21:19.

Built-up Felt and Tar Roofs

For roofs with 2″ or less incline per foot, a permanent waterproof roof can be made by alternating layers of asphalt felt paper and mopped-on coats of hot asphalt. Hence the term *"built-up roof"*. The layers of felt paper are referred to as plies and the combined thickness of all roofing materials is called the roof *"mat"*.

Before starting, the roof deck should be inspected to see that it is dry and clean and that there are no loose or badly warped boards. Any knot holes or other small openings should be protected with pieces of sheet metal to prevent the felt from being broken when the roof is walked on.

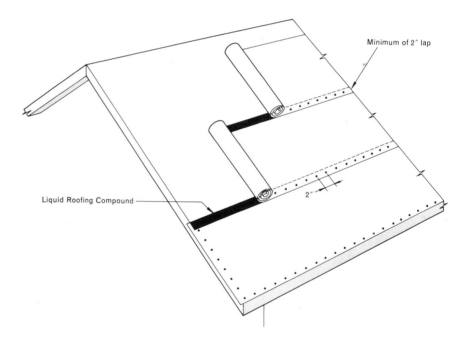

Minimum of 2″ lap

Liquid Roofing Compound

2″

Fig. 21:19   Single Thickness of Rolled Roofing

HOW TO APPLY A FIVE-PLY BUILT-UP ROOF

1. A layer of 45 lb. asphalt felt paper in 36″ strips should be laid over the entire roof. This is referred to as the base sheet. Run the strips at right angles to the slope of the roof. The joints should be lapped 3″ with a

layer of asphalt cement between the two layers of felt. Nail each strip as it is applied at 6″ intervals along the joints as well as two parallel rows spaced 12″ apart. See Figure 21: 20A. Start the nailing from the centre of the strip using 1″ large-head galvanized nails.

2. At the lower edge of the roof and parallel to the eaves, spread a layer of hot asphalt 12″ wide over the base sheet. The asphalt should be mopped on with a roofing mop. Lay a 12″ strip of 15 lb. felt over the hot liquid asphalt, using a stiff, dry push broom to embed the felt into the asphalt.

3. Continue in the same manner with the full 36″ strip. Lap each strip 24½″ over the preceding strips with a coat of hot asphalt between them as well as a coat over the top ply, as shown in Figure 21:20A. Nail the upper edge of each strip at 12″ intervals. The completed roof will then be composed of one base sheet, three thicknesses of light felt, and four coats of liquid asphalt. No two pieces of felt paper should be touching each other; they should be bonded together with the hot asphalt.

The same type of roof can be applied by using a tar-based felt paper and liquid cold tar. Asphalt and tar-based bitumen roofing materials should never be mixed or put next to each other.

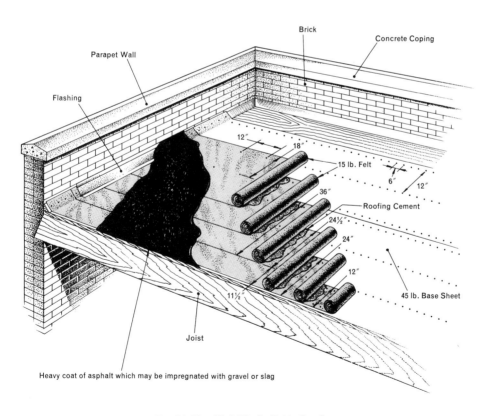

Fig. 21:20   (A) 5-Ply Built-Up Roof

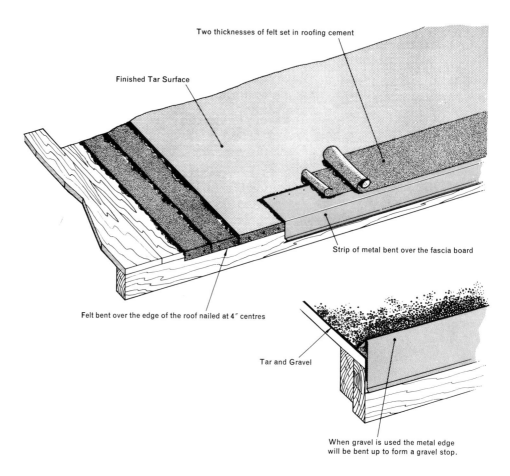

Two thicknesses of felt set in roofing cement

Finished Tar Surface

Strip of metal bent over the fascia board

Felt bent over the edge of the roof nailed at 4″ centres

Tar and Gravel

When gravel is used the metal edge will be bent up to form a gravel stop.

Fig. 21:20   (B) Treatment of the roofing material at the edge of a flat roof.

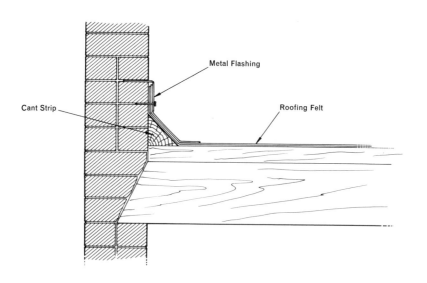

Metal Flashing

Cant Strip

Roofing Felt

Fig. 21:21   Cant strip and flashing at parapet wall.

Heavy Felt Paper Base with Tar and Gravel or
Finely Crushed Stone On Top

A better type of built-up roof can be obtained by spreading a layer of fine crushed stone, slag, or gravel over a heavy coat of hot asphalt or cold tar. This method has the advantage of providing a roof that will withstand more wear from weather and walking. However, it requires a heavier framework to support it as the gravel or crushed stone will add from 300 to 400 lbs. per square. Many modern bungalows use this type of roof with a finely crushed pure white limestone to lower the roof temperature and to create an attractive appearance. On a hot day the temperature of a black roof will be twice that of a white roof, because the black surface absorbs more heat.

There are many other types and variations of built-up roofs being used on both residential and commercial buildings. However, the one shown in Figure 21:20A is similar in principle to most other types.

When a built-up roof meets a vertical wall such as the one shown in Figure 21:21, where a low parapet wall extends above the roof, a "cant strip" should be used. This strip runs the full length of the wall, resting on the sheathing and against the wall. It is cut at an angle to support the felt roofing paper at the angle where it is rolled up the wall a short distance. This prevents the paper from being punctured at this point. The roof should be flashed along the wall as illustrated in the sketch.

Metal Roof Covering

Over door entrances and bay windows as well as on some other parts of the roof, sheet metal is used. All seams should be soldered. The metal used is generally a light-gauge galvanized iron or copper.

Fig. 21:22 Copper roof on a bay window.

269

ASSIGNMENT

Asphalt Shingles

1. Make a drawing of a 3 in 1 asphalt shingle showing the dimensions and the nail locations.
2. (a) What type of shingles would be used on a 1/12 pitch roof?
   (b) How do these shingles differ from those used on steeper roofs?
3. How many squares of shingles would be required to cover both sides of the gable roof shown below?

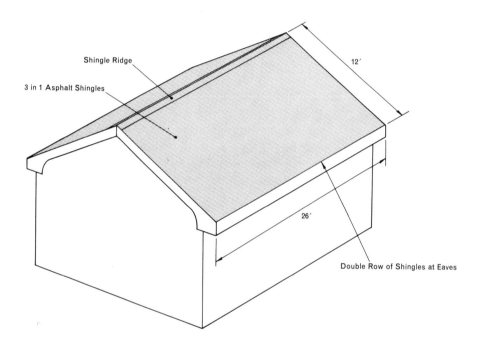

4. What precaution is taken to prevent 3 in 1 asphalt shingles from being damaged in a wind storm?
5. Explain the term *interlocking* shingle.
6. There are two building materials that are often used over the sheathing and under the first course of asphalt shingles. Describe the purpose of these materials and how they are applied.
7. How are the slots in asphalt shingles kept in line from the eaves to the ridge?
8. Why should the shingles be nailed from the centre to the ends?
9. How is an asphalt shingle ridge applied?

Wooden Shingles

10. (a) Into what lengths are wooden shingles sawn?

(b) How much do wooden shingles taper?
11. How much of a 16″ shingle should be exposed to the weather if it is used on a ⅓ pitch roof?
12. How do shakes differ from wooden shingles?
13. Describe the procedure in laying the first course of wooden shingles on a roof.
14. List three methods of gauging the correct shingle exposure to the weather when laying wooden shingles.
15. Make a sketch of three types of ridge coverings used on wooden shingle roofs.
16. List two advantages and two disadvantages of asbestos roof shingles.

Flashing

17. (a) What purpose does flashing serve?
    (b) Where is it used?
    (c) What type of metal is used for flashing?
18. Make a sketch of a roof and chimney intersection and show:
    (a) the base flashing;
    (b) the step flashing;
    (c) the chimney saddle.
19. How is a dormer window whose sill rests on the roof flashed?

Built-up Flat Roofs

20. List the materials used on flat or low-pitched built-up roofs.
21. What type of roof covering is often used on non-permanent buildings?
22. (a) What type of nails is used on rolled roofing?
    (b) How far apart are they spaced?
23. What type of roofing should be used on a roof with less than a 1/12 pitch?
24. Explain what is meant by a four-ply built-up roof.
25. List the advantages and the disadvantages of using crushed stone or slag on a built-up roof.
26. (a) What is a cant strip?
    (b) Why is it used?
27. List the roof areas that often have a metal covering.
28. How are the joints of metal roof coverings sealed?

Chapter 22

ROOF CORNICES

The *cornice*, often called the *eaves*, is that part of the roof that overhangs the wall. Well-designed, properly built cornices are both ornamental and functional. They serve as a protection for the wall by deflecting rain-water and by shading the upper portion of the walls and windows from direct sunlight. Cornices add to the appearance of a building by carrying out the roof lines and providing a neat finish to the exterior trim of the house. The character of the house design is often influenced by the roof overhang. The cornice also provides a flat, vertical surface to which the eavestrough can be attached.

There are a great many types and styles of cornice arrangements to suit different architectural designs. For this reason there is no standard construction that can be described for building cornices. There are, however, some basic details common to all types that can be noted in the illustrations and descriptions that follow.

The cornice that extends up the gable end of a house is referred to as the *rake cornice*. A *return cornice* is that part of the eave cornice that extends around the corner and along the end wall for a short distance, as shown in Figure 22:1.

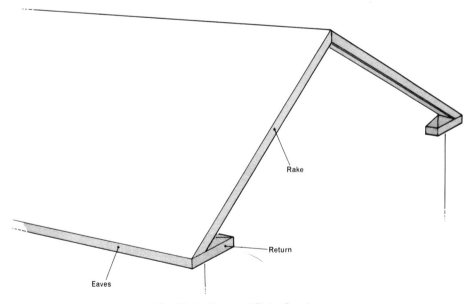

Fig. 22:1 Eave and Rake Cornice

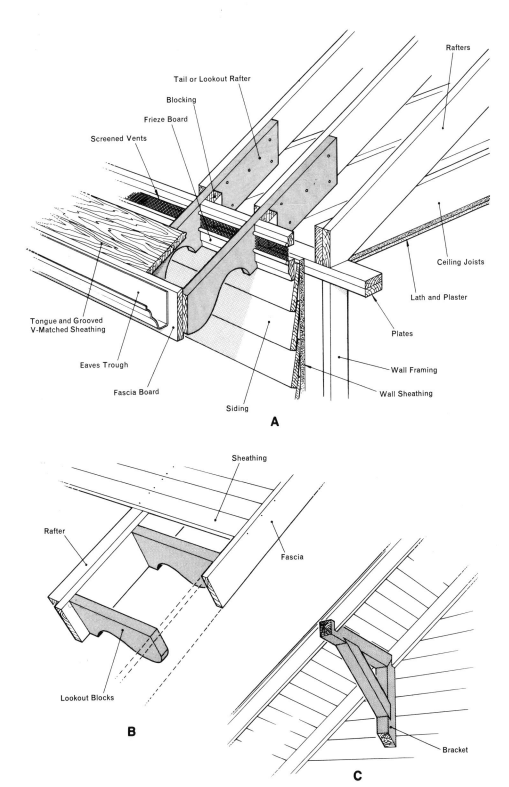

Labels in figure A (clockwise):

Tail or Lookout Rafter

Blocking

Frieze Board

Screened Vents

Rafters

Ceiling Joists

Lath and Plaster

Plates

Wall Framing

Wall Sheathing

Siding

Fascia Board

Eaves Trough

Tongue and Grooved V-Matched Sheathing

A

Labels in figure B:

Sheathing

Rafter

Fascia

Lookout Blocks

B

Labels in figure C:

Bracket

C

Fig. 22:2   (A) Open cornice with ornamentally cut lookout rafters; (B) and (C) Two methods used to support and decorate the gable end open cornice.

273

There are two broad basic classifications of cornices:
1. *open* — in which the rafter ends and the underside of the roof sheathing are exposed to view.
2. *closed* — in which the main roof framing is completely enclosed by the cornice trim members.

OPEN CORNICE

Figure 22:2A shows an open cornice with tail rafters (sometimes called lookout rafters) that have been cut to an ornamental shape and spiked to the main rafters. Tongue and grooved V-matched material is used as sheathing where it is exposed to view. The sheathing must have an attractive smooth surface that will take a good painted finish.

The frieze board is cut to fit tightly between the lookout rafters; it also runs up the gable end and is nailed tight to the wall under the overhanging sheathing. The section of frieze board nailed between the lookout rafters may be in one piece or it may be in two pieces set 1″ to 2″ apart. The opening is covered with screen that is held firmly in place by two strips of moulding, as shown in Figure 22:2A. It is essential that adequate ventilation be provided in the attic space to prevent condensation and to keep the insulation dry.

The lookout rafters may be spiked to the rafters in such a way as to give the roof a sweep effect at the eaves.

The open-type cornice is used more often on cottages and other buildings of similar design.

CLOSED CORNICE

In modern home construction, some form of the closed cornice is the most prevalent. Of these, the *box cornice* is most often used, probably because of

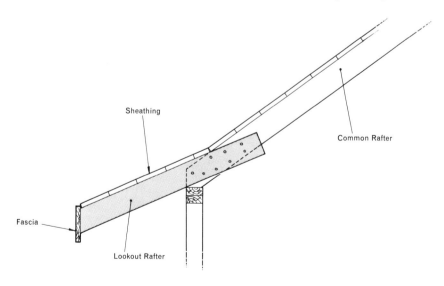

Fig. 22:3   Cornice with a sweep.

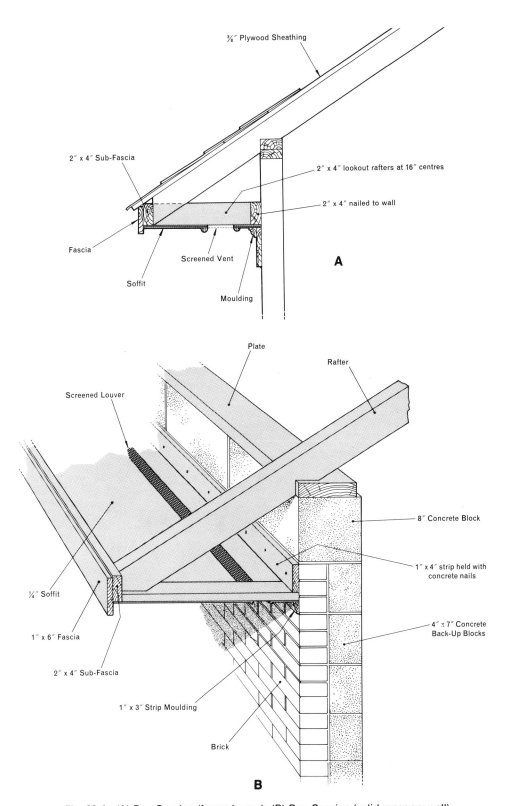

³/₈″ Plywood Sheathing

2″ x 4″ Sub-Fascia

2″ x 4″ lookout rafters at 16″ centres

2″ x 4″ nailed to wall

Fascia

Screened Vent

Soffit

Moulding

A

Plate

Rafter

Screened Louver

8″ Concrete Block

1″ x 4″ strip held with concrete nails

¼″ Soffit

4″ x 7″ Concrete Back-Up Blocks

1″ x 6″ Fascia

2″ x 4″ Sub-Fascia

1″ x 3″ Strip Moulding

Brick

B

Fig. 22:4   (A) Box Cornice (frame house); (B) Box Cornice (solid masonry wall).

its plain, straight appearance and its flat surfaces, which make it easier to paint. A more or less standard box cornice is shown in Figures 22:4A and B.

The box cornice can be adapted to almost any width of overhang from the storey-and-a-half steep roof with an 8″ or 10″ overhang to the low-pitched ranch bungalow with its wide 2′ to 3′ overhang. In general, the flatter the roof slope the greater the overhang. The governing factor in the amount of over-hang a roof has is often the height of the top of the windows. The soffit should be even with the top of the window trim or not more than 1½″ above it so that a piece of light crown mould will cover the gap. This means that neither siding nor face brick will be needed over the window opening. Figure 22:5 illustrates how the slope of the roof may govern the width of the overhang.

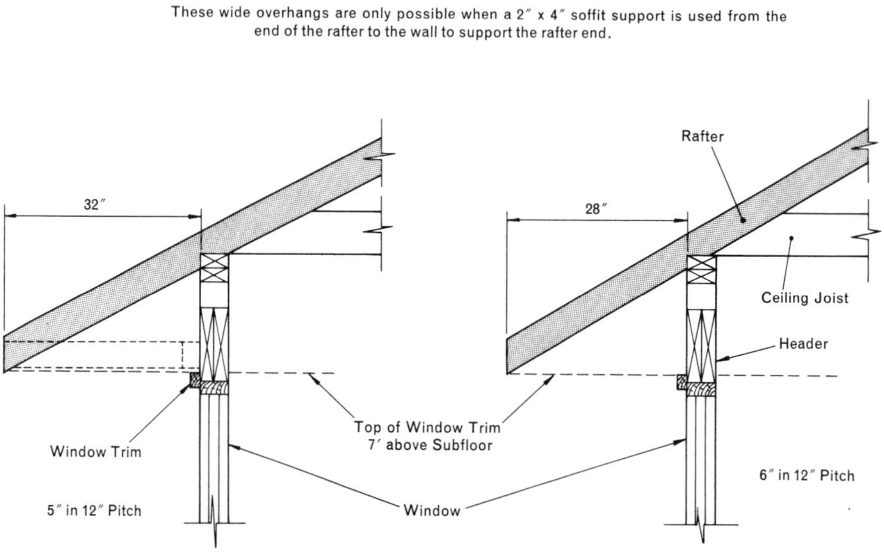

These wide overhangs are only possible when a 2″ x 4″ soffit support is used from the end of the rafter to the wall to support the rafter end.

Fig. 22:5 Maximum roof overhang for low pitch.

If a wide overhang is desired for a storey-and-a-half or other steeper-pitched roof the rafters should be framed to rest on a plate set on top of the floor or ceiling joists as shown in Figure 22:6A.

Another arrangement used for storey-and-a-half houses that provides more living area on the second floor and also raises the roof line is the *cantilever overhang* shown in Figure 22:7. The rafter ends rest on the second-floor joists, which project the required distance over the wall. This is an easy cornice to frame, as all that is required to enclose it is to nail the fascia to the ends and the soffit to the underside of the overhang joists.

A type of cornice that was quite popular on older houses is shown in Figure 22:8A. A board referred to as a *plancier* is nailed to the underside of the exposed rafter overhang. This cornice is now used on modern bungalows where the soffit might otherwise come below the window frame.

276

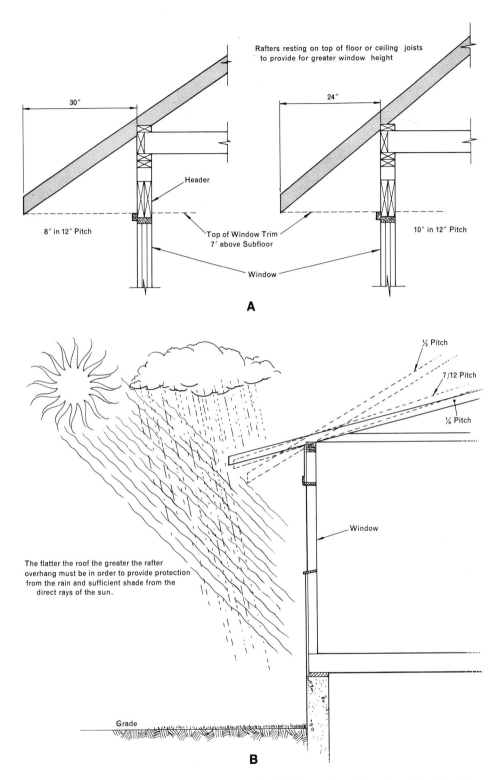

Rafters resting on top of floor or ceiling joists to provide for greater window height

30″

24″

Header

8″ in 12″ Pitch

10″ in 12″ Pitch

Top of Window Trim
7′ above Subfloor

Window

A

⅓ Pitch

7/12 Pitch

¼ Pitch

Window

The flatter the roof the greater the rafter overhang must be in order to provide protection from the rain and sufficient shade from the direct rays of the sun.

Grade

B

Fig. 22:6   (A) Maximum overhang for steep pitch; (B) The angle of the rafter determines the amount of overhang.

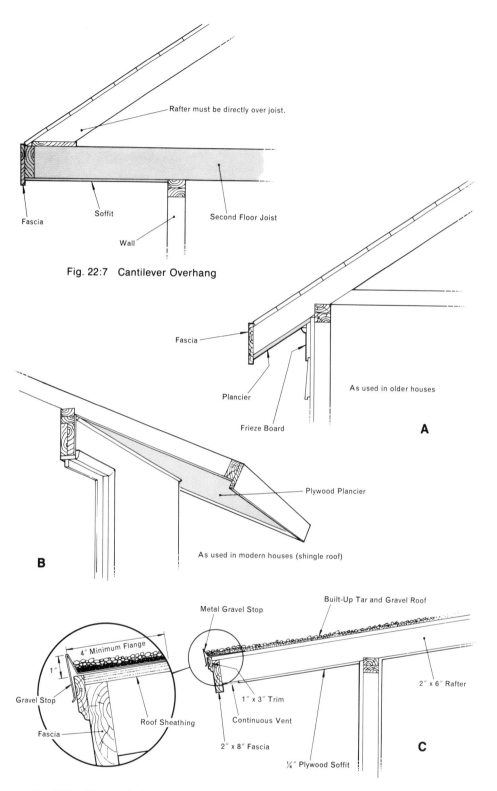

Rafter must be directly over joist.

Fascia

Soffit

Wall

Second Floor Joist

Fig. 22:7 Cantilever Overhang

Fascia

Plancier

Frieze Board

As used in older houses

A

Plywood Plancier

B

As used in modern houses (shingle roof)

Built-Up Tar and Gravel Roof

Metal Gravel Stop

4" Minimum Flange

1"

Gravel Stop

Roof Sheathing

Fascia

2" x 8" Fascia

1" x 3" Trim

Continuous Vent

¼" Plywood Soffit

2" x 6" Rafter

C

Fig. 22:8   (A) and (B) Cornice with a Plancier; (C) Cornice Used on a Built-up Flat Roof.

278

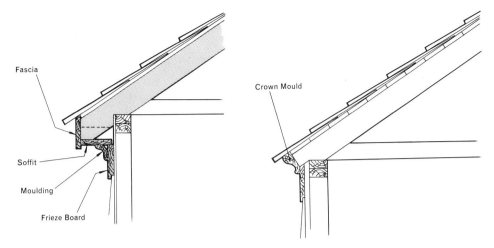

Fascia

Soffit

Moulding

Frieze Board

Fig. 22:9   Box cornice with small overhang.

Crown Mould

Fig. 22:10   Snub Cornice

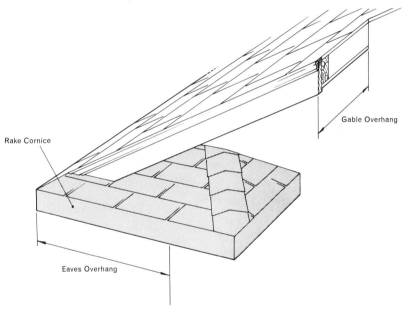

Gable Overhang

Rake Cornice

Eaves Overhang

Fig. 22:11   Return Cornice

Not all houses have large overhangs. A simple box cornice may be built like the one in Figure 22:9. A simpler eave arrangement is the *snub cornice,* in which a piece of crown moulding forms the only roof overhang. This creates a neat appearance but provides little or no protection for the wall. See Figure 22:10.

In the construction of the modern bungalow, the current trend is to wide overhangs at the eaves. These create a low roof line effect and also act as awnings for the windows. However, the gable ends often have considerably less overhang. A short return cornice improves the appearance of such a roof. See Figure 22:11. To break up the end wall, the return cornice is some-

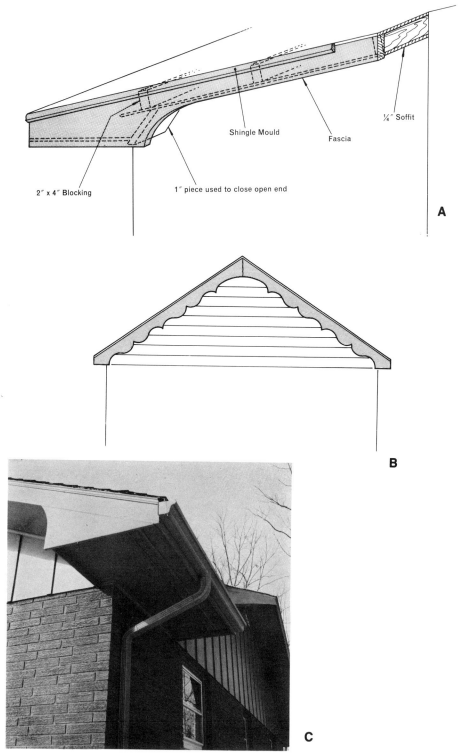

¼″ Soffit

Shingle Mould

Fascia

2″ x 4″ Blocking

1″ piece used to close open end

A

B

C

Fig. 22:12   (A) Rake Cornice; (B) The gable end fascia may be cut to an ornamental shape; (C) Gable End and Eave Cornice (note the aluminum louver strip).

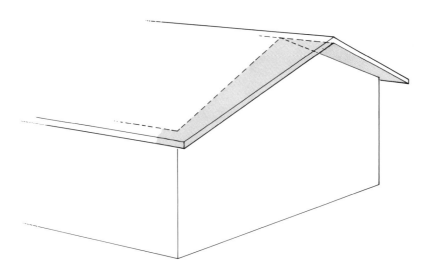

Fig. 22:13   Cornice Wider at the Peak than at the Eaves

times extended all the way across the end wall.

On other roofs, the gable end fascia board is widened and **curved** where it meets the lower horizontal fascia, as shown in Figure 22:12A.

The cornice used in one type of modern architecture is the *tapered gable overhang.* In this design the roof extends farther over the wall at the peak than at the eaves. This serves no functional purpose but is built this way for effect. Figure 22:13 illustrates this type of cornice.

There are several cornice arrangements that can be used on flat roofs; some of them are shown in the following drawings.

For post and beam construction the wide overhang is supported on at least two sides of the roof by the projecting beams. The underside of the heavy sheathing may be exposed to view or the cornice may be totally enclosed except for the supporting beams. The two types are shown here in Figures 22:17A and 22:17B.

Many roof trusses are built complete with horizontal soffit supporting members and blocking attached to the top chord. This provides the roof and cornice framing in one operation and ensures a uniform eave projection and sturdy framework on which to attach the fascia and soffit members. Three types of truss with attached cornice framing are shown in Figures 22:18A, B and C.

Much of the framing for the cornice is done after the rafter ends are lined up, but before the roof covering is applied. If some type of closed cornice is to be used the 2″ sub-fascia is nailed to the rafter ends. If there is to be a large overhang the soffit supports need to be nailed in place to take the spring out of the rafter overhang before it will safely support much weight. The details of this framing are shown in Figures 22:19A and B.

The supporting framework for a wide rake cornice at the gable end requires a series of 2″ x 4″ framing members running from the first rafter, which is set

A

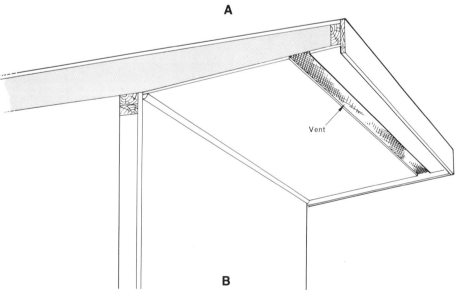

Vent

B

Fig. 22:14   (A) Flat Roof Cornice Framework; (B) Standard Flat Roof Cornice.

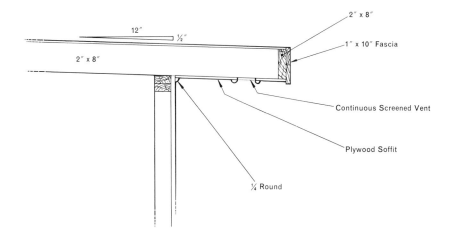

Fig. 22:15 Flat roof with the overhang of the joists tapered to receive a narrow fascia.

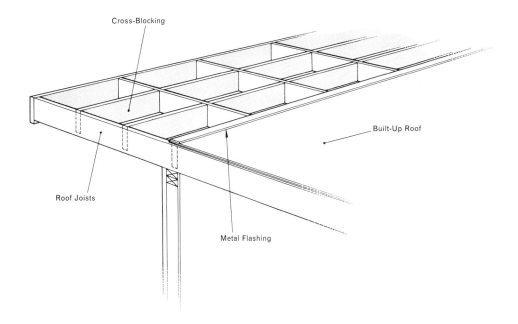

Fig. 22:16 Grid-type cornice used on a flat roof. The roof joists and the cross blocking prevent the direct rays of the sun from coming through and shade the area below, but still permit a circulation of air. This grid-type cornice can be used on both pitched and flat roofs and is generally used only on certain sections of the overhang.

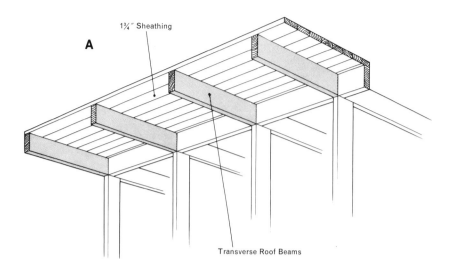

1¾″ Sheathing

A

Transverse Roof Beams

B

Fig. 22:17 (A) Cornice on a Post and Beam Construction (flat roof); (B) Wide gable cornice supported by the extended interior ceiling beams.

284

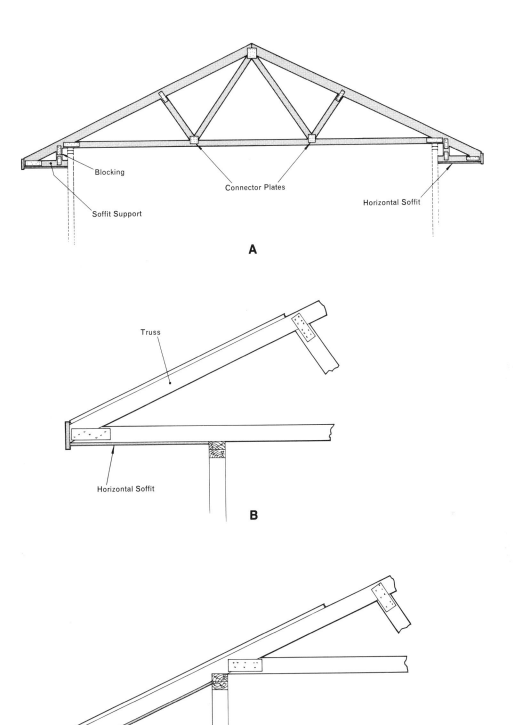

Fig. 22:18 (A) Standard "W" truss built with cornice framing; (B) Trusses may be built with a span to include the overhang with the lower chord acting as the cornice framework; (C) Sloping soffit nailed to underside of top chord.

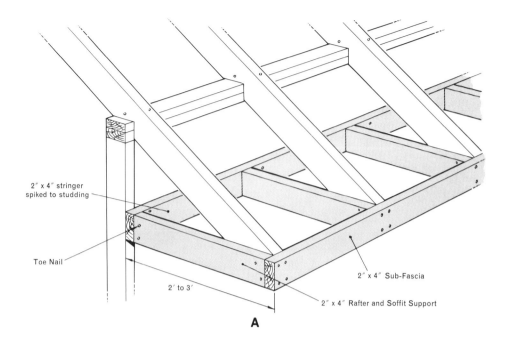

2″ x 4″ stringer spiked to studding

Toe Nail

2′ to 3′

A

2″ x 4″ Sub-Fascia

2″ x 4″ Rafter and Soffit Support

B

Fig. 22:19   (A) Box Cornice Framing; (B) Cornice Framework.

286

16″ or 24″ in from the end wall, to the fascia board. These pieces serve as cantilever lookout members to support the overhang; they also provide nailing support for the soffits as illustrated in Figure 22:20.

Where the gable end overhang is 10″ or less, it can be supported by nailing short pieces of 2″ x 4″ blocks to the underside of the projecting sheathing. The soffit can in turn be nailed to the underside of these blocks as shown in Figure 22:21.

To save on-the-site time, the soffit and the framework to which it is attached may be pre-fabricated and nailed in place as a unit. Or the soffit supports may be made in a sub-assembly ladder-shaped arrangement that can be nailed to the face of the wall and to the ends of the rafters. The plywood or other soffit material is nailed to it later. Or the plywood may be nailed to the framework before the assembly is attached to the wall. Sometimes the soffit section of the cornice is fastened to the wall with the front edge held up by a temporary brace until the rafters are set in place. See Figure 22:23.

On most modern houses at least part of the attic ventilation is provided through the soffit. There are several patented types of aluminum ventilating louvers that can be installed. Probably the most popular is the narrow, continuous strip of perforated aluminum with a copper screen on the back, illustrated in Figure 22:24.

The size and number of vents will depend on the size of the house; how-

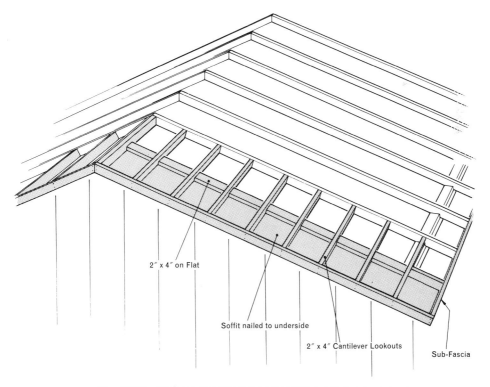

2″ x 4″ on Flat

Soffit nailed to underside

2″ x 4″ Cantilever Lookouts

Sub-Fascia

Fig. 22:20   Framing for Gable End Cornice (wide overhang)

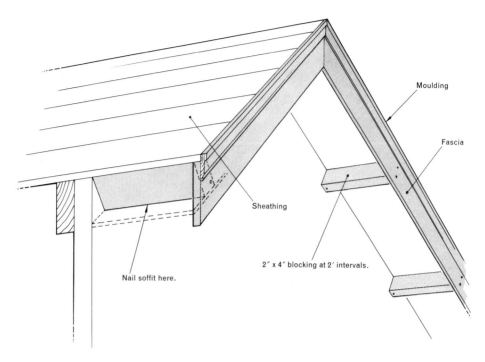

Fig. 22:21 Framing for Gable End Cornice (narrow overhang)

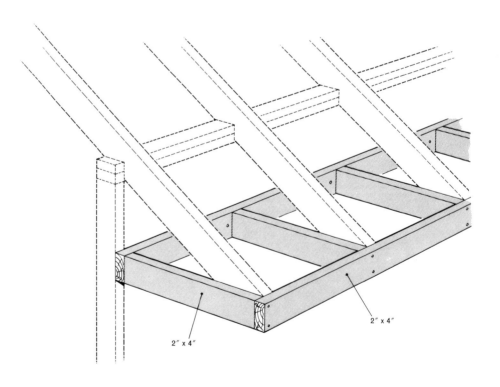

Fig. 22:22 Soffit Framework Sub-Assembly

288

ever, there must be 1 square foot of unobstructed louver opening for every 300 square feet of insulated ceiling area. The ventilating louvers must be designed to prevent the entry of rain, snow, or insects. Louvers are also located at the gable ends, at the ridge, and on the roof slope, as shown in Figure 22:25.

There are several materials that are used for the soffits. The most popular is ¼″ plywood and then ¼″ hardboard. Asbestos sheet stock is also extensively used because of its fire-resistant quality. A pre-finished corrugated aluminum stock is manufactured in rolls in widths to suit most cornices. It

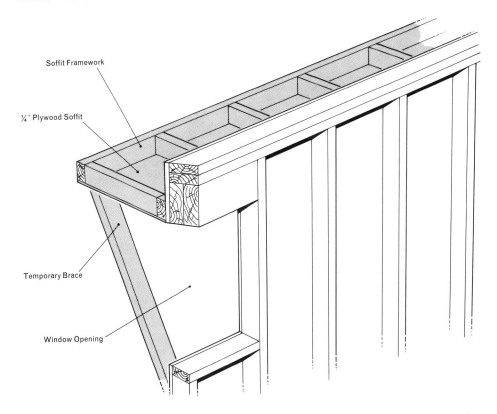

Soffit Framework

¼″ Plywood Soffit

Temporary Brace

Window Opening

Fig. 22:23   Soffit section of cornice nailed and braced in place before rafters are erected.

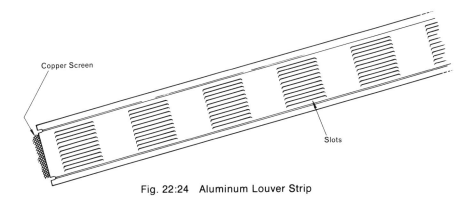

Copper Screen

Slots

Fig. 22:24   Aluminum Louver Strip

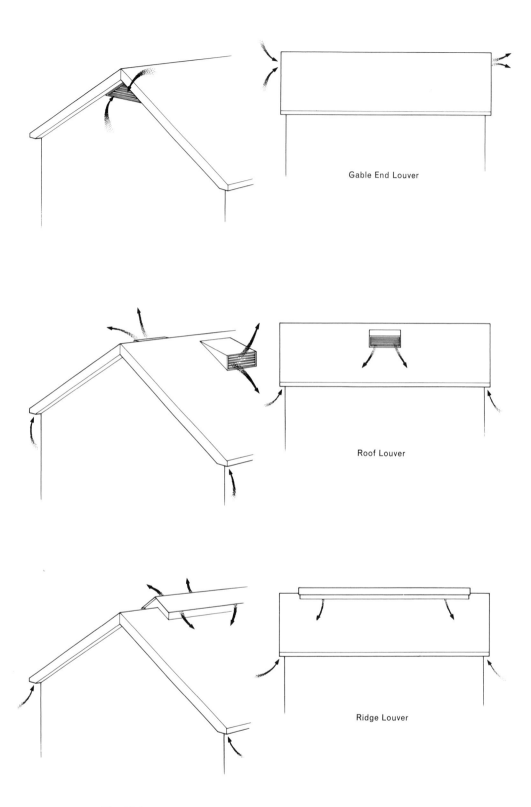

Fig. 22:25 Air flow through various types of ventilating louvers.

Gable End Louver

Roof Louver

Ridge Louver

can be held with screws to the wood framework and produces an attractive finished soffit.

ASSIGNMENT

1. What is the purpose of roof cornices?
2. (a) Where on the building is a rake cornice located?
   (b) Where is a return cornice located?
3. Define the terms "open cornice" and "closed cornice".
4. (a) What are lookout rafters?
   (b) Where are they used?
5. On which types of buildings are open cornices often used?
6. List some of the advantages of the box cornice.
7. What factor often governs the amount of overhang on a roof with a box cornice?
8. Make a sketch of a cantilever overhang and cornice.
9. Where is a plancier board used?
10. What is the disadvantage of the snub cornice?
11. Describe two cornice treatments that are used where the rake and the eave cornice meet.
12. Make a drawing of two types of cornices used on flat roofs.
13. How is the wide overhang on a post and beam construction house supported?
14. Describe two methods used to provide the cornice framework as part of a roof truss.
15. State the two purposes served by the 2″ x 4″ members running horizontally from the rafter ends to the wall.
16. Explain how a wide overhang is supported at the gable end of a house.
17. Which part of the cornice is often pre-fabricated and made up as a sub-assembly?
18. Describe the type of ventilating louver that is generally incorporated into the construction of a box cornice.
19. Why is it important that adequate ventilation be provided above the ceiling insulation?
20. List the materials that are used for the soffits of wide cornices.

Chapter 23

EXTERIOR WALL SIDING AND SHINGLES

There are many materials from which exterior wall coverings are manufactured. They include such materials as solid wood, plywood, fibreboard, asbestos, aluminum, plastics, and asphalt; combinations of these materials may also be used. Finished wall covering may be manufactured and applied in strips, sheets, or shingle-sized pieces.

TYPES OF EXTERIOR WALL SIDING

Many houses have more than one type of wall covering. For example, the main part of a frame house may have one type of siding and the gable ends another. The current trend for masonry houses is to incorporate some panels of horizontal or vertical wood siding above or below the windows or other places which will harmonize with, and complement, the brick or other masonry finish.

We will describe here some of the conventional wall covering products that are in current use in most areas. Some of these have been in general use for many years and their popularity no doubt will continue. Others have been developed more recently. There are also many new wall finishes being developed, which come on the market periodically, in which various materials are used to create different designs and effects.

Bevelled Siding

Often referred to as *lap siding* and sometimes as *clapboard, bevelled siding* is milled from solid lumber. It is generally cut from cedar, pine, or spruce — in widths of 4″, 5″, 6″, 8″, 10″, and 12″. The 10″ width is more extensively used in modern frame construction. There are several types of lap siding; four of these are shown in Figures 23:1 to 23:4.

Lap siding can be used over any type of sheathing. However, if it is used over fibreboard sheathing, all siding joints must be placed over studding because fibreboard will not support nails. If solid 1″ tongue and grooved or square-edged stock is used as sheathing, 15 lb. felt building paper must be placed between it and the siding.

Special galvanized oval-headed siding nails are generally used; the length most suitable will depend upon the type of sheathing. For fibreboard use 2½″ nails and for wood sheathing use 2″ nails. Part of the head will sink below the surface of the wood; however, the slight recess can be filled with putty after the first coat of paint has been applied. This will leave a smooth surface unobstructed by unsightly nail heads.

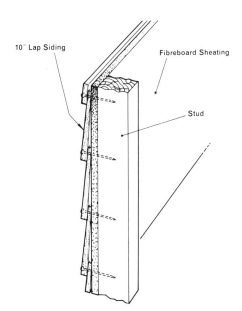

Fig. 23:1 Bevelled Lap Siding. The butt or lower edge varies in thickness from ³⁄₈″ to ⁷⁄₈″, tapering to ¹⁄₄″ to ¹⁄₂″ at the top. In general, the wider the siding, the thicker it will be.

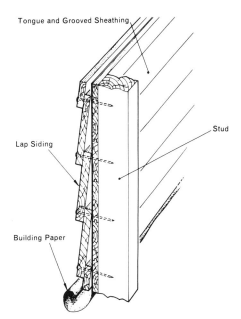

Fig. 23:2 Colonial Siding. Colonial siding is not tapered; the pieces are the same thickness throughout their full width.

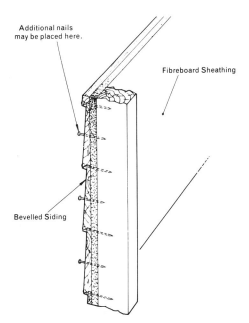

Fig. 23:3 Bevelled Siding with a Rabbeted Edge. This siding has the advantage of having a flat side that fits tightly against the studding. It requires no gauging; the amount of board exposure to the weather is auto-matically set by the rabbeted edge.

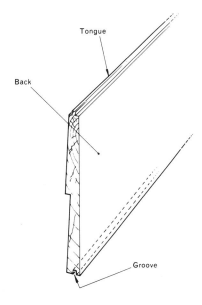

Fig. 23:4 Double Bevelled Siding. Milled with a double bevel and a flat back that fits against the studding, making a smooth interior. It is often used on cottages and garages where no sheathing is needed.

293

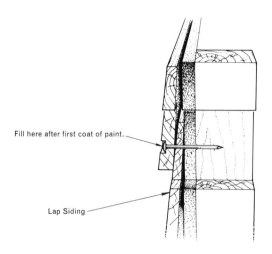

Fill here after first coat of paint.

Lap Siding

Fig. 23:5 Siding Nail

How To Apply Bevelled Siding. We cannot hope to explain in any detail the procedure for the application of all types of exterior wall finishes. However, since wood lap siding is more extensively used for frame construction than any other exterior finish, we will outline some of the steps in its application.

When applying any type of lap siding or wall shingles, the exact amount of lap or exposure will depend on the material used and on the height of the wall to be covered. This distance should be marked off on a *spacing rod*, (a piece of 1″ x 2″ stock slightly longer than the height of the wall from the foundation line to the underside of the soffit). The length of the rod is divided

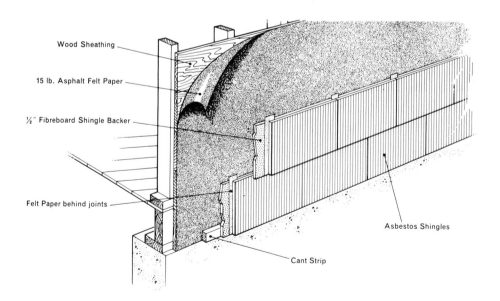

Wood Sheathing

15 lb. Asphalt Felt Paper

½″ Fibreboard Shingle Backer

Felt Paper behind joints

Asbestos Shingles

Cant Strip

Fig. 23:6 Using a measuring rod to lay out the position of siding or shingle courses.

into equal spaces that are closest to that of the desired siding exposure. The idea is to calculate the width of each course so that the courses will fit evenly into the height of the wall to be covered. This will ensure that a partial width of siding will not be necessary at the top of the wall. The tops and bottoms of windows should also be marked on the spacing rod, so that, when possible, the lower edge of a course of siding or shingles will come even with the top and bottom of the window frame. See Figure 23:6.

The marks that were laid out on the spacing rod should be transferred to the wall sheathing at the four corners of the building. This will result in a uniform and level siding spacing on all the walls.

Since the siding is butted against the window and door casing, all window and door frames must be secured in place before the siding is applied. Narrow lap siding is also butted to the corner boards, which must be nailed on first, as shown in Figure 23:7.

The use of 10″ or 12″ lap siding in modern frame construction is becoming more and more popular. The siding at the corners of the building is fitted together by mitred joints or by metal corners similar to the one illustrated in Figure 23:18.

Metal corners may involve less labour, but mitred joints create a much neater appearance, and, if properly fitted and nailed, will remain weather-tight for many years.

How to Cut a Mitred Siding Corner Joint. Start the siding at the bottom of the wall and allow the first board to project 1″ below the top of the foundation. The back of the siding may be kept tight against the sheathing or a furring

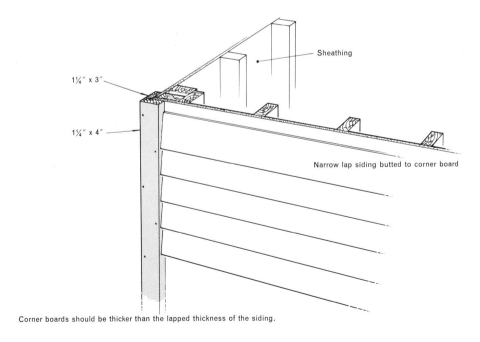

Fig. 23:7   Narrow lap siding and corner boards.

strip may be placed under the bottom of the first course to make it flare out over the foundation wall. See Figure 23:8.

If no furring strip is used, nail the first board temporarily at the correct height and allow one end to project beyond the corner. Take a piece of scrap siding, and, along the top of the board that is to be cut, square a line to point **A**. Do the same at the bottom to point **B**. Join these two points with a line on the face of the siding. With an adjustable square make a 45°-angle lay-out line from point A to B. Carefully cut along the waste side of the layout line. See Figure 23:9.

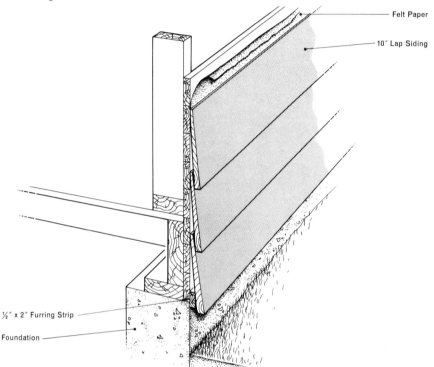

Fig. 23:8 Furring strip used on first siding course.

The second and succeeding siding boards are laid out in the same way except that allowance must be made for the fact that the butt of each piece rests on the siding board below it. Nail each board temporarily in place at the correct height and allow the end to project past the corner, marking it as shown in Figure 23:10.

After each board has been cut to fit, nail it securely in place. When the top of the wall is reached, if the siding courses have been kept to the level of the marks indicated on the spacing rod, a portion of the top board may need to be ripped off to make the top course the same width as the exposed part of the other courses. This, however, will depend on what type of moulding is used between the top of the last siding course and the underside of the soffit. If it is as wide as the lapped portion of the siding, a full-width top siding board can be used.

296

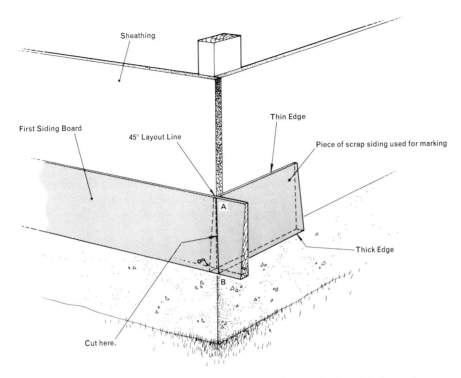

Sheathing

First Siding Board

45° Layout Line

Thin Edge

Piece of scrap siding used for marking

A

Thick Edge

B

Cut here.

Fig. 23:9   Mitre cut layout for first siding course (when no furring strip is used).

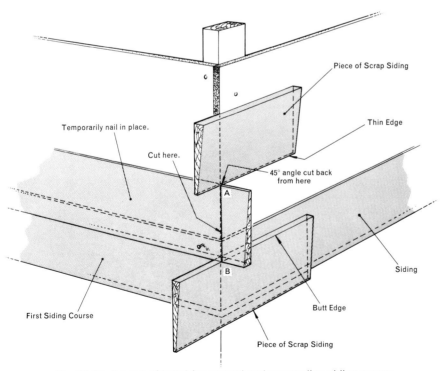

Piece of Scrap Siding

Thin Edge

Temporarily nail in place.

Cut here.

45° angle cut back from here

A

First Siding Course

B

Siding

Butt Edge

Piece of Scrap Siding

Fig. 23:10   Layout of bevel for second and succeeding siding course.

297

Another method of determining the correct height of the siding courses is to use a gauge block as shown in Figure 23:11. The gauge block is hooked under the butt of the last course of siding nailed in place and a mark is made at the top of the gauge to indicate the height of the next course.

A different-shaped gauge block, called a siding hook, can be used for marking the siding to length where it meets the window or door trim. See Figure 23:11.

Rustic Siding

Another type of siding that is used either with or without sheathing is the *rustic*, or *drop*, *siding*; it is milled with a tongue and grooved or shiplapped edge from pine, spruce, cedar, or other softwood. Two varieties are shown below in Figure 23:12.

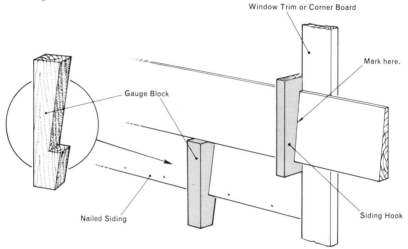

Fig. 23:11   Siding Hook and Gauge Block

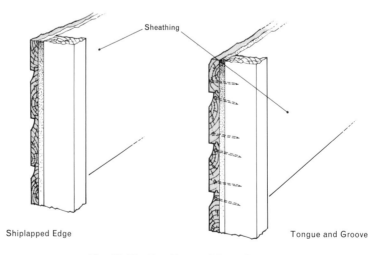

Fig. 23:12   Two Types of Drop Siding

How to Apply Rustic Siding. Cove or rustic siding is always applied horizontally starting from the bottom of the wall. The first board should be allowed to project 1″ over the foundation wall with the tongue edge up. Two nails should be driven into each stud through each siding board as shown in Figure 23:12. To prevent damage to the tongue when the pieces are being driven tight, a short piece of scrap siding should be used as a driving block. See Figure 23:13.

With this type of siding, corner boards are necessary. These may be nailed on top of the siding, or they may be nailed to the frame, and the siding butted into them. The same applies to the exterior window and door trim.

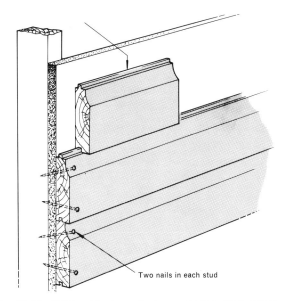

Two nails in each stud

Fig. 23:13 Driving block used when applying drop siding.

There are many types of exterior wall coverings, other than solid lumber, used on frame houses. A few of these materials will be briefly described here; some of them are applied as horizontal lap siding, others are applied in vertical panels.

Fibreboard Siding

The material used for *fibreboard siding* is a wood product made by compressing wood fibres with adhesives into a strong durable strip or sheet that does not easily split, splinter or crack and that forms a good smooth base for paint. Some fibreboard siding is made in a wide range of pre-finished coloured surfaces of baked-on vinyl that does not require painting for ten years or more.

How to Apply Fibreboard Siding. Fibreboard siding may be applied over any type of sheathing. If it is applied over old siding for renovation purposes, the wall must be strapped and building paper used under the new siding.

Fibreboard siding is made in thicknesses ranging from ¼″ to ½″, in widths of 10″, 12″, 16″ and 24″ and in lengths of 8′ to 16′. The strips must have nailing support at all end joints.

This siding may be applied in much the same manner as the conventional bevelled wood siding. However, a wood starter strip ⅜″ x 1⅜″ is nailed along the lower edge of the sheathing. Keep the lower edge of the first siding strip ¼″ below the starter strip. Drive the nails through both the siding and the starter strip into the sheathing and sill. Continue the siding, lapping each course 1″. Use rust-resistant box or siding nails, and drive at least one nail into every stud.

Figure 23:15 shows a method of applying fibreboard sheathing in which a rabbeted furring strip is placed under the butt of each course. This creates the heavier shadow effect desired in certain types of architecture.

A similar shadow effect can be obtained by using the self-locking metal strip shown in Figure 23:16. With this strip, no nails need be driven through the siding. The strip may be vented to allow the siding to breathe, which means the trapped dead air between the siding and sheathing is allowed to escape and be replaced by outside atmosphere. This prevents the condensation caused by trapped warmer air giving up its moisture because of the difference in the temperature of the air on the two surfaces of the siding. Moisture formed within the wall can cause such damage as a serious reduction in the effectiveness of the insulation, resulting in peeled or blistered paint, and decayed sheathing and framework of the wall.

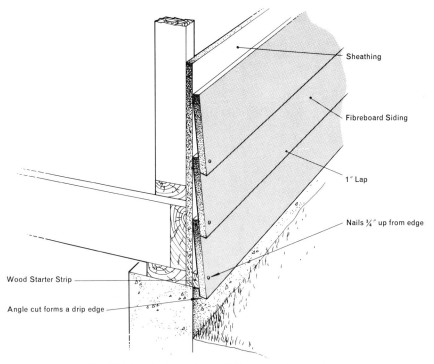

Fig. 23:14 Fibreboard Lap Siding with Starter Strip

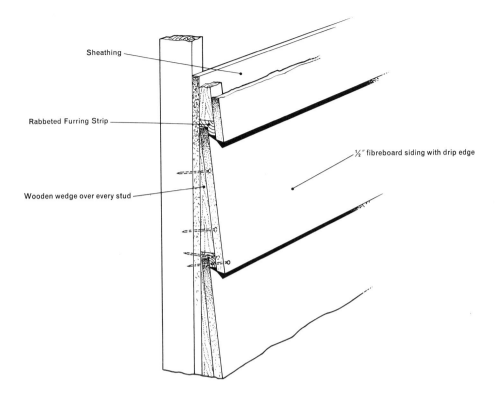

Sheathing

Rabbeted Furring Strip

Wooden wedge over every stud

½″ fibreboard siding with drip edge

Fig. 23:15   Fibreboard Siding with Shadow Effect

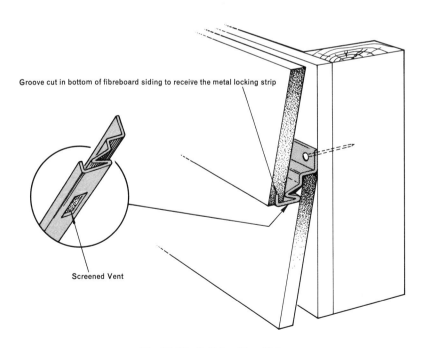

Groove cut in bottom of fibreboard siding to receive the metal locking strip

Screened Vent

Fig. 23:16   Self-Locking Siding

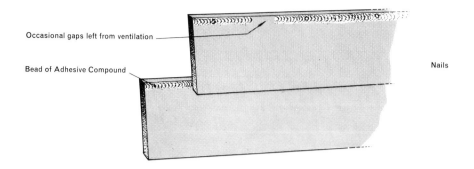

Occasional gaps left from ventilation

Bead of Adhesive Compound

Nails

Fig. 23:17   Fibreboard Siding (top nailed, lower edge bonded).

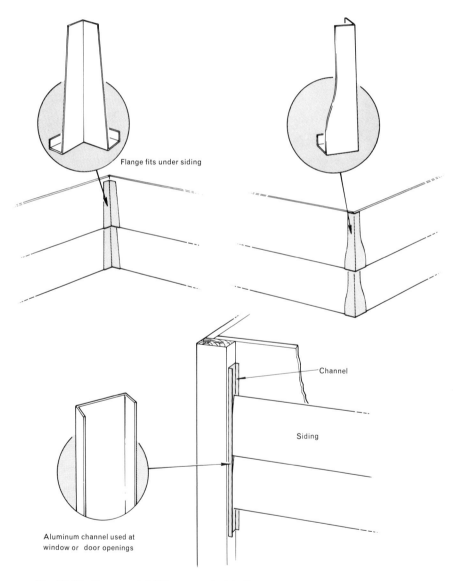

Flange fits under siding

Channel

Siding

Aluminum channel used at
window or door openings

Fig. 23:18   Some metal fittings used with fibreboard, aluminum, or wood siding.

302

Some fibreboard siding is nailed at the top of the strip, with a bead of adhesive compound applied with a caulking gun along this edge and over the nails heads. The next strip is then set in place and the top edge nailed, the butt edge being bonded by the adhesive to the course below. There are no exposed nail heads. See Figure 23:17.

The siding may be butted against the window and door trim, or a metal channel may be attached to the trim into which the siding is fitted. Special metal corners are generally used at the external and internal corners, although wooden corner boards are sometimes used. Figure 23:18 illustrates some metal fittings used in conjunction with fibreboard, aluminum, or wood siding.

Fibreboards may be used in sheet form (generally ½" or ⅝" thick, 4' wide, and 8', 9', or 10' long) for exterior wall covering using either of the following methods. The plain square-edged stock may be used as vertical panels with ½" or 1½" wood battens over the joints. Or the sheets may be scored lengthwise with grooves ½" wide and 3/10" deep at approximately 8" intervals to give the appearance of planks. Sheets used in this way generally have shiplapped edges, as shown in Figure 23:19.

Fibreboard sheets are often used, in conjunction with other types of siding or masonry, either as panels under windows and around doors or on the gable ends.

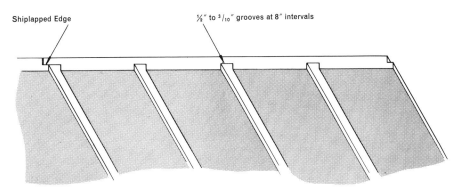

Fig. 23:19   ½" grooved fibreboard sheets used as siding.

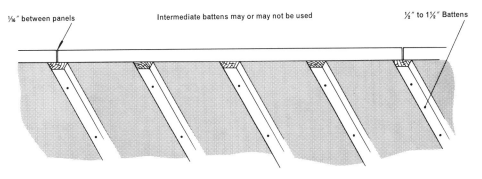

Fig. 23:20   Fibreboard sheets with battens used as siding.

Plywood Siding

Plywood is often used as siding either in 4′ x 8′ or 4′ x 10′ panels that are ¼″ to ½″ thick with square or shiplapped edges and ½″ x 3/16″ grooves 4″ to 16″ apart, or as lap siding in strips of 12″, 16″, and 24″ widths. Both types are sold in an unfinished state or in a wide range of pre-finished solid colours or stains.

How to Apply Plywood Siding. Plywood used as exterior siding is applied in much the same manner as fibreboard.

Either plywood or fibreboard siding can be nailed directly to the studding rather than to the wall sheathing; however, a layer of building paper must be used between the studding and the siding. It is preferable to have the face grain of plywood siding at right angles to the supports. This method does not produce as rigid a wall as the combination of sheathing and siding. The wall must be stiffened with diagonal sway braces. It is a more economical method, however, and it is permissible, provided that sufficient insulation is used between the studding.

A type of plywood that has a masonry surface has recently been developed and is in use in some areas. It consists of ⅜″ plywood that has been pre-heated to remove all the moisture. It is then sprayed with an epoxy-plastic adhesive. While this is still wet, it is sprayed with fine marble and granite particles. This gives the plywood a lifetime pre-finished masonry surface. The 4′ x 8′ plywood sheets can be nailed to the wall with 1″ x 4″ redwood battens over the joints.

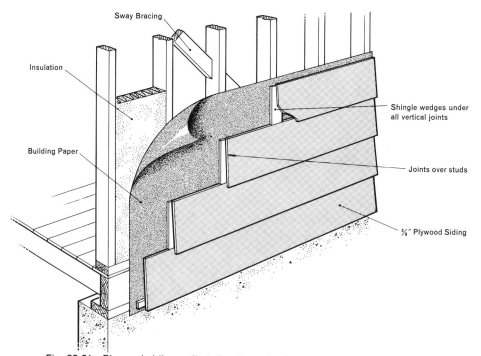

Fig. 23:21 Plywood siding nailed directly to the framework (no wall sheathing).

Aluminum Siding

After a rather slow start as an exterior wall covering, *aluminum alloy siding* is now quite extensively used. At first it was made only with the bright anodized finish, but now it has a baked-on finish in a wide range of colours. Aluminum siding is rust-resistant and will not check, twist, or rot as wood siding often does. The more recent types are manufactured with ½″ thickness of plastic or fibreboard insulation that fit on to the back of the siding strips (as shown in Figure 23:23), to provide the necessary insulation. This is a distinct improvement over the earlier strips of plain aluminum, which, while they provided a hard and permanent-type of siding, had no insulation value at all.

How to Apply Aluminum Siding. Aluminum siding is made in 8″, 10″, and 12″ widths and in 8′ and 10′ lengths. The strips are light in weight and easy to handle and install. There are two main types of aluminum siding, each with its own method of application. With the type shown in Figure 23:22, the siding is started from the top of the wall. The lower flange at the butt of the first strip of siding is nailed through the sheathing into the studding. The top of the second strip of siding is inserted into the groove above this flange. This holds the top of the siding in place and covers up the nail heads on the first course. A moulding under the soffit is used to hold the upper edge of the top course tight to the wall.

The second type of aluminum siding is started from the bottom of the wall. The top of the first strip of siding is nailed to the wall. The flange at the butt

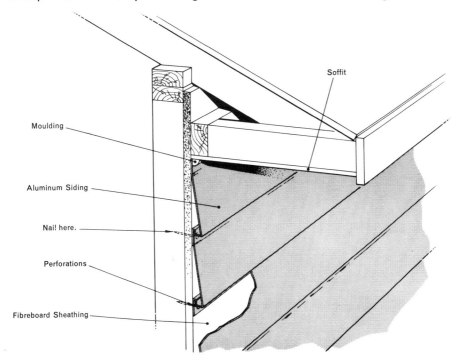

Fig. 23:22   Aluminum siding started from the top of the wall.

of the second strip is inserted into the fold at the top of the first strip, as illustrated in Figure 23:23.

Either of these types of siding may be used with or without a back-up layer of ½″ insulation board. The specially formed metal corners and channels shown in Figure 23:18 are used with aluminum siding.

Some types of aluminum siding are made to be applied vertically. They have interlocking edges that conceal all the nail heads.

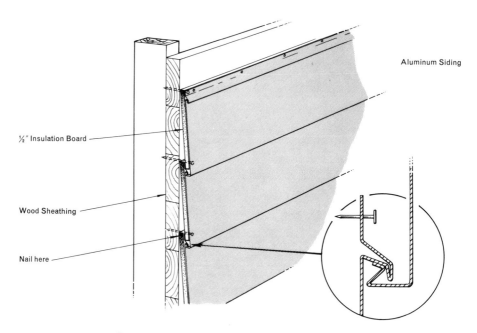

Aluminum Siding

½″ Insulation Board

Wood Sheathing

Nail here

Fig. 23:23 **Aluminum** siding with insulated back.

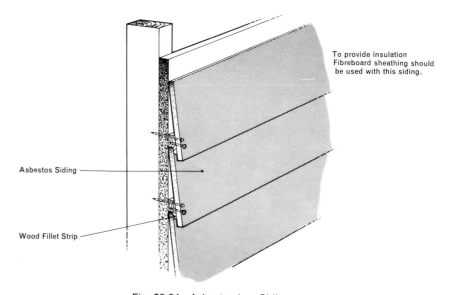

To provide insulation Fibreboard sheathing should be used with this siding.

Asbestos Siding

Wood Fillet Strip

Fig. 23:24 Asbestos Lap Siding

Asbestos Siding

Another type of non-wood exterior wall covering used on frame buildings is *asbestos siding.* This is actually a mixture of asbestos fibres and Portland cement that makes a very hard, durable surface. It has a stone grey colour and need not be painted unless a different colour is desired. Although its insulation value is limited, it is unaffected by extremes of temperature and is rot and insect-proof; its greatest advantage is its resistance to fire.

How to Apply Asbestos Siding. Asbestos siding may be applied in strips that are 9½″, 12″ or 16″ wide and 8′ long. These strips may be lapped tight in the same manner as wood siding. More often, however, they are used with wood fillet strips similar to those used for fibreboard siding. This method of application makes the siding look heavier and gives the wall a shadow effect. See Figure 23:24.

Since asbestos siding is hard and quite brittle, and tends to check when nails are driven through it, the nail holes are pre-drilled. It can be sawn but more often it is cut to length with a special guillotine cutter.

A strip of asphalt felt is placed behind all butt joints of this lap siding to make a weather-tight joint.

TYPES OF EXTERIOR WALL SHINGLES

A more common type of asbestos exterior wall covering is asbestos wall shingles.

Asbestos Shingles

These are made from a material similar to that described for asbestos lap siding. The shingles, however, are made in several colours and with a serrated or grained finish. Asbestos shingles are generally 3/16″ thick, 8″ to 32″ wide, and 12″ long.

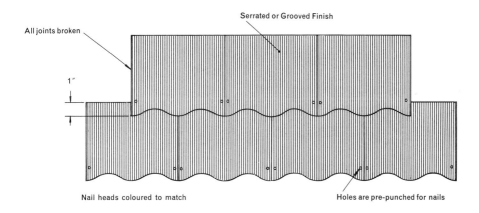

Fig. 23:25   Asbestos Wall Shingles

How to Apply Asbestos Shingles. The 32″ shingles can be applied directly over fibreboard sheathing as they will span two 16″ stud spaces so that nails can be driven into three studs. Narrower shingles must be nailed to wood sheathing or to wood furring strips that have been nailed to the wall.

The butt edge of the shingles may be straight or curved to produce a wavy line as illustrated in Figure 23:25.

Figure 23:26 illustrates the application of square-edged asbestos shingles with a back-up strip of ½″ fibreboard placed behind each course. The back-up strip provides more insulation and makes the shingle surface firmer. The desired shadow effect is created when the shingles are allowed to project

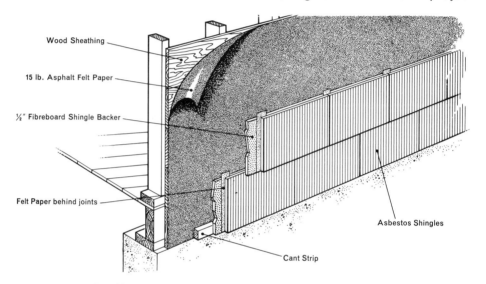

Fig. 23:26   Asbestos shingles with fibreboard backer strips.

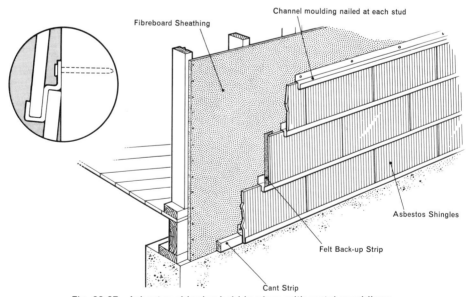

Fig. 23:27   Asbestos shingles held in place with metal mouldings.

308

¼″ below the fibreboard back-up strip. A strip of heavy felt is placed between the shingles and the fibreboard at each vertical joint. A layer of 15 lb. felt is nailed to the wood sheathing before the back-up strips or siding is applied.

When fibreboard or other non-wood sheathing is used, the shingles are attached either by nailing them to wooden furring strips that have been nailed to the studding, or by securing them in metal channel mouldings that have also been nailed to the studding, as shown in Figure 23:27.

Wooden Shingles

Wooden shingles used as an exterior wall covering present a rustic appearance that blends in well with certain types of architecture. They are weather-resistant and extremely durable, as evidenced by the fact that some of our oldest buildings have wooden-shingled walls that are still in good condition.

How to Apply Wooden Shingles. Shingles may be nailed directly to wood sheathing; if they are nailed to fibreboard sheathing, however, the wall must be strapped with 1″ x 2″ or 1″ x 3″ strips that are attached to the studding with 2½″ common nails. The shingles are in turn nailed to these strips as shown in Figure 23:28.

The amount of wall shingle exposed to the weather is greater than the amount of roof shingle exposure, because the problem of water seepage is not as great. For 16″ shingles, the exposure to the weather may vary from 6″ to 12″; for shingles 18″ long, up to 14″ may be exposed.

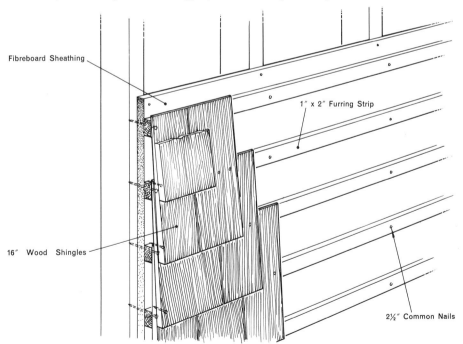

Fibreboard Sheathing

1″ x 2″ Furring Strip

16″ Wood Shingles

2½″ Common Nails

Fig. 23:28   Cedar shingles nailed to furring strips.

Galvanized or other rust-resistant flat-headed 1½″ shingle nails should be used. They may be driven above the exposed portion of the shingle so that the nail heads are covered, or they may be placed near the butt of the shingles.

Wall shingles are often pre-finished or treated with paint or shingle stain before they are applied. This is better than painting them after they are in place, for then only the exposed portion of the shingle can be given a protective coating.

Most wooden wall shingles are sawn in 16″, 18″, and 24″ lengths. They vary in thickness from ⅜″ to ½″. There are five grades of shingles ranging in quality from the No. 1 grade, which is made from clear heartwood, to the No. 5 grade, or undercoursing grade, which may contain large knots.

A type of shingle that presents a very rough and rustic appearance because it is split rather than sawn is the cedar "shake". Shakes may be from 18″ to 32″ long and from ½″ to 1½″ thick at the butt. They are often pre-finished.

Either shingles or shakes may be applied as a single or double course wall covering; Figure 23:28 shows an example of single course construction, and Figure 23:29 illustrates a double course construction. The outer course is applied ½″ below the under course, to create a heavy appearance that will show a shadow line when the sun shines on the wall. Inexpensive, low-grade shingles are used for the under course and a better grade is used for the outer course.

A similar arrangement is used to create a shadow effect when shingles are applied over fibreboard sheathing. A strip of 1″ x 3″ is nailed over one course of shingles just above the height of the next course. The shingles are

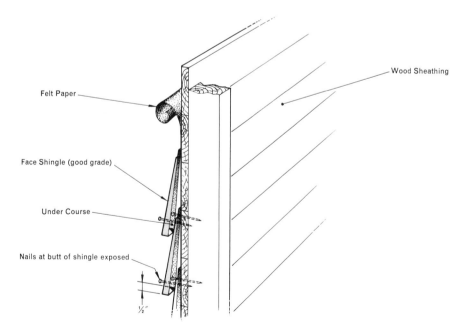

Fig. 23:29   Wood Shingles (double coursing)

then nailed to the strip with the butt projecting ½″ below. The nails should be kept 1½″ up from the bottom of the shingle as shown in Figure 23:30.

The treatment of the shingles at inside and outside corners is shown in Figure 23:31.

Shingles can be kept in line when they are applied by striking a chalk line and keeping the butts even with this line when they are nailed. All joints should be at least 1½″ away from the joint in the preceding course. The number of courses should be determined in the manner that was described for wood lap siding.

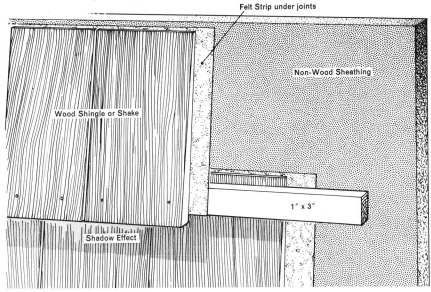

Fig. 23:30   Shingle Wall with Shadow Effect.

Red Cedar Shingle & Handsplit Shake Bureau (B.C.)

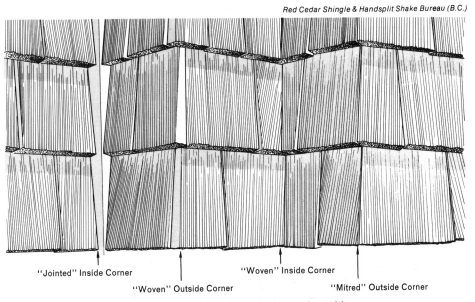

Fig. 23:31   Treatment of shingles at inside and outside corners.

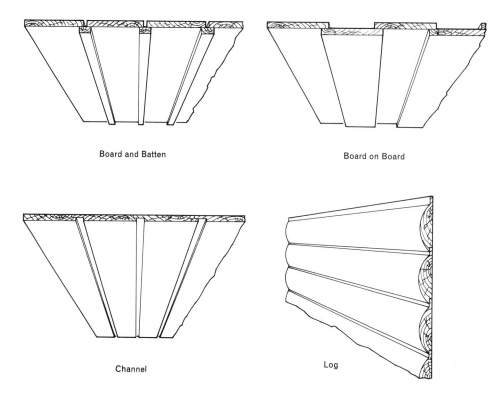

Board and Batten

Board on Board

Channel

Log

Fig. 23:32 Four Types of Solid Wood Siding

Three types of solid wood siding that are generally applied vertically are illustrated in Figure 23:32. Log siding (also shown in Figure 23:32) is generally applied horizontally.

We have dealt in this chapter with only those types of wood, aluminum, and composition exterior wall coverings that are most commonly used. There are others and more are being developed as building research continues. Nor have we mentioned any of the many varieties of masonry products and finishes used for exterior walls, some of which were briefly described in Chapter 4.

ASSIGNMENT

1. (a) List the basic materials from which exterior wall coverings are made.
   (b) List the three general shapes in which siding is manufactured.
2. Make a drawing of four types of lap siding and label each.
3. (a) When fibreboard sheathing is used, where must the lap siding joints occur?
   (b) What type of sheathing requires building paper to be placed between it and the siding?

4. What is a spacing rod and how is it used?
5. Why must all window and door frames be nailed in place before most types of siding are applied?
6. Briefly describe how a mitred corner joint is laid out for the second course of 10″ bevelled siding.
7. Why is the mitre joint of the second course of bevelled siding laid out differently from the joint of the first course?
8. How is a siding hook used?
9. When applying rustic siding, how is the tongue of the boards protected when driving the joints tight?
10. What are the two methods of applying the corner boards when rustic siding is used?
11. List some of the advantages of fibreboard siding.
12. In what thicknesses, widths and lengths is fibreboard strip siding manufactured?
13. How is the first course of fibreboard siding applied?
14. How is a shadow effect created when using fibreboard lap siding?
15. (a) What causes condensation within an exterior frame wall?
    (b) What damage can be caused by condensation in a wall?
16. How is fibreboard siding applied?
17. Make a sketch of three types of metal fittings that may be used when applying wood, aluminum, or fibreboard lap siding.
18. Why are grooves cut in fibreboard or plywood sheets that are used as finished siding panels?
19. How is plywood with a masonry finish manufactured?
20. What precautions must be taken when, in the absence of wall sheathing, plywood siding is applied directly to the wall?
21. List the advantages of asbestos siding.
22. How do the two types of aluminum siding differ in shape and in method of application?
23. List three advantages of aluminum siding.
24. For what purpose are fillet strips used with fibreboard and asbestos siding?
25. In what sizes are asbestos shingles made?
26. What is the purpose of:
    (a) The ½″ fibreboard back-up strips placed behind each course of asbestos shingles?
    (b) The horizontal metal moulding sometimes used with asbestos shingles?

Wooden Shingles
27. What arrangement must be made for wooden shingles to be applied over fibreboard sheathing?
28. Why can wooden wall shingles be laid with greater exposure to the weather than when the same shingles are used on the roof?

29. How do shingles differ from shakes?
30. Explain the difference between:
    (a) Single and double course wall shingles.
    (b) A woven and a mitred shingle arrangement at an exterior corner.
31. What arrangement is made at internal corners when wooden wall shingles are used?
32. Make a sectional drawing of three types of solid wood siding that are applied vertically.

Chapter 24

WINDOW TYPES AND INSTALLATION

Windows are one of the major components of any building, especially for residential construction where light and ventilation as well as appearance are of utmost importance. This chapter will deal with some of the most frequently used window types, and their installation.

Windows involve operations by the carpenter at all stages of construction. The planning and layout of window locations and the framing of the openings have already been discussed in previous chapters. Some of the other operations included in window framing are: the installing of the frame, the fitting of the sash, the cutting of the exterior and interior wall covering to fit the window frame properly, and the installing of the interior trim.

In frame or masonry veneer construction, the window frames are set in place, plumbed, and nailed through the exterior trim to the wall framework. The siding or the brick is then butted to the exterior window trim, as shown in Figures 24:1 and 24:2.

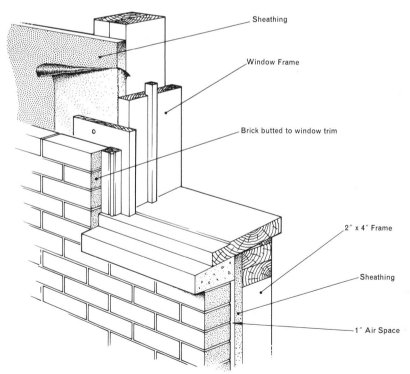

Fig. 24:1 Brick exterior butted to window frame.

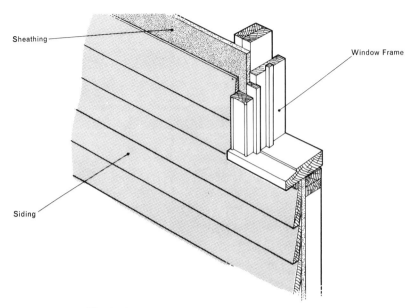

Fig. 24:2   Wood siding butted to window frame.

Most window units have two main parts:
(a) *the window frame* – which consists of the main side members (jambs), the sill, and the exterior trim;
(b) *the sash* – which holds the glass and consists of the top and bottom rails, the side stiles, and horizontal or vertical muntin bars.

In some types of window units no sash is used: the glass is mounted directly into the main frame members; the panes may be either fixed or sliding.

TYPES OF WINDOWS

Although wooden window units are still the most popular for residential home construction, aluminum and steel units are also extensively used. One of the most recent developments in window frame material is the use of hard vinyl, a plastic material that is moulded or extruded into shapes to form the side and head jambs for window frames.

Double Hung Windows

There are many types of windows designed for modern construction, but the type that is most commonly used is the conventional *double hung window.* The double hung window unit consists of a frame and two sashes which slide vertically by each other. The units may be used singly, as shown in Figure 24:3, or two or more may be grouped together to form larger windows. See Figure 24:4. The sections between the units are referred to as mullions; hence the term *mullioned window.*

There are many variations of the double hung window; in some windows only one of the sashes in each unit is movable; in others, one sash is larger

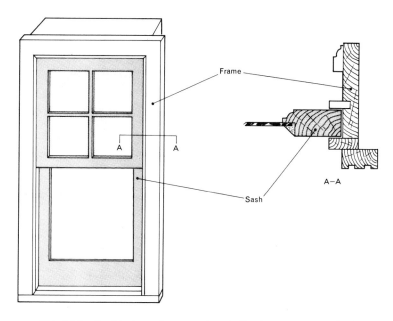

Fig. 24:3 Double hung frame and sash (for frame construction).

than the other to create a special effect. The general construction of the frames, however, is the same. A sectional view of such a frame is shown in Figure 24:5.

The sash used in a double hung window frame is shown in Figure 24:6.

Double hung window units are not always used on a straight wall surface but often form a corner or bay window arrangement as shown in Figures 24:7 and 24:8.

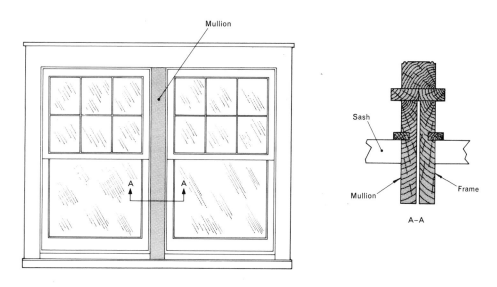

Fig. 24:4 Double hung window with single mullion.

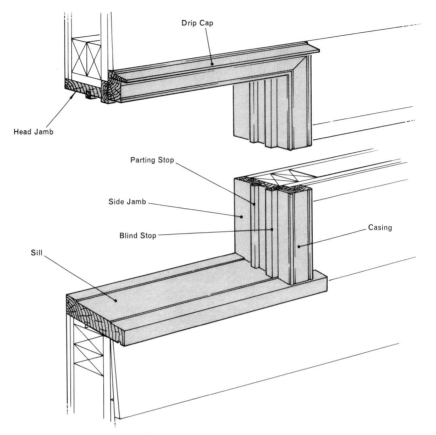

Fig. 24:5   Parts of a double hung window frame.

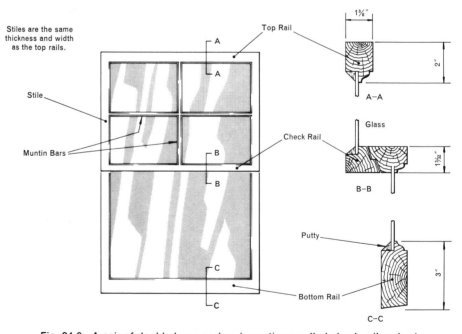

Fig. 24:6   A pair of double hung sashes (sometimes called check rail sashes).

318

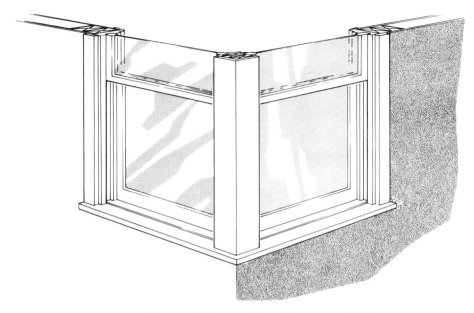

Fig. 24:7 Two double hung units used as corner windows.

Some type of spring balance is required to make the sash lift easily. Light metal glides are often incorporated with the spring balances and are attached to the side jambs. Some windows have a spring between the glide and the window frame. This keeps the sash fitting snugly and yet allows it to slide easily even if it should swell slightly. It also allows the sash to be taken out for cleaning: by pressing it to one side to compress the springs and the glide,

Fig. 24:8 Three double hung units used as a bay window.

allowing the other side of the sash to swing clear of the window stop on the opposite side jamb. One type of spring-loaded glide and weatherstrip is shown in Figure 24:9.

Double hung window units are often placed on each side of a large, fixed, single light of glass to form a picture window as shown in Figure 24:10.

Double hung sashes are made with many glass light arrangements, some of which are illustrated in Figure 24:11.

A window lock is attached to the top of the meeting rail to prevent the sashes from sliding by each other. Either one or two sash lifts are attached to the bottom rail of each lower sash. See Figure 24:9.

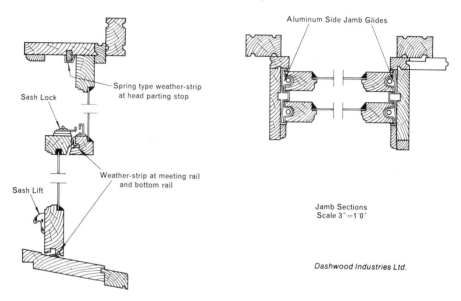

Fig. 24:9   Double hung sash details.

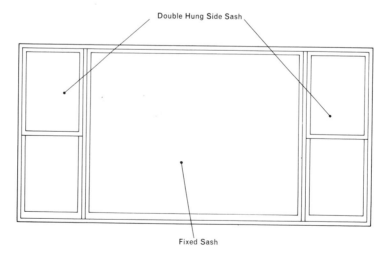

Fig. 24:10   Picture Window

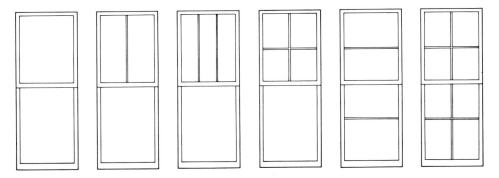

Fig. 24:11 Some of the most commonly used light arrangements in a **double** hung sash.

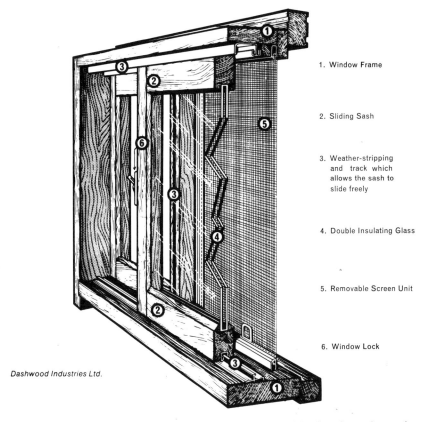

1. Window Frame

2. Sliding Sash

3. Weather-stripping and track which allows the sash to slide freely

4. Double Insulating Glass

5. Removable Screen Unit

6. Window Lock

Dashwood Industries Ltd.

Fig. 24:12 Modern sliding window with double glazed wooden **sash.**

Sliding Windows

The term *sliding window* refers to windows with two or more glass panels that slide horizontally by each other. There are two basic types used in residential construction: (a) those with sashes, which slide between stops or on metal glides such as those shown in Figures 24:12 and 24:13; and (b) those without sashes, in which the glass slides in grooves cut in the sill and the head jamb, or in plastic tracks set in the frame, as shown in Figure 24:15.

Fig. 24:13   Sliding Window

The glass panels used in sashless windows are generally 3/16″ thick. This thickness is often referred to as crystal glass. Some windows have three glass panels, the centre one fixed and the two end panels sliding past it. Others are

Fig. 24:14   Sashless Sliding Window

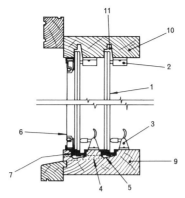

Horizontal section of standard slider unit

1. ³⁄₁₆″ Glass

2. Spring loaded roller to keep glass snug against frame

3. Window Lock

4. Drainage holes for any moisture due to condensation

5. Air space to ensure proper breathing

6. Aluminum Screen

7. Vinyl plastic tracks which allow the glass to slide easily

8. Vinyl weather-stripping on side jambs

9. Wood Sill

10. Side Jambs

11. Head jamb with deep grooves to allow the glass to be lifted out of the frame

12. Removable Storm Sash

Individual light of glass will lift out of the frame.

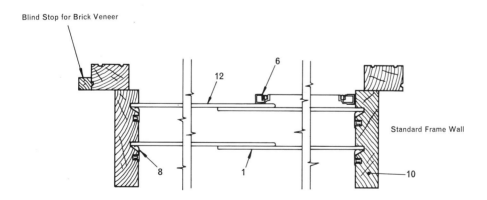

Blind Stop for Brick Veneer

Standard Frame Wall

Vertical section of standard slider unit

Dashwood Industries Ltd.

Fig. 24:15 Horizontal and vertical sections of sliding sashless windows.

divided horizontally, with a wooden cross-bar approximately one-quarter of the way up the window. Mullions may divide the window opening further. The small, lower sections of the window generally have sliding glass panels for ventilation, while the larger top sections are fixed. These two types of windows are shown in Figures 24:16 and 24:17.

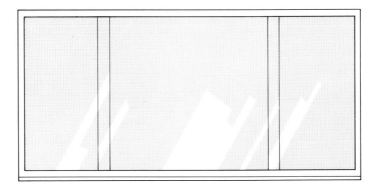

Fig. 24:16   Three glass panels, centre panel fixed, outside panels sliding.

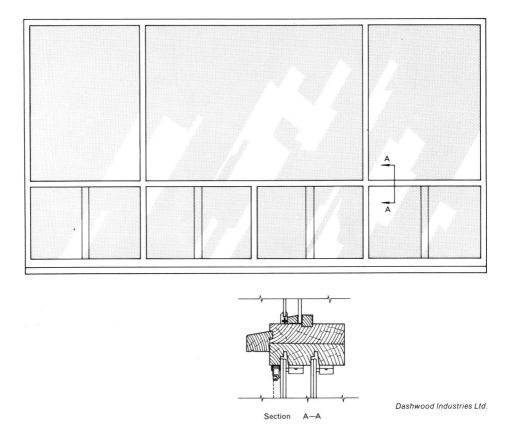

Dashwood Industries Ltd.

Section   A—A

Fig. 24:17   Stacked picture window with sliding and fixed glass.

Casement Windows

The term *casement* refers to windows that swing on hinges. There are two main types: (a) *Inswing*
(b) *Outswing.*

As their names imply, the inswing casement opens inwards and the outswing casement opens outwards. They are generally hinged on either the right or the left side of the sash, although they are sometimes hinged on the bottom or the top. Because the entire glass area of a casement window opens at one time, it can provide twice as much ventilation as a sliding window of the same dimensions.

There are advantages and disadvantages to both types of casement windows. The outswing is probably more popular, because the sash is out of the way when it is open and does not affect the furniture or curtain arrangement in the room. There is the disadavantage, however, that the sash is exposed to the effect of the wind when it is open and must be held with adequate hardware to prevent wind damage. With an inswing window this difficulty is not experienced, but great care must be taken to prevent water from getting in. The sash of an inswing window is located directly over the inner edge of the sill, which must be flat to allow the sash to swing inwards. Therefore, water that runs down the outer face of the sash tends to seep or be blown under it to the inside of the wall. One method that is sometimes used to prevent this is shown in Figure 24:19. A moulding that diverts the water to a lower part of the sill is attached to the bottom rail of the sash.

The most common application of inswing casement windows are those commonly used in basements. The sash is hinged from the top, which allows

A. S. Nicholson & Son Limited

Fig. 24:18   Outswing casement window.

it to swing up and be hooked to a joist or the ceiling. A metal or wood strip is let into the sash to prevent the window from leaking at the sill as shown in Figure 24:20.

Casement windows may be used singly or in groups of two or more units with mullions between them. Some windows combine hinged units and fixed units. Figure 24:21 illustrates a sectional view of an outswing casement window, showing the locations of most of the frame and sash parts.

Casement windows are generally provided with either double insulating glass or a removable storm glass that is attached to the sash for winter pro-

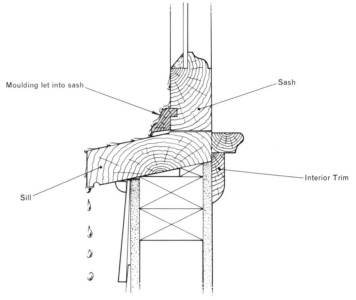

Fig. 24:19   Inswing casement window with moulding to divert water onto the sill away from the sash.

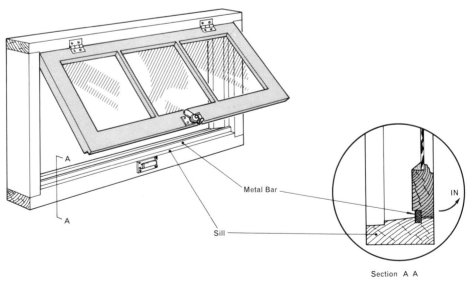

Section A A

Fig. 24:20   Conventional inswing casement basement window.

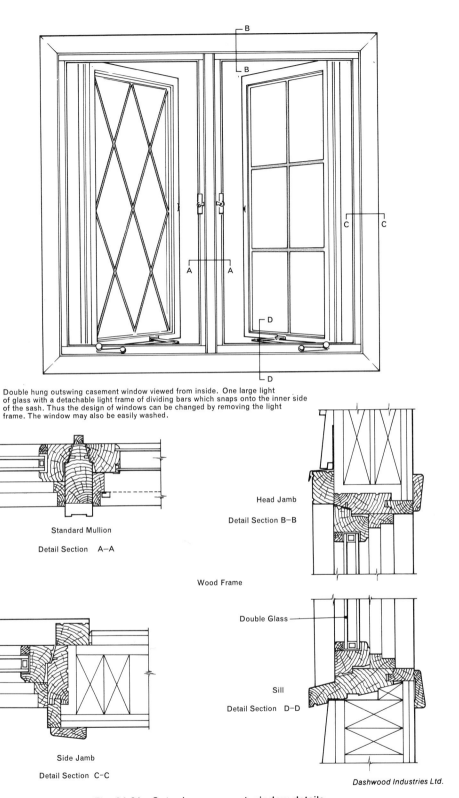

Double hung outswing casement window viewed from inside. One large light of glass with a detachable light frame of dividing bars which snaps onto the inner side of the sash. Thus the design of windows can be changed by removing the light frame. The window may also be easily washed.

Standard Mullion

Detail Section   A–A

Head Jamb

Detail Section B–B

Wood Frame

Double Glass

Sill

Detail Section   D–D

Side Jamb

Detail Section   C–C

Fig. 24:21   Outswing casement window details.

tection. These take the place of the conventional storm sash, which, if fitted over the entire window area, would prevent the sash from swinging open for winter ventilation. On outswing casements the screens are attached to the inside of the frame so as not to interfere with the window action.

A metal winder crank with an arm attached to the sash is fitted on the window stool trim. This allows the sash to be opened and held securely at any position. Casement windows are also fitted with casement locking hardware that will pull the sash in tight against the weatherstrip-lined rabbet on the side and head jambs. Some of the hardware used on outswing casement windows is shown in Figure 24:22.

Another outswing casement window frame used for frame wall construction is shown in Figure 24:23. This frame includes a sub-sill and a vinyl gasket which is let into the back of the exterior trim to make a seal between the window frame and the exterior wall sheathing. The metal weatherstripping is also shown.

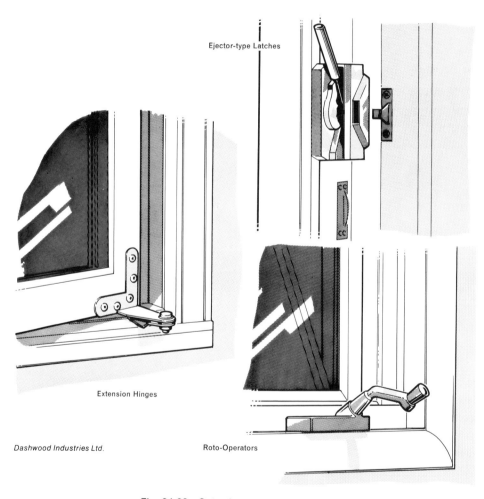

Ejector-type Latches

Extension Hinges

Dashwood Industries Ltd.

Roto-Operators

Fig. 24:22 Outswing casement hardware.

Aluminum flashing, shown in shaded area, is formed and cut to length at factory.

Vinyl gasket, shown in drawing, dovetails into back face of exterior casing.

Andersen Corporation

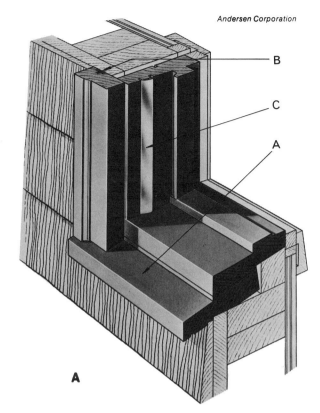

A

A. Subsill is milled and horned for exact fit.
B. Vinyl gasket compressed against sheathing forms weathertight seal.
C. Weatherstrip.

B

Fig. 24:23   (A) Outswing casement window frame; (B) Large outswing casement window.

Jalousie Windows

Some windows have a hinge pivot point that slides on the side jambs and allows the sash to swing out in an awning fashion. These are sometimes referred to as *jalousie* windows. They are operated by a bar attached to either a crank or a lever fastened to the window stool. Sashes that pivot are often used in conjunction with fixed sashes as in Figures 24:24 and 24:25. In Figure 24:26 both sashes open. Jalousie windows may be made from either wood or metal. Figures 24:27, 24:28, and 24:29 illustrate three types of metal units generally used in masonry walls.

A. S. Nicholson & Son Ltd.

Fig. 24:24   Window with one fixed sash and one jalousie sash.

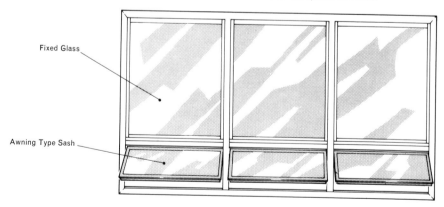

Fig. 24:25   Fixed and jalousie sashes.

330

A. S. Nicholson & Son Ltd.

Fig. 24:26   Awning-type window unit.

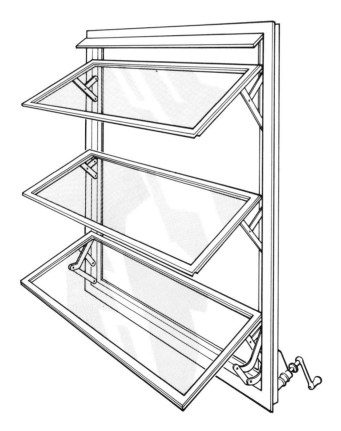

Fig. 24:27   Metal awning-type sash and frame for use in a masonry wall.

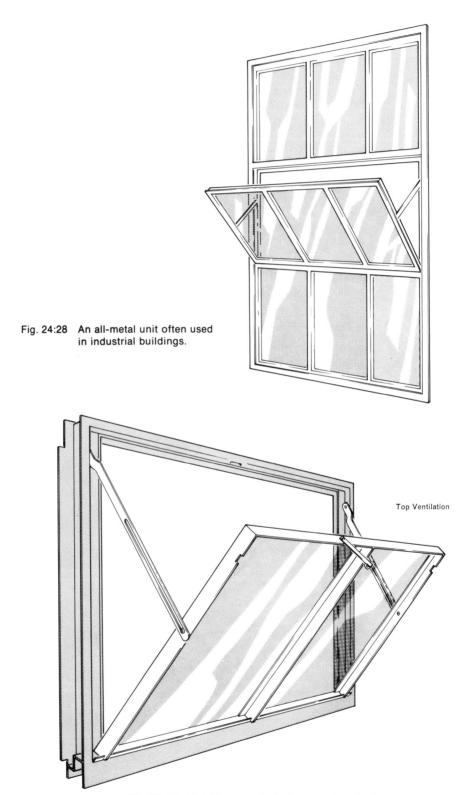

Fig. 24:28 An all-metal unit often used in industrial buildings.

Top Ventilation

Fig. 24:29 Metal basement window unit (inswing).

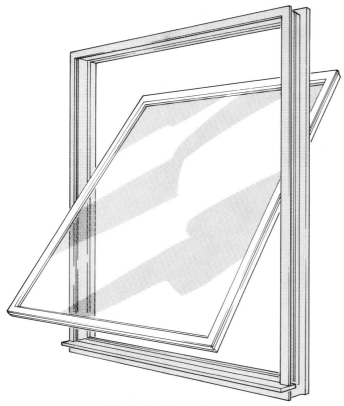

Fig. 24:30   Pivot Window

Pivot Window

A window is manufactured that has a single sash that pivots in the centre so that it completely revolves. The main advantage of this window is that both sides of the glass can be cleaned from the inside. Windows of this type are seldom used for ventilation purposes, serving mainly as fixed windows, because they are difficult to screen. Such a window is shown in Figure 24:30. They are used extensively in air-conditioned buildings.

Bow Window

A popular type of picture window in current use is the *bow*. The bow window is a modernization of the bay window that was popular in older homes. The frame is built in an arc of varying radii depending on the size of window desired. This type of window is generally built with some of the units opening for ventilation. If the window is to be built on the gable end wall, a roof section forms part of the window assembly. If, however, the window is to be placed under the eave overhang no roof is necessary. See Figures 24:31 and 24:32.

For the construction of most types of windows it has often been found to be more economical, when fixed lights are used, to glaze the glass directly into the window frame thus eliminating the sash and providing more glass area. These window frames are generally made from 2″ jamb stock, rabbeted

Bow window with pre-cut roof

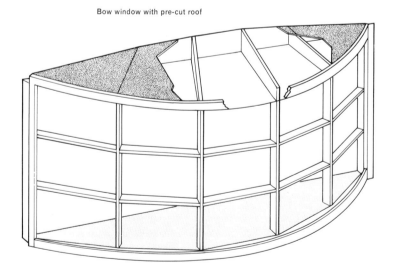

Fig. 24:31   Bow window with metal covered roof.

Fig. 24:32 Bow window set tight under the eaves.

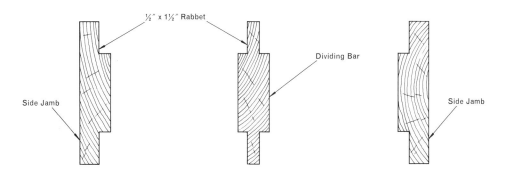

½″ x 1½″ Rabbet

Dividing Bar

Side Jamb

Side Jamb

Fig. 24:33 Jamb and divider bar stock for fixed windows.

on both edges. The horizontal and vertical dividing bars must be rabbeted on both edges of both sides, as shown below. The double rabbet is for either a storm sash or for double glazing. The vertical dividing bars run the full height of the windows and the horizontal bars are fitted into them to the same depth as the rabbet with a dado joint. See Figure 24:34A.

Exterior trim is nailed to the jamb stock but not to the dividing bars. The glass is generally held in place by wooden stops, as shown in Figure 24:34A. The glass is embedded in glazing compound or putty before the stops are nailed in place.

335

In any large glassed-in wall area, or what we might term a window wall, most of the glass is glazed into heavy vertical and horizontal supporting members. Some of the glass, however, is set in sashes that can be opened for ventilation purposes. A portion of a window wall is shown in Figure 24:34B.

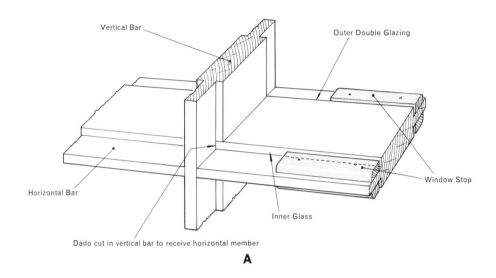

A

B

Fig. 24:34 (A) Divider bars in sashless fixed glass windows; (B) Large window with glass glazed directly into the window frame (post and beam construction).

Some type of vacuum-sealed glass is often used for large lights in fixed windows, and to a lesser extent in other window types. Vacuum-sealed glass is made of two panes of glass ¼″ to ½″ apart, sealed at the edges. The space between is not actually a vacuum, but a dehydrated air space. These double lights of glass can be made in any size or shape.

The chief advantage of vacuum-sealed glass is that no storm sash is required. This is of benefit where large and often odd-shaped lights of glass are used, and where storm sashes would not only detract from the appearance of the window, but would be very difficult to put up and take down.

This type of glass is sold under several trade names. Two types are shown in Figure 24:35.

There are many other types and combinations of types of windows than those described here. However, these are the basic ones in current use.

In present-day building, the carpenter on the building site is seldom called upon to build the window frames used in the building. Such units as window frames and sashes along with the doors and the exterior door frames are made at lumber yards, in special shops, or in factories. This work is classed as "millwork" and constitutes a special branch of the building industry.

It is, however, the responsibility of the carpenter on the job to install the window frames properly in the correct location, and to make certain that they are level, plumb, and weather tight.

In a frame or brick veneer wall, the window opening should be flashed with 15 lb. felt paper as shown in Figure 24:36, in order to make the frame weather-tight. The strip should be approximately 12″ wide and nailed to the face of the sheathing with 4″ of the paper folded over and nailed to the inner face of the 2″ x 4″ rough frame opening.

Where possible, the tops of all window frames should be the same height to keep the exterior trim line level.

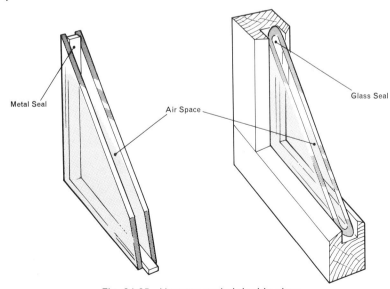

Metal Seal

Air Space

Glass Seal

Fig. 24:35   Vacuum-sealed double glass.

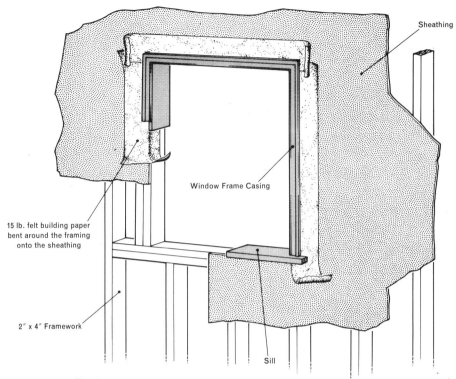

Fig. 24:36 Installation of a window frame (frame construction).

Sheathing

Window Frame Casing

15 lb. felt building paper
bent around the framing
onto the sheathing

2″ x 4″ Framework

Sill

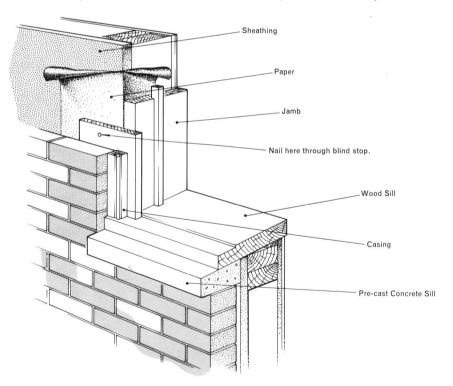

Fig. 24:37 Window frame in brick veneer wall.

Sheathing

Paper

Jamb

Nail here through blind stop.

Wood Sill

Casing

Pre-cast Concrete Sill

338

HOW TO SET A WINDOW FRAME

(For frame or brick veneer construction)
1. Set the frame in place, sliding it into the opening from the outside.
2. Adjust the frame in the opening so that the top is at exactly the correct height and centred sideways in the opening.
3. Temporarily nail the lower end of one of the side casings to the sheathing.
4. Level the sill using a spirit level. Wedge the sill if necessary and nail the lower end of the opposite side casing.
5. Plumb the side jambs and nail the top of the casing.
6. Permanently nail the frame using 2½″ finishing nails at 8″ intervals.
   Figures 24:36 and 24:37 illustrate cutaway views of window frames in a frame construction and brick veneer wall.

In a solid masonry house, the wall is built up to the level of the window sills and the frame is set on the stone or pre-cast concrete sill and braced in place as shown in Figure 24:38. If a poured concrete sill is to be used, the win-

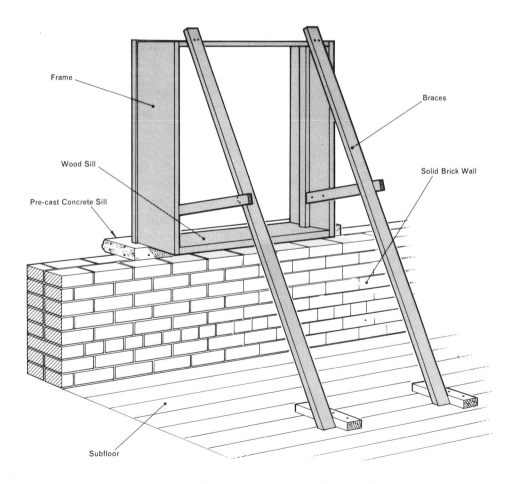

Fig. 24:38   Window frame set in solid brick wall.

339

dow frame is blocked up to the thickness of the concrete sill and the concrete poured after the brickwork has been completed. Sometimes the frames are braced from the outside and the lower end of the braces held by stakes driven into the ground. This provides a clear subfloor on which the masons can work. Special care must be taken to ensure that the sill of the frame is level, the side jambs are plumb, and that both ends of the braces are securely fastened. The inner edge of the frame should project 1½″ past the inside masonry wall so that it will be flush with the finished interior plaster.

Figure 24:39 shows the installation of a metal window frame in a brick veneer wall. The same application is followed if wood or other siding is to be used.

Many builders use pre-fabricated panel units that include the wall framework in which the window frame is built, as well as the portion of the wall above and below the window. These units may include the completely installed frames, sashes and trim as well as the exterior wall covering below the window. Pre-fabricated window panels are extensively used in solid brick construction where one section of the brick wall from foundation to plate can be left out and the panel inserted. Window wall panel sections are also used in frame and other types of construction.

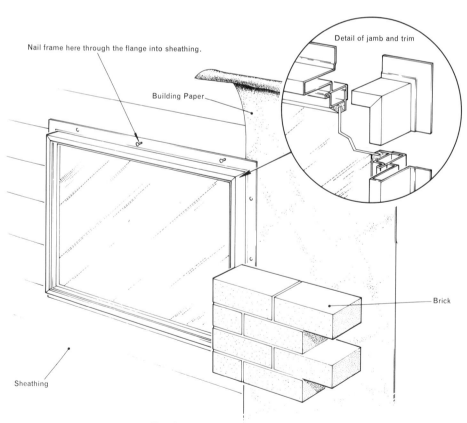

Nail frame here through the flange into sheathing.

Detail of jamb and trim

Building Paper

Brick

Sheathing

Fig. 24:39 Metal window frame.

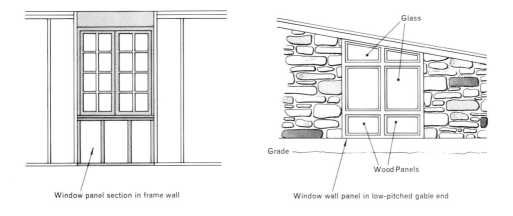

Window panel section in frame wall

Glass

Grade

Wood Panels

Window wall panel in low-pitched gable end

Fig. 24:40 Prefabricated window panel units.

Some special window frames require special installation procedures, which will be determined by the design of the frame and the exterior finish of the building.

ASSIGNMENT

1. Why are windows one of the major components to be considered in residential building construction?
2. Name the two main parts of most window units.
3. Of what materials are windows made?
4. Describe a mullioned window.
5. (a) Make a drawing of a double hung window frame (sectional view) and label all parts.
   (b) Make a drawing (vertical section) of a pair of sashes used in a double hung window frame.
6. Describe the arrangement used to keep the sash of a double hung window fitting snugly while still allowing it to slide freely.
7. By means of a sketch show a four glass light arrangement used in a double hung window.
8. List the two types of horizontal sliding windows.
9. What thickness of glass is most often used in sashless sliding windows?
10. What advantage has a casement window over a sliding window?
11. List the advantages and the disadvantages of the inswing and the outswing casement window.
12. Describe two methods used to prevent inswing casement windows from leaking.
13. Draw a sectional view of the side jamb of an outswing casement window frame and sash.
14. What arrangement is used for storm window protection on outswing casement windows?

15. (a) What is meant by a jalousie window?
    (b) Make a sketch of three types of jalousie windows.
16. State one advantage and one disadvantage of the type of window that has a single sash that pivots in the centre?
17. (a) Describe a bow window.
    (b) The bow window to some extent replaces what type of window that was used in older homes?
18. Draw a sectional view of one of the horizontal dividing bars of a sashless, fixed light window frame.
19. (a) On what type of window is vacuum-sealed glass often used?
    (b) What is the advantage of using vacuum-sealed glass for window lights?
20. The building of window frames and sashes is generally considered to be part of what branch of the building construction industry?
21. Why should the window opening in a frame wall be flashed with building paper?
22. List the steps in installing a window frame in a brick veneer wall.
23. Explain how a window frame is set and held in place in a solid masonry wall while the brickwork is built around it.
24. How are metal window frames fastened to a frame wall?

Chapter 25

PORCHES AND DOOR ENTRANCES

EXTERIOR TRIM MEMBERS

Some exterior trim members have been mentioned in previous chapters in the descriptions of cornices and siding. There are, however, other exterior trim members used in residential construction, especially around porches and entrance ways.

Porch designs have changed considerably from the ornamental style with scroll work, large posts, and hand rails, to the plainer type with concrete floors and small wood or metal posts and wrought iron railings. Many of them are the covered patio type with solid concrete or pre-cast square concrete slabs used as the floor. The trend in porches in modern building is to allow

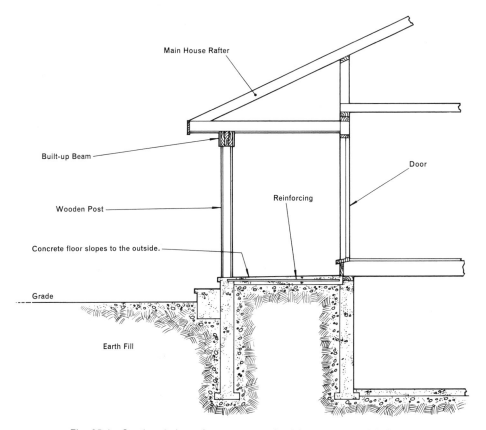

Fig. 25:1 Sectional view of an open porch with a concrete slab floor.

343

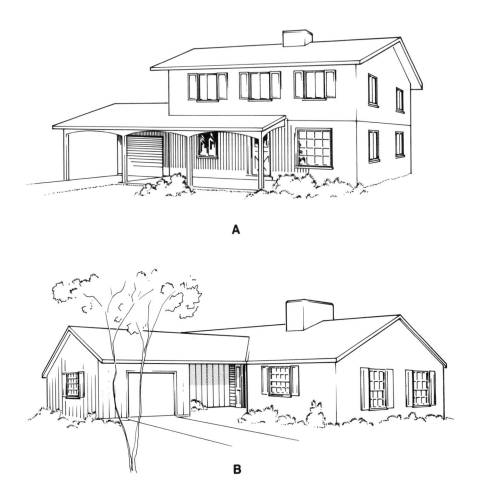

A

B

Fig. 25:2 (A) Open porch on a two-storey house. Concrete floor with square wooden posts; (B) Open porch formed by the recess in the main wall.

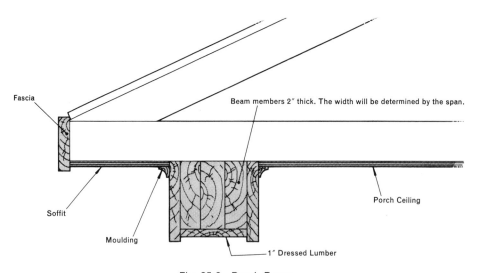

Fascia

Beam members 2″ thick. The width will be determined by the span.

Porch Ceiling

Soffit

Moulding

1″ Dressed Lumber

Fig. 25:3 Porch Beam

344

the main roof either to extend beyond the wall far enough to cover the porch area, or to recess the main wall, thus forming a covered-in area while still maintaining the regular roof line. Figure 25:2B illustrates such an architectural arrangement.

There are two basic types of porches: (a) open; (b) closed. As their names imply they differ in the amount of side wall enclosure provided. They can range from the completely open porches with a concrete slab floor and small steel posts to those with completely enclosed walls, which may be heated and used as a finished living area.

An example of a porch used in many modern homes is shown in Figure 25:1.

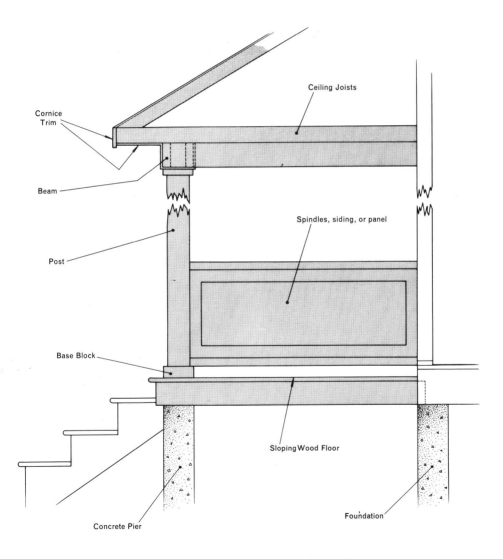

Fig. 25:4 Conventional porch framing and trim.

The only additional exterior trim involved in this type of porch is the posts and the boxed-in, supporting beam, which may be faced with lumber cut in an arch as shown in Figure 25:2A. In many houses the porch roof is formed by a continuation of the main roof and overhang as in Figure 25:1.

There are, however, still many porches built in the traditional method with masonry piers or walls that support one end of wood floor joists, the other end of the joists rest on the main house foundation wall. These porches generally have some type of solid or open railing arrangement between the posts. It is common practice to make the post from 2″ structural lumber boxed in with finished lumber. The beams, too, are finished with dressed lumber. See Figure 25:3.

Figures 25:4, 25:5, and 25:6 illustrate three methods used to afford some side wall protection by filling the space below the railing and between the posts. The rail is generally placed 30″ to 36″ above the floor. In the method shown in Figure 25:6, the siding from the main house is continued around the porch. This is a good arrangement if there is any likelihood of the porch being glassed in at a later date, as the 2″ x 8″ rail can be used as a subsill for the sash or window frames; the lower part of the wall will already have been completed.

The posts or columns may be square and built as in Figure 25:7; either 2″ x 4″s or 2″ x 6″s are used for centre support. Round columns are used in varying lengths and diameters for porch supports. For two-storey colonial homes that have large round columns often two storeys high, the hollow

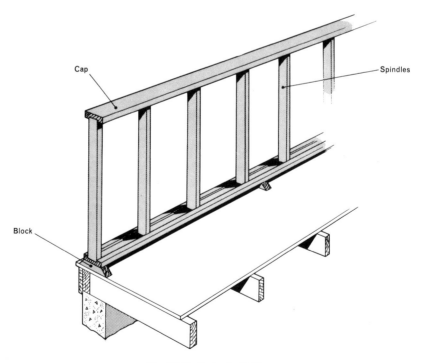

Fig. 25:5 Spindle Railing

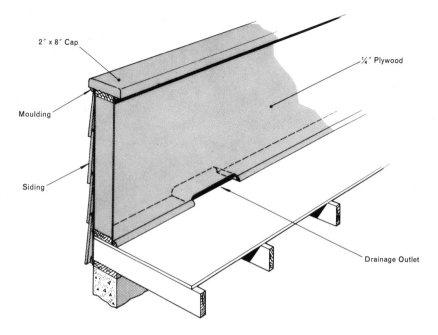

Fig. 25:6 Solid railing between posts.

stave column shown in Figure 25:8 is used. On bungalow homes, smaller-diameter, solid wood posts are used. Metal tubular posts with a plate welded on each end also serve as porch columns.

Wrought iron posts and railings are extensively used on modern homes

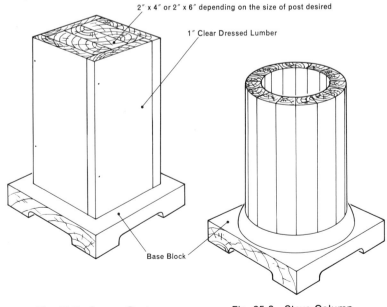

Fig. 25:7 Square Post   Fig. 25:8 Stave Column

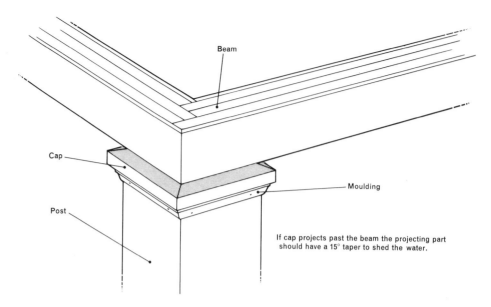

If cap projects past the beam the projecting part should have a 15° taper to shed the water.

Beam

Cap

Moulding

Post

Fig. 25:9   Post Cap and Beam

Fig. 25:10   Wrought Iron Posts and Railing

348

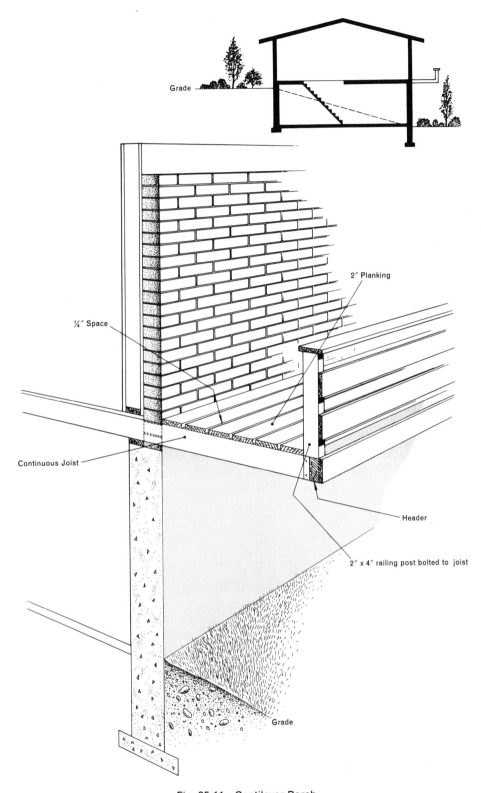

Grade

¼" Space

2" Planking

Continuous Joist

Header

2" x 4" railing post bolted to joist

Grade

Fig. 25:11   Cantilever Porch

349

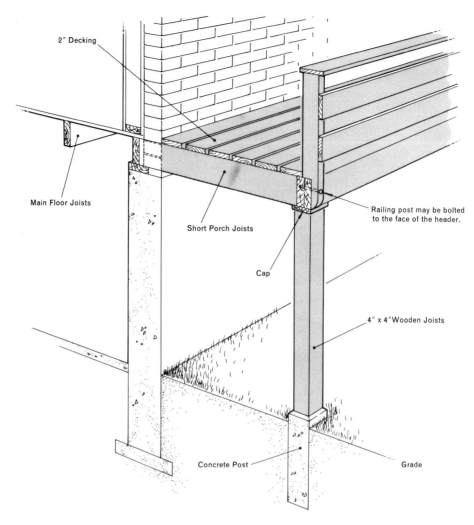

2″ Decking

Main Floor Joists

Short Porch Joists

Cap

Railing post may be bolted
to the face of the header.

4″ x 4″ Wooden Joists

Concrete Post

Grade

Fig. 25:12 Porch deck when the joists are at right angles to those of the main house.

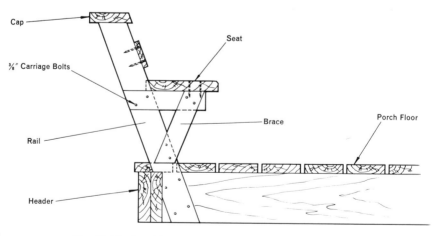

Cap

⅜″ Carriage Bolts

Rail

Header

Seat

Brace

Porch Floor

Fig. 25:13 Combination seat and rail. Use all 2″ red cedar.

where the porch is built on a concrete slab floor. The corner supports generally consist of two or three 1″ x 1″ metal posts with scroll work welded between them as shown in Figure 25:10.

A popular platform arrangement that can be classed as a porch, although it is seldom covered with a roof, is the *cantilever porch*, (sometimes referred to as a deck or balcony). This type of porch is used on many new homes, especially those built on a sloping lot. See Figure 25:11.

The platform is often supported by allowing the floor joists to project beyond the wall, in which case no posts are required. This method of support is only possible when the main floor joists run at a right angle to the deck floor. If the joists run in the opposite direction, the deck must be supported by short joists running from the foundation to a double header which in turn is supported by posts. See Figure 25:12.

The flooring of the deck is generally made from 2″ cedar planking laid with a ½″ open joint between the planks to allow water to run through.

Some type of railing must be provided for safety and appearance; a seat arrangement may be incorporated as one of the railing members. Figures 25:12 and 25:13 show two types of railings.

Many styles of wood railing can be used as well as the popular wrought iron type.

Another type of porch extensively used is the "breezeway", the partially or totally enclosed area between the main house and the garage. The breezeway has a concrete slab floor at the grade level, which is generally one or more steps below the floor level of the main house. The roof level is generally below that of the main house because of the drop in floor level. The cornice should correspond to that of the rest of the house. One style of breezeway is shown in Figure 25:14.

There are many other architectural arrangements, such as covered entrances, sun decks, patios, and step platforms, that can be loosely termed as porches, but they are too numerous and varied to be described here. However, their construction is similar in most respects to one of the types illustrated here.

Fig. 25:14   Open Breezeway

DOOR ENTRANCES

The front entrance is often the most distinctive feature of a home and the focal point of interest, symbolizing a welcome to all who approach. For this reason the special attention of the architect and the builder is required to provide an attractive entrance that will harmonize with the rest of the house.

A more or less standard exterior door frame that is used for side and back doors and also sometimes for the front door is shown in Figures 25:15 and 25:16. Many front door entrances, however, are more elaborate, with side lights or heavy trim. The entrance may be recessed for protection and appearance or it may be covered by an ornamental canopy. See Figures 25:17 and 25:18.

The door frames must be well constructed from heavy material and properly installed to support heavy doors and to withstand the rugged wear and constant jarring they receive from the doors being slammed.

Standard exterior door frames are sold by the lumber mills as pre-assembled units, ready for installation. For ease of shipment they may be delivered as knocked-down units, with all parts cut to length, fitted and bundled, ready for assembly on the job. Front door frames may differ from the standard frame shown in Figure 25:15, in that the exterior casing or trim member is wider and thicker and may be decorated with fluted, half-round cuts running all or part of the way up the door trim. Extra blocks and pieces of moulding are often added to the side casing. The most ornamental part of a front door frame, however, is often the head trim, which may be cut as a semi-circle or in some other shape to create the desired architectural effect. Some designs are shown in Figures 25:20, 25:22, and 25:23A.

Figure 25:23 illustrates a frame with double doors. This arrangement requires a wide entrance hall and creates an effective front entrance, especially when used on larger, two-storey homes.

The current trend in front entrances is the use of side lights, to provide light to the entrance hall and style to the front of the house. The lights can be arranged in several ways. There may be a sash on only one side of the door or there may be a sash on both sides, as shown in Figure 25:24. In this design the lower third of the side sections is enclosed with a solid wood panel with the sash filling the remainder of the space. Either clear or obscure glass may be used. The side lights may be protected with storm sashes or they may be made of vacuum-sealed glass.

A threshold of some type is installed in most exterior door frames. Two types are shown in Figures 25:28 and 25:29.

When setting a door frame in a brick veneer or frame wall, the same procedure as that for setting a window frame is followed. The door frame is centred in the opening and the side jambs are plumbed and securely nailed through the exterior trim into the 2" x 4" framing.

In a solid masonry wall, the door frame should be set on the wall in the correct location, plumbed, and levelled before it is securely held with braces. See Figure 25:30. The masonry wall can then be built around it. When side

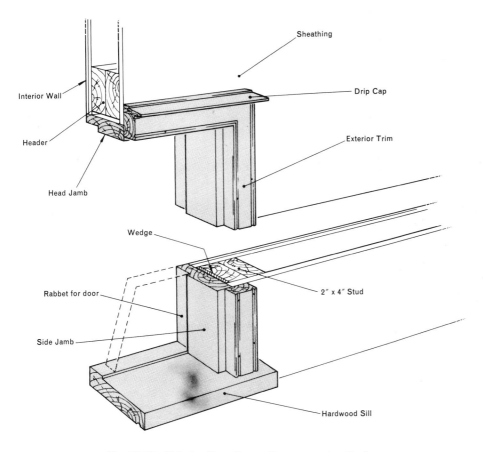

Fig. 25:15   Exterior Door Frame (frame construction)

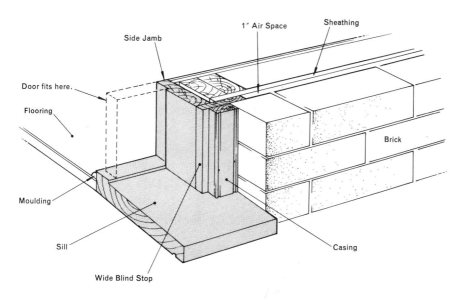

Fig. 25:16   Exterior Door Frame (brick veneer construction)

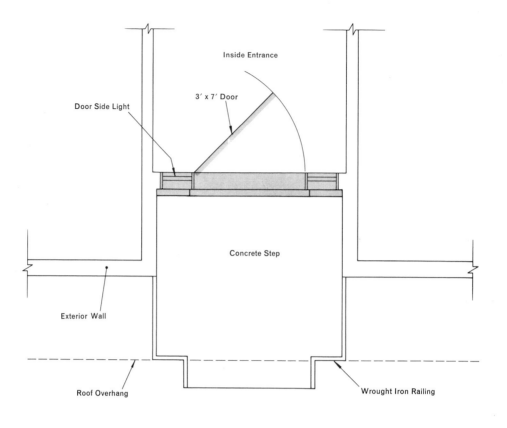

Inside Entrance

3' x 7' Door

Door Side Light

Exterior Wall

Concrete Step

Roof Overhang

Wrought Iron Railing

Fig. 25:17 Recessed Front Door Entrance

Fig. 25:18   Front entrance with copper-covered canopy.

Fig. 25:19   Roof bracket sometimes used over back and side doors.

Fig. 25:20   Front entrance with wide trim members and pilaster posts.

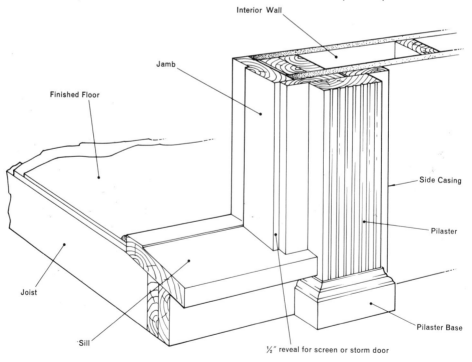

Interior Wall

Jamb

Finished Floor

Side Casing

Pilaster

Joist

Sill

Pilaster Base

½″ reveal for screen or storm door

Fig. 25:21   Base of door frame and trim.

356

Fig. 25:22   Front entrance with pilaster posts
and ornamental arched head.

A

Fig. 25:23   (A) Front entrance with
a double door.

B

C

Fig. 25:23   (B) Double doors with imitation shutters;   (C) Double doors in recessed entrance.

Fig. 25:24   Front entrance with side lights.

Fig. 25:25   Horizontal section of door frame with side lights.

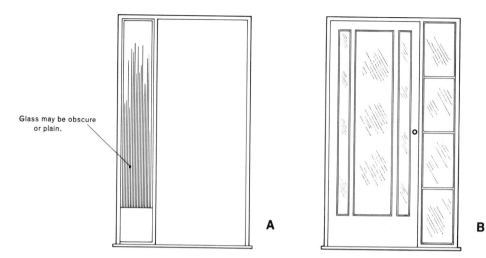

Glass may be obscure
or plain.

A

B

Fig. 25:26   (A) and (B) Door frames with a single full-length side light.

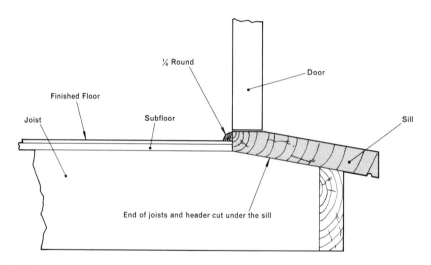

¼ Round

Door

Finished Floor

Joist

Subfloor

Sill

End of joists and header cut under the sill

Fig. 25:27   Exterior door frame sill where no threshold is used (frame construction).

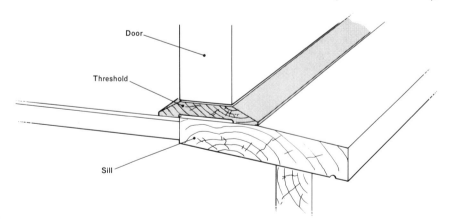

Door

Threshold

Sill

Fig. 25:28   Wooden Threshold

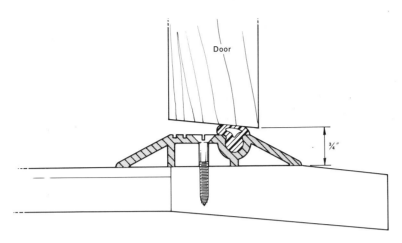

Fig. 25:29   Aluminum threshold with vinyl plastic insert.

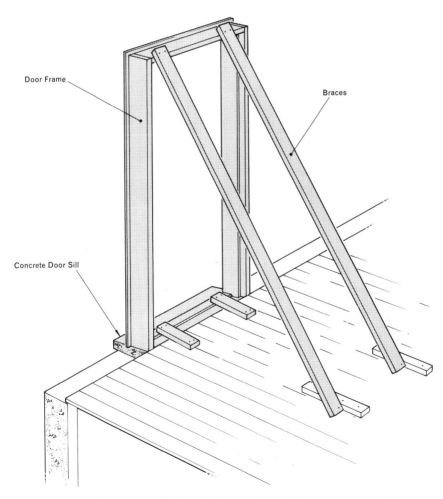

Door Frame

Braces

Concrete Door Sill

Fig. 25:30   Door frame set on the foundation wall before the masonry wall is built.

Panel Doors

Plywood Slab Doors

Plank Doors

Fig. 25:31 Exterior Doors

lights are included in the entrance they are incorporated in the frame, making it a complete entrance unit.

Exterior doors are made in many styles and designs, that can be classified as: (a) panel; (b) plywood slab; (c) plank. There are many variations of each of these types and most of them have one or more panes of glass, often in odd shapes. Some of the door designs most often used are shown in Figure 25:31.

Exterior doors are made in three stock sizes: 2'8" x 6'8", 2'10" x 6'10", and 3' x 7'. They are generally 1¾" thick.

The sliding glass door unit is extensively used in modern residential building. This unit consists of a 3' wide wood or aluminum door with one large light of glass and a 3' stationary panel of glass over which the door can slide. The sliding glass door unit is used chiefly for porches and patios. The door

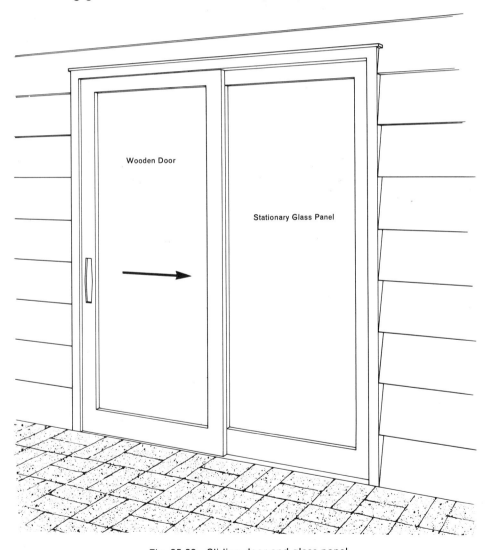

Fig. 25:32 Sliding door and glass panel.

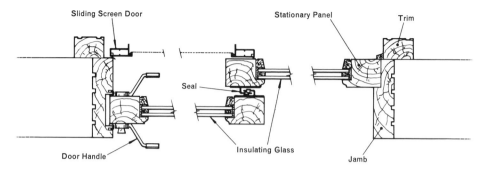

Fig. 25:33   Vertical section of a wood and glass sliding door with a stationary glass panel.

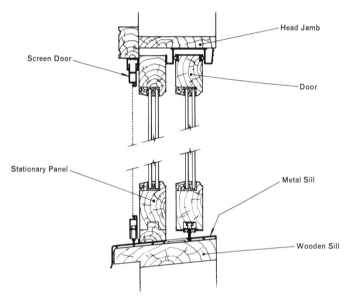

Fig. 25:34   Horizontal section of a sliding wood and glass door.

slides or rolls on an aluminum or vinyl track. A special aluminum member similar to the one shown in Figure 25:34 is used at the sill to act as a track and to prevent the door from leaking. A screen door unit is also mounted on this track.

Although aluminum sliding door units have been extensively used, some difficulty due to condensation has been experienced during our Canadian winters. Condensation causes an undue amount of moisture at the sill and makes it difficult to operate the door. Because wood has much greater insulation value than aluminum, it has been found that there is considerably less condensation when wooden sliding doors are used. The glass in the door and the panel beside it should be of the double insulating type. Some sliding door units are now being manufactured with nearly all of the non-glass parts made from hard vinyl plastic. Time will determine the effectiveness of this material in withstanding the Canadian climate.

Only a few of the many types and styles of doors and front entrances have been mentioned here but these are representative of the rest.

ASSIGNMENT

Porches

1. How has the architectural design of porches changed in recent years?
2. What is the structural difference between an open and a closed porch?
3. How are porch joists supported?
4. Make a sectional drawing of a beam used to support a porch roof.
5. Describe three methods of filling in the space between the railing and the porch floor.
6. On what type of homes are long, round, wooden columns often used?
7. When a porch has wrought iron posts and railings, what type of floor is generally used?
8. Explain the two methods of supporting a porch deck considering the direction of the main house joists.
9. What type of flooring is generally used on a cantilever deck?
10. Make a drawing of two types of railings used on porch decks.
11. Explain the location and construction of a breezeway.

Door Entrances

12. Make a drawing of a standard exterior door frame and name the parts.
13. How does the exterior door frame that is used for a brick veneer house differ from one used on a frame house?
14. What is meant by
    (a) A pre-assembled door frame unit?
    (b) A knocked-down door frame unit?
15. Describe the features of an exterior door trim for a front entrance that make it different from the trim used on a standard exterior door frame.
16. When double doors are used for a front entrance, what special interior design feature must be incorporated in the floor plan?
17. (a) What is meant by doors with side lights?
    (b) What purpose do the side lights serve?
    (c) List some of the side light arrangements that can be used.
18 Why is a vinyl insert used in some door thresholds?
19. Explain how an exterior door frame is set in:
    (a) a frame wall
    (b) a solid masonry wall.
20. Make a drawing of one door design from each of the three types of exterior doors.
21. Doors are manufactured in three stock sizes. List the sizes.
22. Describe the two sections of an exterior sliding door unit.
23. Why are sliding doors made of wood considered to be superior to those made of aluminum?
24. What type of glass is used in sliding doors?

Chapter 26

ELEMENTARY STAIR BUILDING

The building of stairs is often considered to be one of the more advanced operations in home building and is reserved for the fully qualified carpenter. In fact, stair building is often considered to be a trade in itself, or at least, a specialized branch or subtrade within the construction industry. This is especially so when the tradesman has, as well as a full knowledge of all aspects and types of stairs, the experience and skill of a craftsman to build them properly in all their complicated detail. Such men are in great demand by good construction companies and command a high rate of pay.

Elementary stair building, however, is not as difficult nor as involved as we

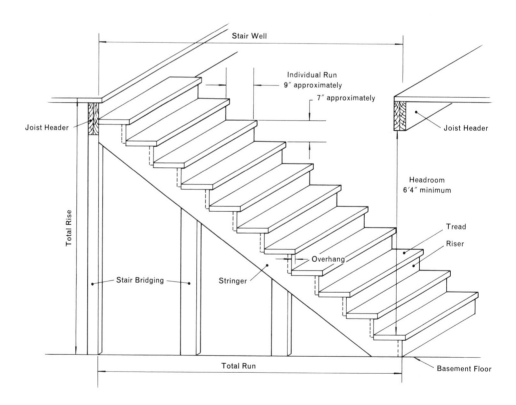

Fig. 26:1   Basement Steps. Parts and terms.

are sometimes led to believe. If you can read architectural working drawings, understand elementary mathematics, have a working knowledge of stair terms and the principle of stair layout, and are a careful and conscientious tradesman, you should have no difficulty mastering elementary stair building.

We will limit this chapter to the elementary stair building information that the average carpenter would be expected to understand. The more complex aspects of stair construction can be left to a more advanced study of the subject.

There are two general classifications of stairs; they differ in their type and their location in the home.

1. *Steps.* The term *steps* refers, in general, to a simple structural arrangement used to descend from a porch to the sidewalk or from the main floor to an unfinished basement.

2. *Stairs.* The term *stairs* refers, in general, to flights of stairs reaching from the main floor of a house to the second floor or to a finished basement. In split-level homes and commercial buildings, stairs are built in various other places as well. Stairs often span a greater distance than steps. They involve more labour and material and are more complex in their construction requiring a better finish and a higher degree of precision and skill to build.

Figure 26:1 illustrates a set of basement steps and also shows the names of the main step parts as well as some stair terms with which you should become familiar. Study this drawing.

DEFINITIONS OF THE MAIN STAIR PARTS

The same parts and terms apply to both steps and stairs, although stairs have additional parts.

Stringers
The main supporting diagonal members cut to receive the treads and risers.

Treads
The main horizontal members, which are walked on.

Risers
The vertical members that enclose the space between adjacent treads. They run from the back edge of one tread to the underside of the tread directly above it.

Stair Well
The framed floor opening through which the stairs ascend or descend.

Headers
The double 2″ x 8″s or 2″ x 10″s that form the ends of the stair well, and on which the top of the stringer rests.

STAIR TERMS

Total Rise
The vertical distance of the stairs.

Total Run
The total horizontal distance from the face of the bottom riser to the face of the top riser.

Individual Rise
The vertical distance from the top of one tread to the top of the next. It is sometimes called the tread rise.

Individual Run
The horizontal distance from the face of one riser to the face of the next. It is sometimes called the tread run.

Head Room
The vertical distance from the header at the end of the stair well to the face of the tread directly below it.

Tread Overhang
The distance the tread projects over the face of the riser. This is sometimes called the nosing. See Figure 26:2.

Some steps are built with the riser omitted; the treads are merely housed into the stringers as shown in Figure 26:3.

The material used for outside or basement steps generally consists of —

Stringers: 2″ x 10″

Treads:　2″ x 10″, or for outside, two 2″ x 6″s may be used to make up the tread. See Figure 26:4.

Risers:　1″ x 8″.

For basement steps pine or spruce is often used. Steps to be used outside are generally made of cedar, a lumber less susceptible to decay when exposed to the weather.

Before starting the necessary calculations to determine the number of risers and treads and the width of each, we must consider some basic rules devised by architects and endorsed by the National Housing Act and by most local building codes:

1. All individual treads and risers shall have uniform rise and run in any one flight of stairs.
2. Seven inches is the best average height for individual risers.
3. The height of individual risers must be proportional to the width of the tread.
4. Except in special cases there is one more riser than treads, as the top floor acts as a tread. This means the stairs start and end with a riser.

When these rules are adhered to, the result will be "easy flowing stairs" that are safe and comfortable to walk up and down.

There are several formulas for arriving at the correct ratio between the individual rise and tread. These formulas are based on the length of the average stride. The reasoning is that if a person steps up a long distance he cannot, at the same time, step very far forward, or vice versa. The formulas are these:

1. the tread + 2 risers = 24″
2. the tread + rise   = 17″
3. tread × rise   = 70″

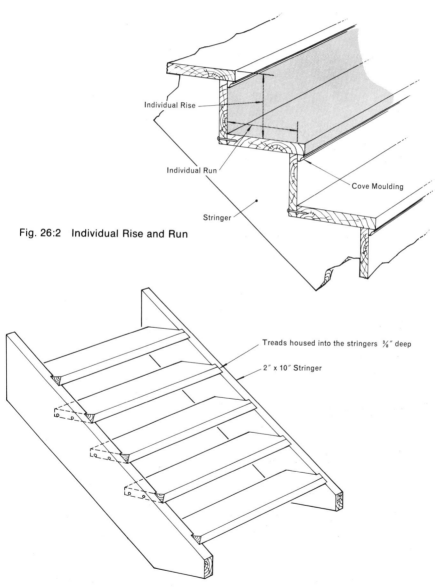

Fig. 26:2   Individual Rise and Run

Fig. 26:3   Open Steps. No risers.

369

When it is not possible to adhere exactly to these formulas because of conditions in the house such as the placement of a door or some other factor, it is permissible to make a 10 per cent variation. *Residential Standards* regulations state that the maximum height of each riser shall be no more than *8"* and that the minimum run of each step shall be *8½"* with a minimum tread width of *9½"*, that is, each tread should have at least *1"* overhang.

STAIR MATHEMATICS

If stairs are to be correctly framed, it is important that care be taken with the mathematics involved in calculating the number of treads and risers and the width of each. It is necessary first to determine the *"total rise"*. This is the most important measurement in any stair layout problem.

Let us take, for example, the set of verandah steps with a cutout stringer, shown in Figure 26:4. The total rise, or the distance from the porch floor to the sidewalk, is 36¼". Since 7" is the best individual rise height, 7 should be divided into 36¼.

$$36¼ \div 7 = 5.178$$

Since all risers must be of equal height the closest whole number will be taken, which is 5. It can be assumed, then, that there will be five risers.

To find the exact height of each riser divide the total rise by 5.

$$36¼ \div 5 = 7¼$$

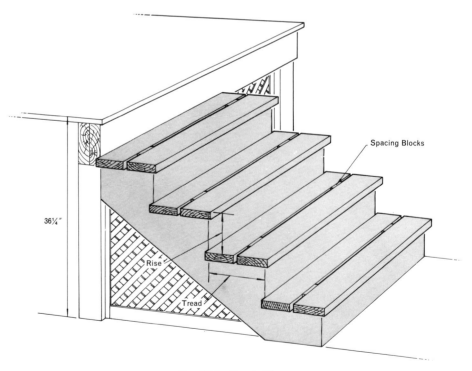

Fig. 26:4 Porch Steps

This means there will be five risers, each 7¼" high.

Since there is no definite location where verandah steps must end, we can adhere strictly to the formulas given in determining the width of each tread.

There will be four treads (one fewer tread than risers). It can be noted from formula 2 that the rise + the tread should be 17". If we subtract the already determined riser height (7¼") from 17" the remainder is 9¾" which will represent the individual tread run. This does not take into account the tread overhang on each step, which is generally from 1" to 1½". This would mean that a small amount would have to be ripped off standard 2" x 12" stock for the treads. Quite often two pieces of 2" x 6" material are used for treads on outside steps, as in Figure 26:4. They are spaced a small distance apart to allow water to run away and to prevent rot by providing ventilation.

TO LAY OUT A CUTOUT STRINGER

Using the same example for the layout of the stringer, find the approximate length of the stringer by measuring diagonally between the tongue and the body of the framing square, from the figure representing the total run on the body to the figure representing the total rise on the tongue. Since the arms of the square are too short for using these dimensions full scale, some convenient scale can be used. For short steps it might be ½" = 1", for longer steps ¼" = 1". When cutting the rough stock allow an extra 2" or 3" in length. In this case the total run would be 4" x 9¾" = 39" and the total rise is 36¼". If a ¼ scale were used, the measurement would be taken from the 9¾" mark on the body of the square to the 9 1/16" mark on the tongue, which would be 13¼". Multiplying this by 4 to bring it to full size gives us 53", the approximate length of the step stringer. Add 3" for cutting. See Figure 26:5.

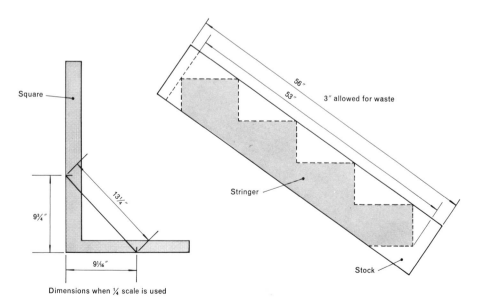

Fig. 26:5 Calculating the approximate length of step stringer.

371

By finding the rough stringer length, the material can be estimated and ordered or cut from longer stock on the job.

Before making the actual layout on the stringer it is a good idea to equip the framing square with a fence; this reduces the layout time, but more important, it ensures a more accurate layout. If a fence is not available, one similar to the one shown in Figure 26:6 can be made. Metal stair gauges can be used for the same purpose. See Figure 26:7.

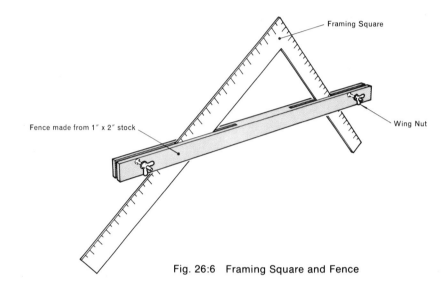

Fig. 26:6   Framing Square and Fence

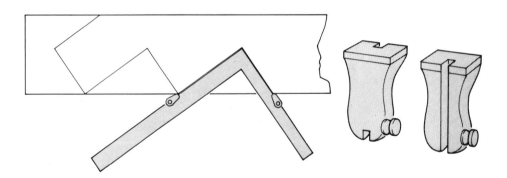

Fig. 26:7   Stair Gauges

1. Set the fence or the stair gauges to the height of the riser on the tongue, and to the tread run on the body of the framing square. In this case it would be 7¼ ″ for the rise and 9¾ ″ for the tread.
2. Place the stringer on a pair of saw horses.
3. Commence the layout by marking the location of the bottom step, and have this end of the stringer to your right. If the stringer stock has no extra length a short straight-edge can be placed at the edge of the stringer which

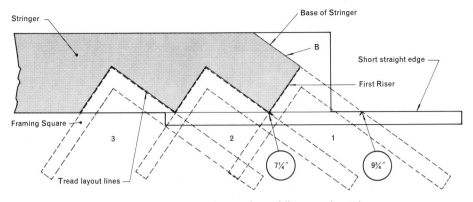

Fig. 26:8 Laying out the riser and tread lines on the stringer.

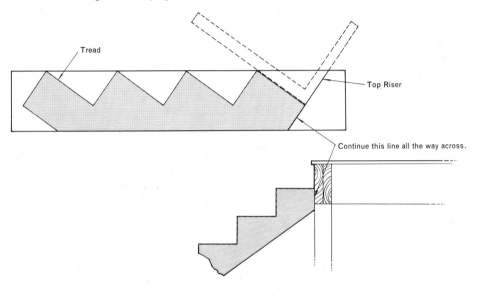

Fig. 26:9 Layout at top of stringer.

will act as an edge for the square in making the bottom step layout. See Figure 26:8. In this way no lumber is wasted. While the square is in this first position lay out the bottom riser line, (line B, Figure 26:8). Continue this line across the stringer to form the base line, or the bottom of the stringer. This will be the part of the stringer that will rest on the sidewalk.

4. Move the square along to position two, and mark along the body and tongue to form the layout lines for the second step.

5. Move the square along the stringer, stopping as many times as there are individual steps. In this example four steps are required. Mark along the tongue and the body of the square, each time making sure the fence or stair gauges are tight against the edge of the stringer. Number the steps as you progress.

6. When the square is in the fourth position continue the riser line all the way across the stringer as shown in Figure 26:9. The top riser of the steps will be formed by the joist header and the fascia nailed to it.

7. Since the thickness of the tread forms a part of the first riser, the riser layout on the stringer must be reduced by this amount. This is sometimes referred to as "dropping the stringer". Thus, the stringer is shortened, which makes all the risers exactly the same height. The principle of the stringer drop is shown in Figure 26:10.

8. All layout lines should be squared across the edge of the stringer. The exception to this occurs when the risers are mitred into the stringer so that the end grain of the riser will not be visible. The majority of better-quality outside steps are built in this manner. This method will be described here.

9. From each riser line, draw a line at 45° across the edge of the stringer. This line should be drawn towards the top of the stringer as in Figure 26:11.

TO CUT OUT THE STRINGER

1. When the layout is complete, cut out the first stringer. Cut on the lines using a sharp cross-cut hand saw or a portable electric saw.

2. When one stringer is cut set it on top of the other stringer face to face.

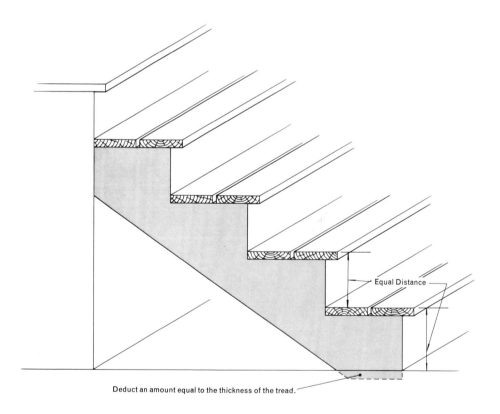

Equal Distance

Deduct an amount equal to the thickness of the tread.

Fig. 26:10 Dropping the stringer.

Mark the second stringer as shown in Figure 26:12. In this way you can be assured that the stringers will be cut in pairs with the long side of the mitre cuts facing out to make the risers fit properly.

3. Since the stringer stock for outside steps is generally made from 2″ material, and the risers are made from 1″ stock, two methods can be used to make the joint between the two members. If an electric portable saw is used, the joint shown in Figure 26:13 can be made. This joint is considered superior to the one shown in Figure 26:14, which can be cut with either a hand or power saw. Study these two figures.

   If the steps are more than 3′ wide a third stringer should be used in the centre of the span as illustrated in Figure 26:15.

4. Cut the risers to width and length with a 45° angle cut on each end. The length of the risers should be equal to the distance from the outside of one stringer to the outside of the other. The bottom riser will be narrower than the rest by the thickness of the tread stock.

5. Cut the treads to length, making allowance for the distance they overhang the stringers, which will usually be equal to the front overhang. The tread run in this case is 9¾″ with the maximum overhang of 1¼″; the width of the tread stock should then be approximately 11″. Stock size 2″ x 12″ material could be used for treads if ¾″ were ripped off one edge. Better

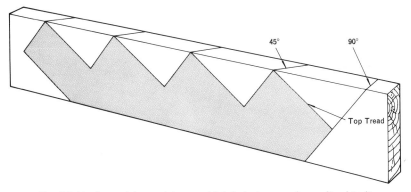

Fig. 26:11   Layout for a stringer which is to have a riser mitred to it.

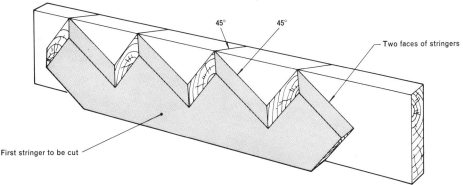

Fig. 26:12   Laying out stringers in pairs.

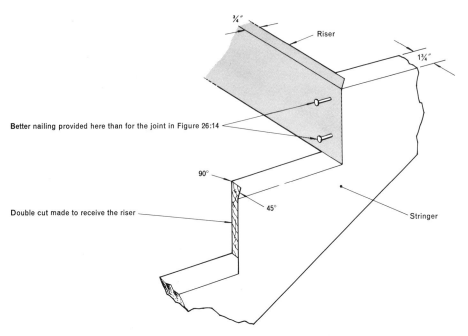

Fig. 26:13   A good method of attaching the risers to the stringer.

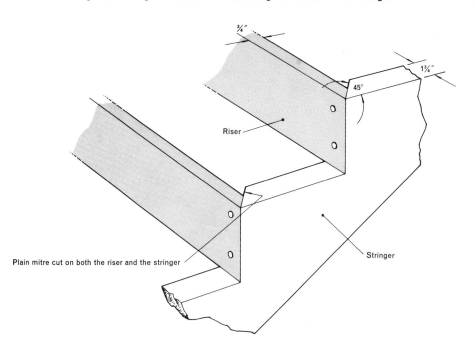

Fig. 26:14   Alternate method of mitring riser to tread.

treads for outside steps would result from the use of two pieces of standard 2″ x 6″ stock with ½″ space between them as shown in Figure 26:16. It would be necessary to rip a strip 1″ wide off one of the pieces to make a total tread width of 11″.

376

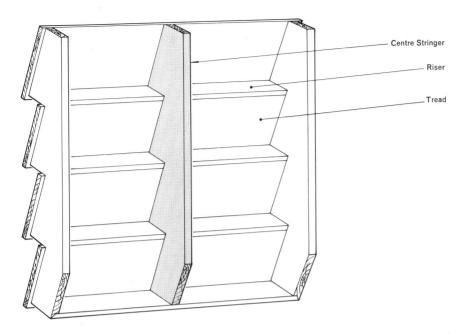

Fig. 26:15   Wide steps as viewed from the back, showing third stringer.

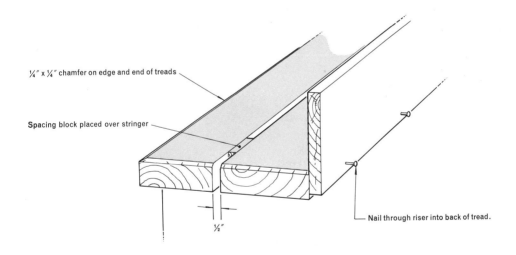

Fig. 26:16   Tread made from two pieces of stock.

TO ASSEMBLE STEPS

1. Set the stringers on edge on a pair of trestles. Nail the top and bottom risers in place with 2½″ finishing nails.
2. Square the stairs using a framing square as shown in Figure 26:17. Nail a temporary diagonal brace to the underside of the stringers as shown in the same Figure. This will keep the steps square until all the risers and treads are nailed in place.

3. Using 2½" finishing nails, secure all the other risers.
4. Nail the treads in place with 4" spikes. Allowance should be made for the correct amount of overhang at the stringers. If the tread is to be made up of two pieces, a ½" spacer should be used between them.

    Care should be taken when assembling steps that all nails are driven straight and that there are no hammer marks. The finishing nails should be set below the surface and the spikes flush with, or slightly below, the surface. Stairs and steps, as well as being functional, are part of the trim of a house and should be built in a craftsmanlike fashion.
5. The steps should be attached firmly. They can be attached to the porch fascia by toe-nailing the stringers or by nailing the top tread to a 2" x 2" strip, which in turn has been spiked through the fascia into the joist header. See Figure 26:18. For additional support, vertical pieces called "stair bridging" may be set under the stringers. The top tread should be level lengthwise. It is, however, desirable for the treads to slope towards the front at an angle of approximately 5° to enable water to run off. The base of the stringers must rest on a solid level base, preferably one made of concrete.

All parts of the steps should be well painted to prevent rot. This is probably more important with wooden steps than with any other part of the house, since, owing to their proximity to the ground and their constant use, steps are

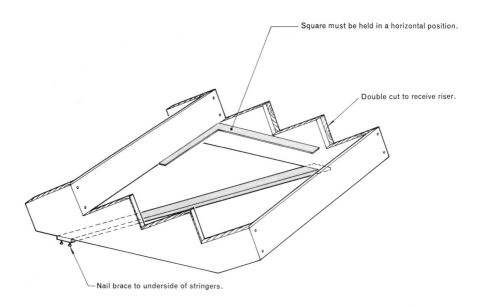

Square must be held in a horizontal position.

Double cut to receive riser.

Nail brace to underside of stringers.

Fig. 26:17   Square framework of steps.

very susceptible to rot and other deterioration.

Because it is periodically necessary to replace outside steps that are made from wood, the use of concrete steps is becoming more prevalent. The mathematical formulas used for the stringer layout can also be used for building the forms for reinforced concrete steps.

Since it is the purpose of this book to deal principally with the exterior frame structure of homes, we have described here only the cutout type of steps that are mainly used for exterior or basement steps. As has been pointed out, there are many other types of stairs that are built and installed in the interior of homes. Many of these are quite complex; the principles involved in stair layout, however, are the same and are applicable to all types and lengths of stairs.

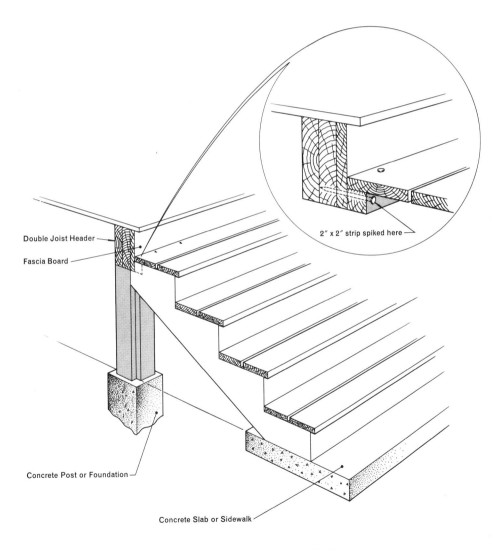

Fig. 26:18 Steps supported and in place.

ASSIGNMENT

1. Why is stair-building often considered to be a special sub-trade in the construction industry?
2. What qualifications should a person have to be able to do elementary stair-building?
3. The terms *steps* and *stairs* have distinct meanings within the building industry. Briefly give your interpretation of these two terms.
4. Make a sketch of a short set of steps. Label your sketch with these parts and terms: stringer, tread, riser, total rise, total run, individual rise, and tread run.
5. What size stock is generally used for these step parts: stringer, treads, and risers?
6. Why should all the individual treads and risers have the same rise and run?
7. What is considered to be the best height for individual risers?
8. Explain the statement "the height of individual risers must be proportional to the width of the tread".
9. A set of steps has three treads. How many risers will it have?
10. List two formulas for arriving at the correct ratio between the height of the individual riser and the width of the tread.
11. (a) State the maximum height of an individual riser.
    (b) State the minimum width of treads.
12. The distance from the top of a porch floor to the top of the sidewalk is 29″.
    (a) How many risers will be required for the steps?
    (b) What would be the height of each riser?
    (c) How many treads would be required?
    (d) What would be the width of each tread?
13. What is the advantage of using two pieces of 2″ x 6″ stock as treads for outside steps?
14. How is the approximate length of the stringers determined?
15. What are "stair gauges"? Why are they used?
16. How is the layout made to mark out the bottom step if the square must project over the end of the stringer?
17. Which members generally form the top riser of a set of steps?
18. Explain the term "dropping the stringer".
19. Why are mitre joints made between the risers and the stringers?
20. When transferring the layout lines from one cutout stringer to another, why are they placed face to face?
21. When should three stringers be used in a set of steps?
22. How far should the treads overhang the risers?
23. How are the stairs squared while they are being assembled?
24. How are steps secured to a wood porch?
25. Why should the treads on porch steps have a 5° slope to the front?
26. Why should all parts of wooden steps be well painted?

Chapter 27

PORTABLE POWER TOOLS

Automation is taking place in the building industry through the increased use of improved power equipment. A great deal of time and labour is saved by the use of the many types and sizes of portable electric or pneumatic power tools that are made to meet the needs of the building industry and the home owner. They are designed to perform operations that cannot be done on stationary machines, and that were formerly done with hand tools.

TYPES OF PORTABLE POWER TOOLS

Portable Electric Hand Saw

The piece of equipment that has done the most to save manual labour and time in the building industry is the portable electric saw. It can be used to make almost any cut that was formerly made by a hand saw. It is estimated that an electric portable saw will cut through a 2″ plank 25 times faster than a hand saw and with 1/85 of the effort on the part of the operator. When one first uses an electric saw one begins to appreciate the implications of "power tools". The speed of the blade and the ease with which the saw can be pushed ahead, together with the whirr of the blade and the discharge of the sawdust, proclaim the power and capacity of the machine. As long as we treat this power with proper respect, and use the saw in the correct manner, it will perform wonders in saving us both time and effort and it still will be a safe tool to use.

Portable power saws are made in varying sizes and weights. Because these saws are often lifted to head height when vertical cuts are being made, they are manufactured as light as possible, but they are still rugged enough to stand up under hard use. The frames are generally made of light steel or aluminum alloy.

Many of the operations performed on the stationary variety table saws can be performed with portable saws, although not to the same degree of accuracy. When rip sawing, a guide line must be drawn. There is generally a V-shaped notch at the front of the saw base that is in line with the blade. If the point of this V follows the line, a straight cut can be made for either rip sawing or cross-cutting. A small rip saw fence is provided on most portable saws that serves as an aid in making straight cuts. The saw base is adjustable to vary the depth of the cut so that grooves or dados can be made. The base also tilts so that angles, bevels, or chamfers can be cut.

The conventional rip and crosscut, as well as combination and planer blades, are used for various woodcutting operations. An abrasive disc can be used in place of a blade for cutting building materials such as tile, concrete, and marble. The diameter of the blade determines the size of the saw; blades range from 6″ to 8″. A typical portable saw is shown in Figure 27:1.

Portable electric saws will not replace the conventional table saws either

Stanley Tools

Fig. 27:1   7″ Portable Electric Saw

Stanley Tools

Fig. 27:2   Rip sawing with an electric hand saw

for accuracy or for ease of operation. Their value is in their portability, which makes them easy to transport to the job site, and to use in any area of the structure. The fact that they can be so conveniently used on long stock and in places where the material is fastened to the building adds to their usefulness. Portable power saws may be used on saw horses, but on large jobs special cutting benches are built for their use.

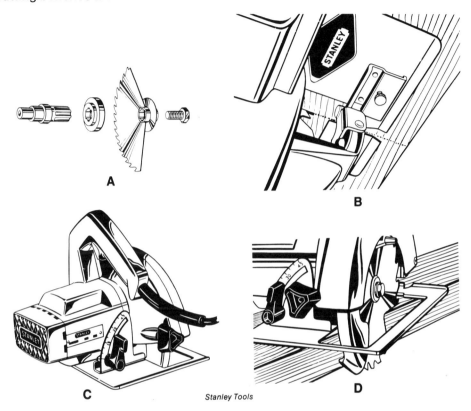

Stanley Tools

Fig. 27:3 (A) Blade mounting which allows the blade to stop independently of the motor, thus protecting the motor when the blade strikes something hard; (B) Note the notch at the front end of the saw base and its relation to the saw cut; (C) Saw guide will automatically rise above the blade as it enters the wood when making an angle cut; (D) Adjustments at rear of saw.

Pointers on Use of Portable Electric Saw

1. Draw guide lines at the desired location of cut.
2. Use the correct blade for the cut to be made.
3. Adjust the depth and angle of the blade to suit the cut to be made.
4. See that the work is held firmly on a trestle or bench. (Where possible, it is a good idea to clamp the work.)
5. When starting the cut allow the blade to reach its full speed.
6. Use a guide when possible. If a long cut is to be made in a plywood panel a straight-edge should be clamped to it and used in place of the rip guide provided on the saw.
7. Cut on the waste side of the line.

8. Push the saw ahead steadily but not so rapidly that the r.p.m. will drop below efficient cutting speed.
9. When not in use the saw must be disconnected. Many accidents have occurred after the cut has been made and the saw shut off but with the blade still coasting. Some manufacturers have installed a brake on the switch that stops the blade in ½ second.

SAFETY PRECAUTIONS THAT *MUST* BE OBSERVED

Portable electric saws are useful and efficient tools but they are also a potential source of danger if not handled with precision and care. No person should operate a portable power saw until he has been given instruction in its use.

1. These saws are fitted with a spring-loaded retractable guard which should spring back over the blade after the wood has been cut. See that this guard operates freely.
2. When operating the saw hold it firmly with both hands and avoid careless handling of the saw or stock.
3. Make sure all adjustments are tight.
4. Do not cross-cut a board between the two supporting points. It will cause the blade to bind and may throw the saw out of control.
5. Use the correct blade, and make sure it is assembled on the saw so that the teeth point up on the forward edge of the blade.
6. Connect the saw only to a grounded electrical outlet.
7. Make sure the blade is sharp. A dull blade will make it difficult to push the saw and if forced will burn and discolour the wood and may cause the blade to stall or the saw to go out of control.
8. Always wear safety goggles when using a metal-cutting blade or abrasive disc on the saw.

Most accidents occur from over-confidence. The portable electric saw demands all your attention even after you have become accustomed to its use.

Sabre Saw

Although the *sabre saw* might be considered a basement tool for the hobbyist or handyman, it is also used as a building construction tool. There are many cutting operations such as curved fascia boards and kitchen cabinet work for which a portable electric sabre saw is the most convenient tool to use.

The portable scroll or sabre saw has a narrow, stiff blade that moves up and down allowing it to cut curves or intricate patterns. It will do much the same work as a jig saw, but has the advantage of being portable so that it can be taken to the work. Any sized piece or any angle or radius can be cut. The cuts may be made at a right angle to the surface or at any angle up to 45° by adjusting the tilting saw base.

In spite of its light weight (generally about 5 lbs.), the sabre saw is a rugged tool. It can be fitted with various types of blades that cut not only wood up to

2″ thick, but aluminum, brass, steel, and other metals as well as plastic, leather, and asbestos. Figure 27:4 shows a typical sabre saw.

Pointers on Use of Sabre Saw. Although the sabre saw is an easy and comparatively safe tool to use, there are some procedures that should be followed to ensure a good job.
1. Lay out the pattern to be cut and make heavy lines that can easily be followed. Never cut free-hand or by guess. If a part or project is worth making, a proper outline should be drawn on the work.

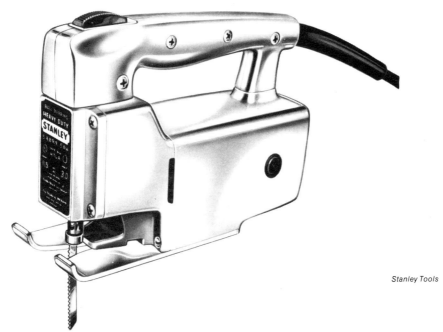

Stanley Tools

Fig. 27:4   Sabre Saw

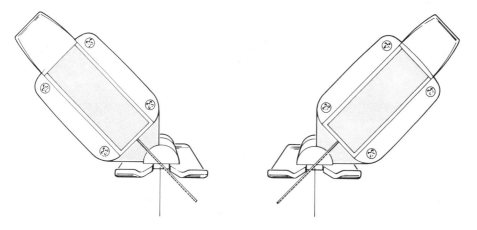

Fig. 27:5   Angle cutting with a sabre saw.

2. Use the proper blade for the type and thickness of the material and the radius to be cut.
3. Install the blade correctly and make sure the swivel base adjustment is tight.
4. If the work is small, clamp it to a bench or secure it in a vise.
5. When cutting hold the saw firmly and press downward and forward.
6. Cut on the waste side of the line.
7. If straight cuts are to be made, clamp a straight-edge to the work that will act as a ripping fence.
8. When making internal cuts, bore a hole larger than the width of the blade to start the cut.

SAFETY PRECAUTIONS THAT *MUST* BE OBSERVED

1. Before adjusting or changing the blade make sure the saw is disconnected.
2. Hold the saw and the work so that the fingers are well away from the blade and the line of cutting.
3. Before removing the saw from the work turn off the switch. There is danger of breaking the blade if the end strikes the work while the saw is being removed when it is still in operation.

Stanley Tools

Fig. 27:6 All-purpose Power Saw

For heavier work several companies make general purpose portable saws with blades that have an up-and-down action similar to the blade of a sabre saw. These saws, however, are larger and heavier, and can be fitted with larger blades. They are *not* used for scroll work or cutting small radii. These saws are used extensively in building construction to cut holes for heating and ventilating ducts and plumbing pipes. A wide range of blades are made that will cut through wood, nails, plaster, aluminum, fibreglass, metal pipe, soil pipe, and sheet metal. The blades can be mounted so that the saw will make vertical or horizontal flush cuts. One of these saws is shown in Figure 27:6.

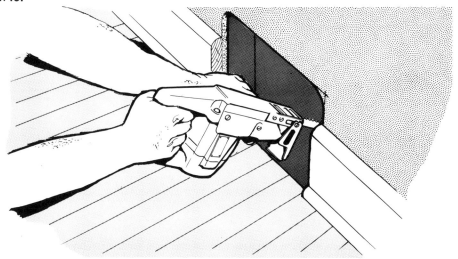

Fig. 27:7   Cutting a hole in a wall and floor for heating register with an all-purpose power saw.

Portable Electric Hand Drills

Portable drills are probably the most exclusively used of all portable power tools. They are used by almost all tradesmen involved in the building industry. They are light and easy to handle, which makes them ideal for drilling holes in wood, metal, or almost any other material. With suitable attachments the drill can be used for sanding, sawing, grinding, buffing, polishing, driving screws, and even stirring paint.

Portable drills are made in many types and sizes, the size being determined by the largest size of drill bit that can be fitted in the chuck. The ¼″ and ⅜″ are the two sizes most commonly used for light general work. Figure 27:8 illustrates a ¼″ portable drill. It has an aluminum alloy frame; the other main parts are the motor, switch, chuck, and handle.

A larger drill used for heavier work in construction is shown in Figure 27:9.

To drill holes in wood with a ¼″ or ⅜″ drill, a twist drill bit is generally used. This bit is similar to those that are used to drill metal except that they are made of mild steel and are sharpened with a longer taper at the point.

With the larger portable drills, double-spur, multi-spur, forstner, or centre bits may be used. For larger holes in thin material, hole saws and fly cutters are sometimes used. A fly cutter is shown in Figure 27:11.

One disadvantage of most portable drills is that the speed cannot be regulated. Some portable drills are now being made, however, that have a variable speed arrangement for use in drilling various types of material.

For working in or around buildings that have no electric power, a ¼″ drill is manufactured that is driven by a light power pack battery.

Fig. 27:8   ¼″ Electric Hand Drill

Fig. 27:10   Hole saw for use in an electric portable drill or drill press.

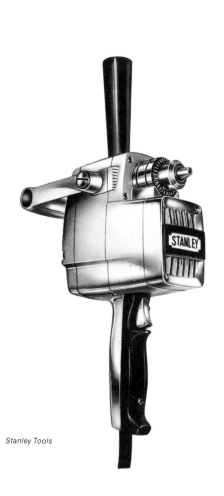

Fig. 27:9   ½″ electric drill which can be used for restricted or overhead areas.

Fig. 27:11   Fly cutter used in a portable electric drill.

Pointers on Use of Electric Hand Drills. Electric portable drills are not difficult to operate, but there are some procedures that should be followed if good results are to be obtained.

1. Accurately locate the position of the hole to be drilled. If the hole is to be drilled in wood, mark the location with a scratch awl. If the hole is to be drilled in metal, mark the location with a centre punch.
2. Hold the drill firmly and perpendicular to the face of the work.
3. If the hole is to be drilled at an angle, it is a good idea first to drill the hole at the correct angle in a scrap piece of wood and clamp this to the work as a guide or jig. The drill will be thus prevented from sliding off the starting point.
4. A back-up block can be used to ensure a clean hole on the underside of the work.
5. Do not shut off the drill until the bit has been withdrawn from the hole.

SAFETY PRECAUTIONS THAT *MUST* BE OBSERVED

1. Use only grounded electrical outlet and cord.
2. Disconnect the drill before changing the bit.
3. If work is small, it should be clamped to a bench.
4. Hold the drill securely, especially if a large drill bit is being used. When a hole saw or fly cutter is used, the work should be clamped as in Figure 27:11. If the drill is not securely held, and the bit or cutter sticks or grabs, the torque of the motor may cause you to lose control of the drill or the work.

The Electric Router

The *electric router* is often considered to be a cabinet-maker's tool. However, it is equally valuable to the carpenter in building construction. It is used for such operations as cutting hinge gains in doors, mortising locks, cutting the housed joints in stairs, trimming arborite on counter tops and many other operations.

The heavy duty 1¼ h.p. router is generally used by builders because of the heavy cutting operations required and the rugged use to which it is subjected during construction. Such a router is shown in Figure 27:12A.

For routing the hinge gains on doors the special jig shown in Figure 27:13A is used.

There are more than two hundred shapes and sizes of bits and cutters available for use with the router; a few of these are shown in Figure 27:14. The bits are held in a chuck which, in turn, is attached to the end of the motor shaft.

Pointers on Use of Electric Router. Because of the high speed of the router (from 18,000 to 24,000 r.p.m.) it will cut parallel with, or at right angles to, the grain. The router must, however, be kept moving. If it is allowed to remain in a

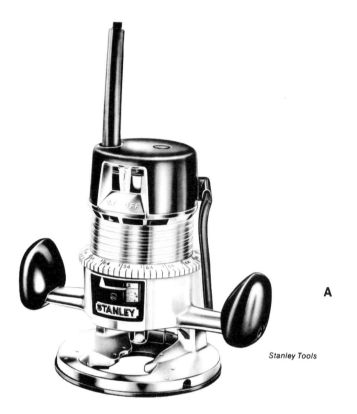

A

B

Fig. 27:12   (A) 1¼ h.p. Router; (B) ½ h.p. Router with a cove bit that has a pilot to regulate the depth of cut.

390

A

B

Fig. 27:13 (A) Door and Jamb Butt Template; (B) Stand used to hold the door firmly on edge while routing out hinge gains.

391

stationary position the revolving knife will burn the wood. The base of the machine should be kept flat on the surface of the wood. The depth of cut can be regulated by lowering the frame on the motor unit and tightening it with a lock nut. For smooth, even cuts the bits and cutters must be kept sharp.

SAFETY PRECAUTIONS THAT *MUST* BE OBSERVED

1. Keep your hands well away from the revolving bit.
2. Make sure the work is securely held before making the router cut.
3. Do not attempt to route stock that is too short.
4. Hold the router firmly, especially at the start of the cut, to overcome the torque of the motor.

The router motor unit can be fitted into a planer frame attachment that converts it into a portable electric plane. These planes can be used for fitting doors and sashes or for planing any long stock when no jointer is available. A spiral cutter is used for the planing operation. See Figure 27:14B.

The Electric Sander

The *belt* and *orbital sanders* are illustrated here. Both are extensively used as finishing tools when building cupboards, installing trim and performing many other operations. Sandpaper belts of varying degrees of coarseness are available to suit the operation. These sanders operate best on flat surfaces. Allow the sanders to operate under their own weight only. Never push down on the sander as this will make an uneven surface and will also be hard on the sander. Keep the sander in motion or there is danger of making hollows in the surface being sanded.

Nailing Devices

The most basic of all operations in building construction, that of driving nails, is being automated. The use of some types of mechanical nailing device is widespread in home construction. These devices range from the spring-operated *stapler* used to attach insulation to the studding, to the heavy compressed-air-operated *gun nailer* used to nail roof sheathing to rafters. These guns are easily loaded by inserting strips of attached nails or staples into the magazine cartridge. The fasteners can be driven as fast as the gun can be moved from location to location and the trigger released. Pneumatic tools will drive common or finishing nails with a plain or galvanized finish, up to 2½″ long. They may have the standard-shaped head, or T- or L-shaped heads that are better adapted to the driving head of the machine. The air pressure required to operate the pneumatic nailing gun is generally provided by a small portable air compressor and tank that can easily be moved from job to job. A light air hose must be run from the compressor to the nailing gun. Figure 27:17 illustrates a pneumatic nailer and some of the applications for which it can be used.

Some nailing devices are activated by striking their heads with a heavy rubber mallet. This type is extensively used for nailing hardwood floors.

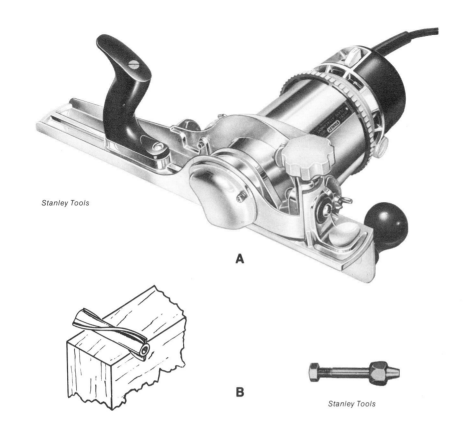

A

B

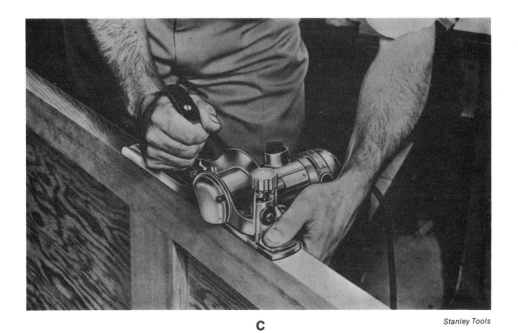

C

Fig. 27:14   (A) Planer Attachment; (B) Cutter and Arbour; (C) Portable power plane in action.

393

Fig. 27:15   Belt Sander

Fig. 27:16   Orbital Sander

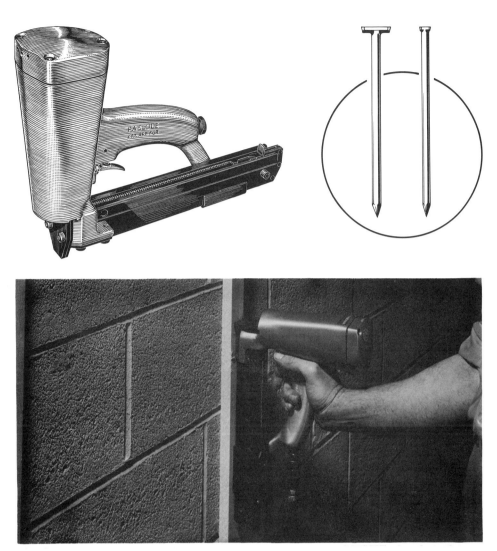

Nailing strapping to concrete block wall.

Nailing Baseboard.

Fig. 27:17   Pneumatic nailer and
how it is used.

Paslode Company,
Division of Signode Corporation

The automatic staplers may be pneumatically powered or they may be manually operated by a spring action. Figure 27:18 illustrates a *stapling hammer* that is operated by swinging the stapler hammer-fashion. Another type is shown in Figure 27:19. This type can be used either by hand or by striking it with a mallet.

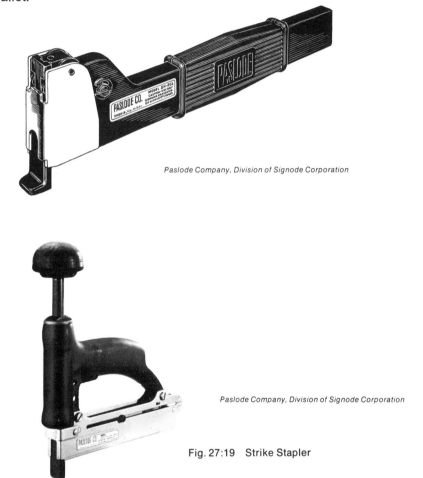

Paslode Company, Division of Signode Corporation

Paslode Company, Division of Signode Corporation

Fig. 27:19   Strike Stapler

Some of the places in home construction where automatic nailing guns and staplers may be used are on roof decks, wall and roof sheathing, subflooring, shingles, siding, bridging, and interior and exterior trim. They may also be used in many other nailing situations.

There are many more types of automatic power-driven tools and machines both in use and in process of being developed. These will substantially reduce the labour, increase the speed, and lower the cost involved in building housing units in Canada. In an effort to keep abreast of the most recent developments in power-driven automatic tools and equipment in the building industry, you should observe the methods used by the progressive home builders in your area. You should also study all the construction trade catalogues and literature available.

Paslode Company, Division of Signode Corporation

Fig. 27:20 Fastening subfloor with a pneumatic nailer. Note the air filter-lubricator attached to the operator's belt. This filter is necessary to keep the nailer operating efficiently.

Fig. 27:21 Fastening sheathing with a pneumatic stapler.

ASSIGNMENT

1. State one method by which the building industry is being automated.
2. (a) List the types of blades used on the portable electric saw.
   (b) What type of blade is used to cut non-wood building materials?
3. Outline the special features of portable electric saws that make them of special value as building construction tools.
4. (a) List four general pointers that should be followed when using the portable electric saw.
   (b) List five safety precautions that *must* be observed while operating the portable saw.
5. Explain the principle of the cutting action of the sabre saw.
6. (a) List four pointers concerning the use of the sabre saw that will help to ensure a good job.
   (b) List three safety precautions that *must* be observed while operating the sabre saw.
7. (a) For what operations are all-purpose portable saws used?
   (b) If the proper blade is used, what materials can this saw cut?
8. When attachments are used several operations can be performed with the portable electric drill besides drilling holes. List these operations.
9. What factor determines the size of an electric hand drill?
10. List three types of bits that are used in the large portable electric hand drill.
11. Make a sketch of:
    (a) a fly cutter   (b) a hole saw.
12. List four general procedures that will aid you when drilling holes with an electric hand drill.
13. What precaution should be taken when cutting a hole with a fly cutter?
14. List four operations for which the electric router can be used in residential home construction.
15. Make a drawing showing the shape of four router bits.
16. How is the depth of the cut regulated on the router?
17. Explain how the router can be used for planing the edge of a door.
18. List two types of sanders in general use by carpenters.
19. Why should electric portable sanders be allowed to operate only under their own weight?
20. Several sources of energy may be used to operate automatic nailing and stapling machines. List these sources.
21. List the building materials that are quite often fastened in place by automatic nailing or stapling devices.
22. How can one attempt to keep abreast of the most recent developments in power tools in the home building industry?

CONSTRUCTION SAFETY

Human life is our most precious resource; in spite of this fact many workers are killed and many more are seriously injured because of unnecessary accidents each year in the construction industry. Unnecessary, because accidents do not just happen; they are caused. What are the causes of these accidents? In general, they are caused by two factors: the human element and the failure of equipment or facilities. Since the latter is nearly always the result of someone's neglect or carelessness – although seldom the victim's – we find that almost all accidents result from ignorance, negligence, or incompetence on someone's part, and could have been prevented had the proper action or precautions been taken.

It is reasonable then to assume that most accidents can be avoided when building tradesmen are properly informed, and when they have developed a safety attitude and a concern for the welfare of their fellow workers as well as for themselves.

An organization that has done much to promote safety by publicizing the need for safe habits and working conditions in the building industry is the *Construction Safety Association of Ontario.* This association is very actively concerned with the safety of workers in all branches of the construction industry. Its main purpose is to prevent construction accidents by conducting effective educational campaigns. It is an independent organization sponsored by the building contractors of the province of Ontario and is financed through a percentage of the assessment paid to the Workmen's Compensation Board. This association has this to say in regard to construction safety:

Safety Education and Accident Prevention in construction is much more than an attempt to equip all workmen with hard hats and safety shoes. A safety program will only be successful when it is established as a philosophy by all those who work in the industry. The most important persons to control a safety program are, of course, the owners and executives of construction companies who, by using their authority, can insist on correct safety procedures in accordance with formalized effective safety programs for their specific type of construction work. *The safety of workers is the moral responsibility of both the employer and the employee,* and until this is clearly recognized and established as the prime method by which work is performed the accident frequency rate will continue to be simply a matter of probability and chance.

The first mandatory principle in any organization is that all personnel, from the superintendent to the unskilled worker, must be instructed that the policy of the organization is such that accidents which could have been avoided will not be tolerated.

The second requirement is that all employees must be trained so that they are thoroughly familiar with the safety requirements of their own specific work. This, of course, assumes that the job superintendent is completely responsible for safety procedures on the whole project, that the foreman is responsible for the safety of workmen in his specific area, and that the tradesmen and labourers are thoroughly familiar with the method by which they perform their work in a safe manner, to protect both themselves and their fellow workmen.

The Ontario Government, through the Department of Labour, has shown its concern for construction workers by passing such legislation as:
(a) The Construction Safety Act;
(b) The Department of Labour Act — Safety Provisions;
(c) Modern Regulations for Work in Compressed Air Tunnelling;
(d) Construction Hoists Act;
(e) Operating Engineers Act;
(f) The Industrial Safety Act.

All these statutes and their regulations, which are published in book form, list in detail the safety rules and precautions that must be followed in the various fields of the construction industry. The regulations of all these acts are explicit and detailed. They have been carefully assembled by competent persons and are in themselves an excellent guide to safety procedures on construction. Contractors and tradesmen are advised to be completely familiar with all the foregoing acts and their regulations. Government and municipal inspectors enforce the acts and their regulations.

Another government-sponsored agency that is vitally concerned with accident prevention is the *Workmen's Compensation Board*, which pays the medical expenses and a percentage of the wages of workers who suffer lost time because of industrial accidents. The Board is supported by a levy placed on all industries on a per-employee basis. In 1965 the Board paid out almost $18 million in workmen's compensation and benefits on behalf of workers in the construction industry.

We ought to be appalled by the number of industrial accidents predicted for the coming year by the Workmen's Compensation Board, as we should when we read in the newspaper the number of highway deaths predicted during a holiday week-end by the Canadian Highway Safety Council. It will only be when everyone connected with the building industry realizes the gravity of the accident rate and decides to take an active part in accident prevention, that the rate will decline.

It has been difficult to control accidents, and to assess the responsibility for them in home construction because so much of the work is done by small sub-contractors. Until recently, each of these small sub-contractors was responsible for the safety of his own men. The owner-builder or the general contractor had little or no responsibility for persons employed on a project.

In consequence, the Construction Safety Act was amended in 1964 to make the "general contractor" or the "owner-builder" responsible for all persons who work on the building site and for making provision for all safety precautions.

Construction is *not* a dangerous occupation. Work is usually performed on a new site, free from potential hazards, and a great many safety devices have been established for equipment, tools, and materials. The procedures employed by responsible contractors are designed to create safe working conditions. Every conceivable precaution is outlined by both government and reputable contractors for the safety of the personnel employed on the building projects.

Why then, you may well ask, does not the accident frequency rate show a consistent improvement? Probably because of the ignorance and blatant irresponsibility of a small number of individuals, both contractors and workmen, who perform their work with complete disregard of the existing safety laws and established procedures, as outlined by such organizations as the Construction Safety Association of Ontario.

Ignorance and irresponsibility are no excuse when it comes to obeying safety laws. All workmen must know how to work safely, and do their work in a manner that will protect both themselves and their fellow workers.

GENERAL SAFETY RULES

We will list here some of the safety rules that should be observed in general construction, and hope that you will be sufficiently impressed with the value of safety that you will take these rules seriously and realize their importance.

1. Have the correct mental outlook toward the job; that is to say, be safety-conscious. This attitude is best acquired by being efficient and interested in the job. "Seldom is a good mechanic injured" is an old maxim in which there is a great deal of truth.

2. Be physically fit and mentally alert. No tradesman suffering from illness or from the effects of fatigue is in any condition to perform efficiently or safely.

3. Be properly dressed for the construction work to be done. The hard hat has become a status symbol and should be proudly worn by those working in the building industry. Many serious accidents have been prevented by their use. On most construction jobs it is mandatory for all persons working on or visiting the site to wear them. For most construction work safety shoes should be worn. The reliability of safety shoes with their heavy soles, steel insert, and reinforced toe caps is well recognized as a safety measure. These shoes are made so that they fit comfortably and are neat in appearance. In some types of construction work protective apparel such as aprons, coveralls, or gloves are necessary for the safety of the worker.

4. When accidents do occur report them at once. Even if the injury is slight, first aid should be obtained; small cuts, scratches, or abrasions

may become infected. A full report of all accidents requiring medical attention must be made to the Workmen's Compensation Board if compensation is to be paid for lost time.

5. Keep all hand tools in first-class condition. Chisels should be sharp. More accidents are caused by using dull chisels than by using sharp ones.

Hammer heads should be tight; a loose head can fly off and might

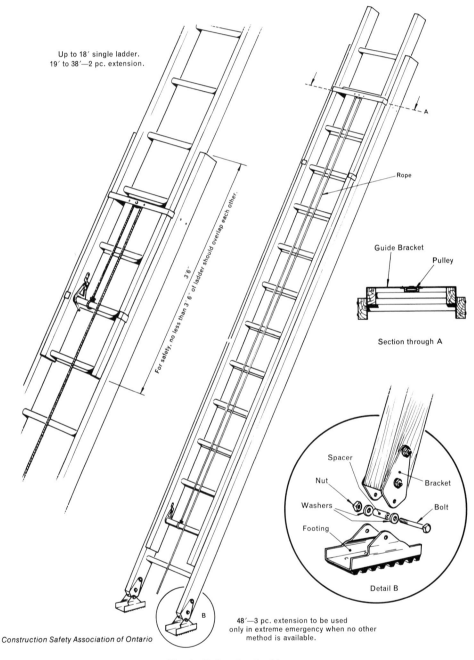

Up to 18′ single ladder.
19′ to 38′—2 pc. extension.

For safety, no less than 3′-6″ of ladder should overlap each other.

3′-6″

Rope

Guide Bracket

Pulley

Section through A

Spacer

Nut

Bracket

Washers

Bolt

Footing

Detail B

B

48′—3 pc. extension to be used only in extreme emergency when no other method is available.

Construction Safety Association of Ontario

Fig. 1   Extension Ladders

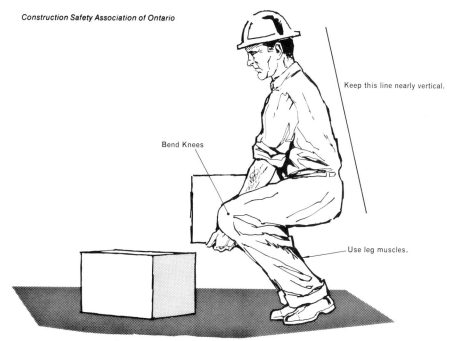

Keep this line nearly vertical.

Bend Knees

Use leg muscles.

Fig. 2   Proper method of lifting a heavy weight.

injure a fellow worker. The face of the hammer should be clean and slightly convex.

Always use the correct tool for the job at hand. Never make do with a substitute tool such as a screw driver instead of a chisel, or pliers instead of a wrench. Specific tools are designed for a specific purpose; use them for this purpose.

6. Ladders of all types are very necessary equipment in the building industry. They are also, however, the source of many accidents if they are in poor repair or are improperly used. Never attempt to reach higher than the top of the ladder upon which you are working. Make sure ladders are in good condition. Extension ladders should be equipped with rubber-based swivel levelling feet as shown in Figure 1. Broken or cracked rungs are death traps.

7. Insulated or non-conducting tools should be used when working around electrical conductors. Never use electric portable tools unless both the outlet and the tool are grounded.

8. Do not work on a pitched roof that is wet or frosty. Wear shoes with a rubber or composition sole when working on a steep roof.

9. Keep the work area clean. Arrange building materials neatly and keep all waste and rubble in a safe place. Many accidents are caused because of falls due to poor footing on a littered building site.

10. Many building materials are heavy or awkward to handle. Heavy material should be lifted by bending the knees, rather than the back. See Figure 2. When moving long material, take care not to endanger those working around you. See Figure 3.

11. A good workman should not have to be told that horseplay or practical jokes have no place on a construction job. They will only increase the hazards and probability of an accident. This does not mean that a workman should lose his sense of humour, or his natural cheerfulness, but there is a great difference between good humour on the job and stupid physical pushing and scuffling, or taking advantage of new and less experienced workers by sending them on false errands, or subjecting them to some other practical joke. The new employee should be given all the help and encouragement possible.

12. Temporary guard rails should be built around all stair or other floor openings while the building is under construction. An accident may be

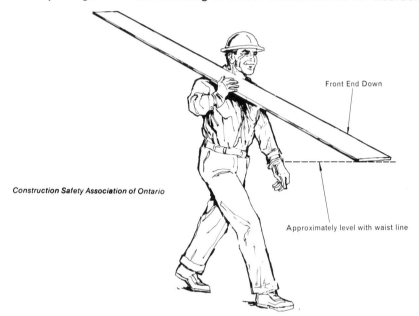

Construction Safety Association of Ontario

Front End Down

Approximately level with waist line

Carry lumber this way. Keep front end low when carrying long objects by yourself.

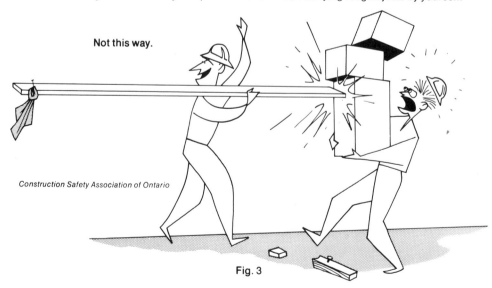

Not this way.

Construction Safety Association of Ontario

Fig. 3

caused by failing to observe any one of these safety precautions. More often, however, one occurs because of a combination of factors that involve the infraction of a number of safety rules or precautions, each of which is partially responsible for the accident.

EXPLOSIVE ACTUATED TOOLS

Explosive actuated tools (sometimes called *powder actuated tools*) are excellent fastening devices that depend on an explosive charge to drive pins or studs into most types of masonry or steel, making it possible to attach electrical, plumbing, or heating materials, and also units such as door and window frames, wall strapping, hanging ceilings, partitions, or any other type of building material, to existing walls or ceilings.

The specially hardened studs are inserted into the barrel of the tool, the cartridge is fitted into the breech, and the tool is closed. When the trigger is released the cartridge is fired, driving the stud into the wall. The size of the stud and the type of material into which it is to be driven determines the strength of the charge, or the amount of powder in the cartridge.

There are two basic types of explosive actuated tools: the standard *high velocity fastening tool* and the *low velocity piston fastening tool.*

High Velocity Fastening Tool

In the high velocity tool the force of the exploding cartridge is exerted directly against the drive pin or stud. This tool is used for operations where a considerable amount of holding power is required, such as supporting a heavy bracket or a suspended ceiling. A protective shield or guard must be attached to the muzzle of the tool to protect the operator from flying particles and to prevent the escape of ricocheting studs or pins.

Ramset Fasteners Ltd.

Fig. 4   High velocity explosive actuated fastening tool. Note the safety shield attached to the muzzle.

Low Velocity Piston Fastening Tool

The low velocity piston fastener is considered to be a safer tool to use than the high velocity tool. The cartridge explodes against the top of a piston, which, in turn, drives the fastener into the material. The fastener itself is propelled at a considerably lower speed with less kinetic energy. This tool is used where less holding power is required. A protective shield is not neces-

Ramset Fasteners Ltd.

Fig. 5   Low velocity piston-set explosive actuated fastening tool. Note the small muzzle; no shield required.

Ramset Fasteners Ltd.

Fig. 6   Strapping being attached to a concrete wall with a standard high velocity fastening tool.

sary. Low velocity piston fasteners are used extensively for operations such as the securing of metal window frames or the fastening of wooden strapping to masonry walls.

High and low velocity fastening tools and some of the operations performed with them are illustrated in the following figures.

The most important aspect of explosive actuated tools is safety. These tools must be used in the correct manner by competent men who have been thoroughly instructed in their use. When improperly used they can be as lethal as any firearm.

Explosive actuated tools used in Canada should be certified by the "Canadian Standards Association". This Organization has published a safety code concerning the use of such tools in an attempt to eliminate hazardous conditions caused by either misuse or inadequate equipment. Some of its safety recommendations are similar to those listed below.

Ramset Fasteners Ltd.

Fig. 7 Low velocity piston-set fastening tool being used to attach partition channels to a masonry wall.

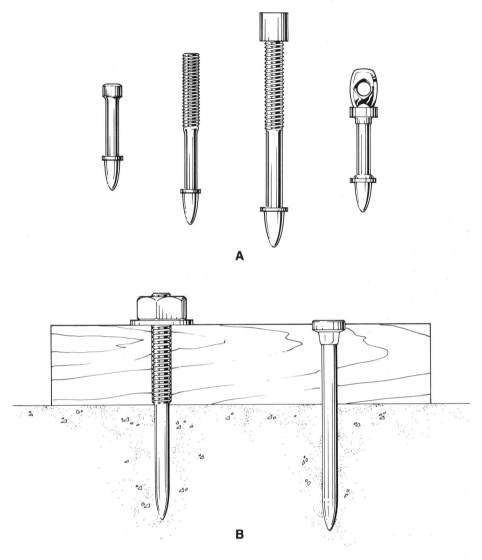

Fig. 8   (A) The four basic types of fasteners that are used with explosive actuated tools;
(B) A threaded stud and a drive pin holding wood to concrete.

Safety Precautions That *Must* Be Observed

1. Before using an explosive actuated fastening tool, the operator should be properly trained in its use and completely familiar with its safety features and limitations. It has been strongly recommended that all operators of these tools should hold a qualified operator's certificate issued by the manufacturer which would guaranty that the operator fully understood the operation of the tool and had demonstrated his ability to use it correctly and safely.

2. The tool must be carefully checked before it is used to see that it is in good operating condition.

408

3. The operator should wear goggles, gloves, a safety hat, and other protective clothing.
4. The operator must not attempt to drive explosive fastener pins into building materials that are harder than the pins. Such building materials include: glazed tile or brick, glass, spring steel, cast steel or cast iron. If in doubt, one of the pins can be used as a centre punch. If the fastener point is blunted, then the material is too hard; if the material shatters, it is too brittle.
5. The operator must never use an explosive actuated tool to drive fasteners into steel less than 3/16″ thick.
6. The fastener must be driven at least two inches away from any weld; the pins will not penetrate a welded surface.
7. The operator must never drive fasteners closer than ½″ from the edge of steel.
8. The strength of charge and size of fastener recommended for the operation being performed should be used.
9. Fasteners must not be driven closer than three inches from the edge of a concrete slab with an explosive actuated tool. Otherwise, the concrete may crack and the fastener ricochet.
10. High velocity tools are equipped with safety shields and guards to prevent flying particles or studs from causing injury. The proper shields and guards should be in place at all times.
11. If uncertain of the correct charge, the weakest cartridge should always be tried on the first trial shot. If the penetration is not sufficient, the operator can increase the charge to the next heavier load.
12. The operator must never attempt to drive a fastener through a pre-drilled hole.
13. The tool should be loaded in strict accordance with the manufacturer's instructions.
14. The tool should always be unloaded when not in use. It should be cleaned and stored after each day of service.
15. Before firing, the muzzle of the tool must be held firmly against, and at a 90° angle to, the working surface.
16. Explosive actuated tools must be treated with the same respect as any other firearm. They must never be pointed at anyone.

There is a considerable amount of research being carried out to develop new explosives and propellants that will improve the efficiency of explosive actuated tools.

SCAFFOLDS

Scaffolds are very necessary pieces of equipment and are used in all construction work. In the interests of safety and working convenience, scaffolds must be well-planned, of a good type, and sturdily built. Many accidents have been caused by improperly built or makeshift scaffolds.

There are two basic types of scaffolds in general use:

1. Single or double post, all wood scaffolds that are built on the site; and
2. The all-metal, sectional, self-supporting scaffolds that may be owned by the contractor, or that may be rented from equipment companies.

Single Post Scaffold

Figure 9 illustrates a *single post scaffold* that is supported by one set of posts. 2″ x 4″ cross-bars or "ledger boards" are spiked to the posts and to blocks that are, in turn, attached to the wall sheathing. Where feasible, the

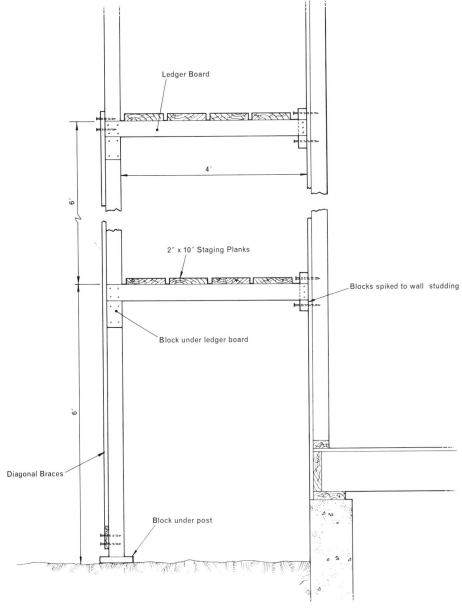

Fig. 9   Single Post Wood Scaffold

410

wall end of the ledgers is spiked to the studding around the window or door openings. The posts should be placed 8' to 10' apart.

Diagonal cross-braces made from 1" x 4" or 1" x 6" material are nailed to the posts to stiffen the scaffold and to keep the posts upright. It is essential that all supporting posts be kept perfectly vertical. A scaffold post that is at even a slight angle is dangerous.

Short pieces of plank must be placed under the posts to keep them from sinking into the ground. All ledger boards should be level, both with each other and from the posts to the building. The vertical distance between ledger boards, or stagings, may be 6' to 9' depending upon the work to be done.

Short pieces of 2" x 4" stock should be spiked to the posts below the ledgers to support the weight. The planks used for the platform or staging should be 2" x 8" or 2" x 10", in long lengths and of good quality.

Double Post Scaffold

Double post scaffolds are built in a similar manner, except that an inner set of posts and extra diagonal braces are required. This scaffold stands free of the building which makes it possible to apply any type of siding or masonry veneer to the face of the wall.

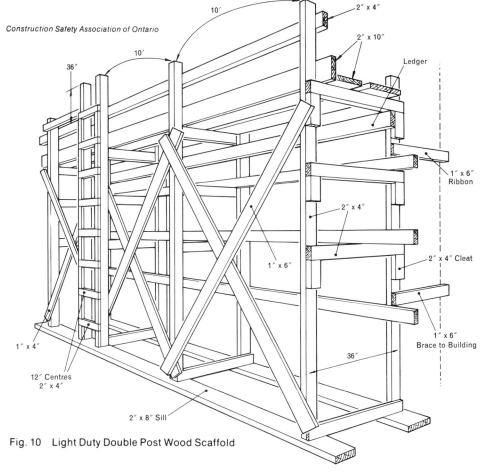

Fig. 10 Light Duty Double Post Wood Scaffold

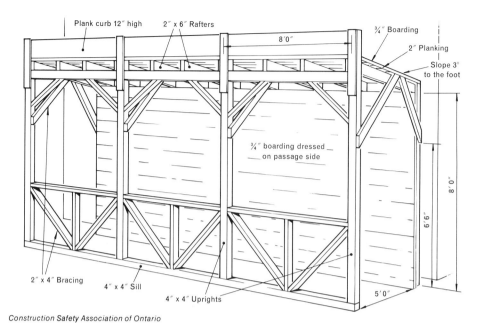

Construction Safety Association of Ontario

Fig. 11   Covered way. When commercial buildings are constructed adjacent to sidewalks the public must be protected. Some type of gantry, commonly called sidewalk sheds, which will prevent falling building materials from injuring pedestrians must be provided.

All-Metal, Sectional Scaffold

Most large construction companies now use *sectional metal scaffolding.* The initial cost of this scaffolding is greater than for most wood scaffolding, but it has the advantage of being quickly and easily erected and conveniently stored. It is also considered stronger. There are many varieties of metal sectional scaffolds but most of them are similar in design and are assembled in the same manner. The main supports are flat, rectangular frames made from light steel tubular stock. See Figure 28:12A. The frames are approximately 4′ wide and 6′ high with solid pins in the lower end of the long members that will fit into the top end of the members on another frame (sometimes separate pins are used). This allows the frames to be stacked to make a scaffold of the desired height. The frames have cross-bars to support the staging planks. Diagonal braces are also made from tubular stock and are held to the upright frames by bolts and wing nuts which makes the scaffold easy to dismantle.

Scaffolds used inside a building are often equipped with swivel castors so that an 8′ or 10′ section may be easily moved when the work in one section of the room is completed.

Scaffold Safety

The best-designed scaffolds are safe only if they are built and used correctly. Some of the rules that must be followed are:

(a) inspect the scaffold before using it;

412

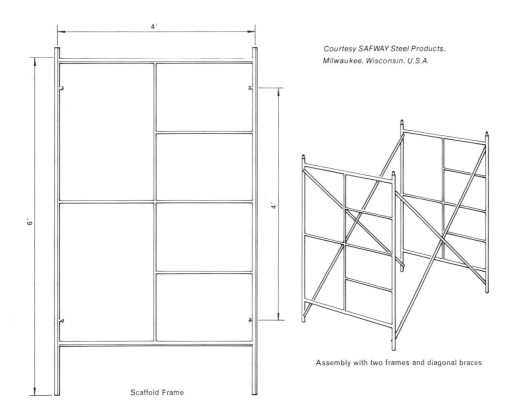

4'

6'

4'

Courtesy SAFWAY Steel Products, Milwaukee, Wisconsin, U.S.A.

Scaffold Frame

Assembly with two frames and diagonal braces

Courtesy SAFWAY Steel Products, Milwaukee, Wisconsin, U.S.A.

Fig. 12 Metal scaffolding used for home construction with raised platform for building materials.

Fig. 13   Metal Scaffold

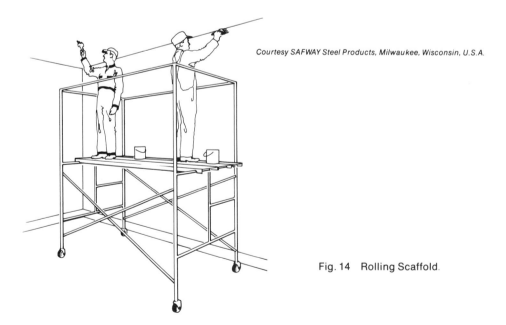

Courtesy SAFWAY Steel Products, Milwaukee, Wisconsin, U.S.A.

Fig. 14   Rolling Scaffold.

414

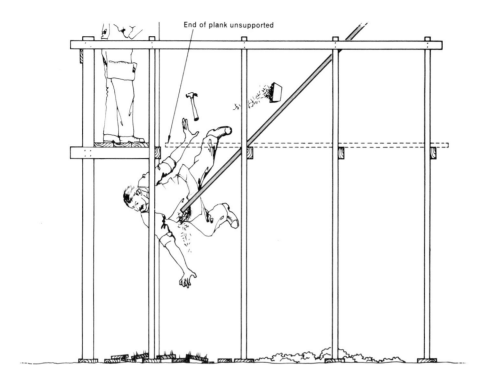

Fig. 15   Scaffold Trap

(b) use a base plate under all posts;

(c) make sure all supporting posts or frames are plumb;

(d) fasten all diagonal braces securely;

(e) do not climb on the diagonal braces;

(f) large scaffolds must be tied to the building every 30′ in length and 25′ in height of the scaffold;

(g) use guard rails above the staging planks;

(h) be careful of power lines around metal scaffolding;

(i) do not use ladders or any makeshift arrangement on top of scaffolds to increase its height;

(j) do not overload scaffolds;

(k) use only a good grade of lumber for staging planks;

(l) planks must have a 12″ lap over each other or extend 6″ past the support. An unsupported scaffold plank is referred to as a trap. Such a situation is illustrated in Figure 28:15.

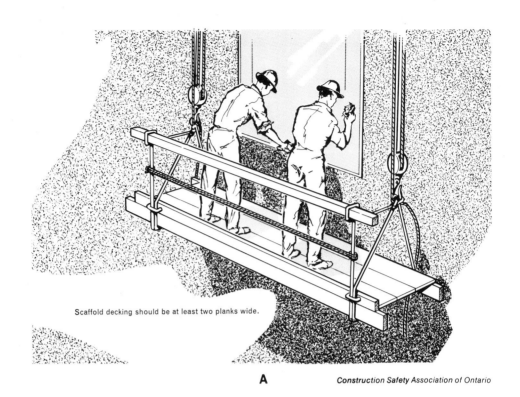

Scaffold decking should be at least two planks wide.

A

B

Fig. 16   (A) Hanging Scaffold; (B) Boatswain's Chair.

(m) When rolling scaffolds are used, the castors must be equipped with "brakes". The brakes must be applied at all times when the scaffolds are not being moved.

There are other scaffold arrangements such as swing scaffolds, and boatswain's chairs, as well as wall-mounted and ladder-mounted scaffold brackets, all of which require special safety precautions.

GLOSSARY OF TERMS

abutment: a side support

acoustic quality: the ability of a building material to transmit or retard the passage of sound

anchor bolt: a bolt that is threaded at one end and hooked at the other and is used to hold down a structural member

apex: the peak of a triangle; the highest point

apprentice: a learner in a trade, bound by contract to his employer for a specified period of time

asbestos: fibrous mineral that can be woven into a fireproof fabric

asphalt: mineral pitch; a bituminous composition used for paving, flooring, roofing, etc.

back-up blocks: blocks used for the inner face of a wall

barbed nails: nails with rows of barbs along their length to give them greater holding power

batten: a strip of wood placed across the joints of boards to prevent warping, and to strengthen them

bearing: the portion of a beam or truss that rests on the supports

bearing partition: a partition that bears the weight of the floor joists and other partitions above it

bearing plate: a plate of the thickness and area required to distribute a given load

blue: to toughen steel by a special heating and cooling process which gives it a bluish-black finish

blueprint: an architectural drawing or plan that has been transferred to chemically treated paper

board foot: unit of measure for lumber. One foot square and one inch or less thick

boxwood: a hard, close-grained wood of a pale yellow colour, used for rules, scales, and tool handles

bridging: a method of bracing joists or studs by the use of short strips of wood or metal

canopy: a roof-like covering over a door

cant strip: a projecting sloping member fitted around a building to deflect rain water from the wall

cantilever: a beam or girder fixed at one end and free at the other

ceiling joist: one of the timbers to which a ceiling is attached by lath and plaster or by other means

chamfer: a cut-off corner

chord: the principal member of a truss, either top or bottom

chuck: a device for holding a rotating tool during an operation

cleat: a strip of wood or metal nailed across a joint

column: a vertical pillar, usually round

cornice: part of the roof that overhangs the wall

course: a row

cripple rafter: a rafter which extends from a hip to a valley rafter

cripple studs: short studs used above and below a window opening

crown: curve

dormer: a small, upright window projecting from a sloping roof

double hung window: a window consisting of upper and lower sash, both carried by sash cords and weights

eaves: the projecting edges of a roof

elevations: views of the exterior of a building on a vertical plane

epoxy-plastic adhesive: a synthetic resin liquid glue used to bond wood to wood, or wood to metal, plastic, or masonry

explosive actuated tools: tools operated by an explosive charge

fascia board: trim member of a roof that extends along the eaves and up the gable end

flange: a projecting rim

flashing: pieces of metal or roofing material shaped to the valley of a roof, or around chimneys and windows to prevent leaking

floor joist: heavy piece of timber laid edgewise to form a floor support

flute: an ornamental, vertical groove cut into the surface of a column or other member

footing: a foundation for a column, etc.

frieze board: the decorated upper part of a wall, below the cornice

furring strips: pieces of wood attached to a surface, as for lathing

galvanize: to coat iron with zinc

girths: short pieces of wood nailed between studs to prevent them from bowing

glaze: to equip with window panes

graduation: one of the equal divisions on a graduated scale

grain: the direction or arrangement of wood fibres in a piece of wood

gusset: a wood or metal plate attached to one or both sides of a joint to increase its holding power

header: the joist into which the common joists are framed around stair and chimney openings, etc.

heartwood: the wood in the centre of a tree

hexagon: a six-sided figure

hip rafters: the rafters that form the hip of a roof, running at a 45° angle from the plate to the ridge

insulation: a special covering that prevents the passage of electricity or heat

isometric: a type of perspective drawing in which receding parallel lines do not converge

jack rafter: a short rafter joining a hip rafter to the eaves, or a valley rafter to the ridge

jamb: one of the upright sides of a doorway or window frame

jig: a device that holds and locates parts while they are being assembled, cut, or drilled

joist hanger: an iron forging shaped like a stirrup and bent so that it can be hung on a beam to provide end support

journeyman: a qualified tradesman who has served his apprenticeship

laminate: to build up wood in plies; to glue

lath: a strip of wood about 1½″ wide and ⅜″ thick, used as a foundation for plaster

layout: an outline or details set down in preparation for work on stock

lead hand: assistant foreman

ledger board: a wooden member bolted to a beam to support abutting joists

light: a pane of glass in a window

lineal foot: a foot in length as opposed to a square foot or a cubic foot

lintel: the horizontal top piece over a door or window opening

live load: a moving load that varies in its application

man-hour: work done by one man in one hour

meeting rail: the horizontal bar dividing the upper and lower sash of a window

mitre box: a device used as a guide in sawing mitre joints

mitre joint: a joint between two pieces at an angle to one another of 90° in such a way that the line of junction bisects the angle

modular construction: construction conforming to the modular dimensional standards. Houses are designed with wall lengths in even feet, thus making it possible to utilize standard-sized building materials.

module: a standard unit of measurement in building construction, generally two or four feet.

monoplane: single, flat surface

mortgage: a legal document that transfers property from one person (the borrower) to another (the lender) as security for a loan. It is redeemed upon repayment of the debt.

nominal size: the size by which a material is known and sold, but which differs slightly from the actual size

octagon: an eight-sided figure

offset: a recess in a wall

parallel: side by side and at equal distance at all points

parapet: a low wall around the edge of a roof or terrace

partition: an interior wall that divides a building into rooms

pitch: the slope of a roof

plate: the top horizontal member of a wall to which are fastened attic joists, roof rafters, etc.

plumb cut: a perpendicular cut

pneumatic power tools: tools operated by air pressure

polygon: a many-sided figure

Portland cement: the building cement of common use, made by heating clay and lime substance

Pythagoras: Greek philosopher and mathematician living in the sixth century B.C.

rabbet: step-shaped cut along edge of wood to receive edge or tongue of another piece

rafters: the ribs that run from hip or ridge to eaves in a roof

ratchet: a gear with triangular-shaped teeth

ratio: relative value; proportion

recess: an indentation in a wall such as an alcove

ridge line: the top of a roof where two slopes meet

rise: the vertical distance from the top of the wall plate to the top of the ridge board

riser: the vertical part of a step

run: the distance from the outer edge of the plate on one wall to the centre of the building

run and rise: term meaning the degree of incline

sash: the frame in which window glass is set

scarf joint: a joint made by notching and lapping the ends of two timbers, fastening them together with bolts or straps

seat cut: a horizontal cut

sheathing: wide boards or sheets of other material nailed to studding or to the roofing rafters to form a foundation to which the outer surface covering of the walls or roof of a house is nailed

shingles: small pieces of wood or other material used for covering roofs and side walls

shiplap: boards that are rabbeted along both edges, one rabbet on each side

siding: lumber or other material used for finishing the exterior walls of a building

slag: the fused refuse of ores

slat deck: open roof sheathing

soffit: the underside of an arch, staircase, cornice or the like

spall: to damage the heads of pins or studs by riveting or bending them

span: the distance between supports such as walls and beams

staging: a platform or walkway used by workmen during the construction of a building

stiffener: a plate or other shape fastened to a member to ensure rigidity

stile: an upright piece of framing

storm sash: an extra or outer sash used as a protection from severe winter weather

straight edge: a straight strip of wood or metal used to gauge linear accuracy

strapping: a term for battens fixed to the inner faces of walls as a support for laths and plaster

strength-weight ratio: relation between the weight and strength of a material

stringer: a main supporting diagonal member of a staircase.

stud: an upright beam in the framework of a house

subfloor: a wood floor laid over the

floor joists on which the finished floor is laid

surveying: the science of measuring land

timbers: trees that have been sawn into large squared sizes

toe-nail: to drive a nail slantingly into the end of a piece of lumber to attach it to another piece

tongue and groove: a board that has a projecting bead cut along one edge and a groove along the other

torque: the force created by a rotating shaft, bit, or cutter

transverse beam: beam that runs from one side of a house to another

tread: the horizontal part of a step which is walked on

trim: ornamental parts of wood or metal used to cover the joints between jambs and plaster wall around a door or window

trimmer: a joist that supports a header

truss: a built-up framework of triangular units for supporting loads over long spans

valley rafters: the rafters that form the intersection of an internal roof angle between the main part of the building and an L or other projection

vapour barrier membrane: a thin, moisture-proof film of tar, light asphalt treated building paper, or one of the light transparent polyethylene films, used to prevent the passage of moisture into walls or ceilings

veneer: a thin layer of wood or other material attached to the surface of an inferior material to lessen cost and to give a superior effect

wing: a separate, projecting part of a building

wing nut: a nut that has two flat wings extending from opposite sides

BIBLIOGRAPHY

ANTHONY, G. H., *Architectural Technology.* Toronto: Sir Isaac Pitman (Canada) Ltd.

BURBANK, N. L., and SHAFTEL, O., *House Construction Details.* New York: Simmons-Boardman Books.

DAHL, A., and WILSON, J. D., *Cabinetmaking and Millwork.* Chicago: American Technical Society.

DURBAHN, W. E., *et al., Fundamentals of Carpentry.* Chicago: American Technical Society.

GRAHAM, F. D., and EMERY, T. J., *Carpenters and Builders Guides.* Indianapolis: Howard W. Sams and Co. Inc.

JONES, R. P., *Framing, Sheathing and Insulation.* Albany, N.Y.: Delmar Publishers Ltd.

LAIR, Elbert A., *Carpentry for the Building Trades.* New York: McGraw-Hill Book Company.

MIX, F., and CIROU, E. H., *Practical Carpentry.* Homewood, Ill.: Goodheart-Willcox Co. Inc.

NERVI, P. L., *Structures.* New York: McGraw-Hill Book Company.

RAMSEY, C. G., and SLEEPER, H. R., *Architectural Graphic Standards.* New York: John Wiley & Sons, Inc.

SMITH, R. C., *Principles and Practices of Light Construction.* Englewood Cliffs, N. J.: Prentice-Hall, Inc.

TOWNSEND, G., *Steel Square,* 2nd. ed. Chicago: American Technical Society.

WILSON, J. D., and ROGERS, C. M., *Simplified Carpentry Estimating.* New York: Simmons-Boardman Books.

WILSON, J. D., and WERNER, S. O., *Simplified Roof Framing.* New York: McGraw-Hill Book Co.

WILSON, J. D., and WERNER, S. O., *Simplified Stair Layout.* Albany, N.Y.: Delmar Publishers Ltd.

Canadian Wood Frame House Construction. Ottawa: Central Mortgage and Housing Corporation.

Canadian Woods — Their Properties and Uses, Forest Products Laboratories. Ottawa: Queen's Printer.

Good Building Practice. Ottawa: Central Mortgage and Housing Corporation.

National Building Code of Canada. Ottawa: Queen's Printer.

Residential Standards. Supplement to the *National Building Code of Canada.* Ottawa: National Research Council.

Wood Frame House Construction. Washington, D.C.: United States Department of Agriculture.

INDEX

Page numbers in italic indicate illustrations

37 47 57 67   **BP**   9 8 7 6 5

lintel
metal tie
double plate

double rafter
lookouts
rough fascia
fascia board
moulding
soffit
screened vent
trim

interior wall finish
vapour barrier
insulation
stud framing
sheathing
building paper
air space (behind brick)
brick veneer
steel angle lintel & flashing
window frame
sole plate
sub-floor
brick ties
weep holes
damp proof course (d.p.c.)
joists
bridging

damproofing to grade line
crushed stone
weeping tile

details of house construction

CENTRAL MORTGAGE AND HOUSING CORPORATION,   OTTAWA, ONTARIO